18·75

C000152864

Introduction to Civil Engineering Construction

Roy Holmes

College of Estate Management

*No part of this publication may be reproduced
by any means, electronic or mechanical,
including photocopying, without permission
in writing from the publisher.*

© 1983 College of Estate Management
First published February 1975
This edition September 1983

ISBN 090213279 2

Printed and published by the
College of Estate Management
Whiteknights Reading RG6 2AW

Preface

There has long been a need by students and those in practice for a book broadly covering the field of civil engineering but which is not too mathematical or specialised. A particular need arises among those who need to understand civil engineering technology but who are never called upon to design such work.

The quantity surveying profession are one such body of people requiring this form of civil engineering knowledge, particularly in the area of professional examinations. With the latter in mind The Royal Institution of Chartered Surveyors Quantity Surveying (Civil Engineering) Working Party examined the study material available to establish the parameters for a suitable book. The working party found that no one book covered the wide scope required by the professional examination syllabuses and that books on individual subjects were either too specialised or too mathematical.

It was considered that the study notes on civil engineering used by the College of Estate Management and written by Kenneth Powell had the correct approach and that such a format might be followed and extended to include a wider range of topics. With these factors in mind the author was invited to write the book.

The book has been written for those who are not qualified engineers and must be read with that thought uppermost. It is specifically aimed at quantity surveying and other professions who work with civil engineers. The purpose of the book is two-fold; firstly, it seeks to present a broad-based understanding of civil engineering methods without a complicated mathematical text, and secondly, it seeks to provide the reader with sufficient knowledge to be able to make valid contributions within a civil engineering team. No book of this size can possibly provide comprehensive information on the topics dealt with, and this has not been the intention; neither can such a book be limited to those methods of construction used by major civil engineering contractors. A balance between depth of knowledge and principles of construction is difficult to achieve in any text but pains have been taken to explain the principles involved and to include the most recent processes and equipment.

Throughout the book photographs and simple sketches readily show the principles or processes involved. The technical content has been checked by experts in appropriate fields but they are in no way responsible for any omissions or errors.

Some chapters deal with topics which are encountered on many contracts and they therefore contain much in the way of detail, other chapters are concerned with topics which are limited, by way of specialism or low incidence, to a small number of civil engineering contractors, and they therefore contain basic principles only.

Bristol Polytechnic, December 1974   *R. Holmes*

Preface to the Second Edition

It has been a privilege to talk to staff and students who have made use of this book over the past seven years and I am grateful for the many helpful comments that I have received. The original intention was to provide a suitable civil engineering text for students in the quantity surveying profession, but it has been particularly gratifying to learn that students in both building and civil engineering have also been using the book.

When the book was first conceived a great deal of effort went into checking developments and into forward writing — that is to say that research developments, anticipated as being in use during the decade, were included. That work has proved worthwhile for it has reduced the amount of revision necessary in this edition. However, not all developments prove to be economically viable and some may go out of use in the short term; it is difficult to say 'for all time' since many do make a successful come-back. This has been borne in mind in the revision, some methods which have been slow to gain popularity being retained while others have been omitted.

Most chapters have required revision, some greater than others, and I am indebted to Dr J G Gibb (ICI-Explosives Division) for his help in updating the sections on the use of explosives, to S Flavel, a colleague of mine, for his helpful critique on Tunnelling, and to British Rail for their comments on Railway Trackwork.

The major revision has been in Chapter 5, Tunnelling. The text has been brought into line with predominant current practices; for instance the bentonite tunnelling machine has been omitted, not because it has become obsolete, indeed the technique has recently been developed in the Far East, but because the student is more likely to encounter other methods.

A number of British Standards have been or are being revised and reference to these have also been revised wherever practicable.

Bristol Polytechnic, March 1983   *R Holmes*

Acknowledgements

The author is indebted to the following individuals and companies who have given help and advice during the preparation of this work and who have given permission, where necessary, to reproduce photographs and other information.

The author is particularly indebted to the Civil Engineering Working Party of the Royal Institution of Chartered Surveyors who verified the typescript and gave expert advice and guidance as the need arose. The working party was composed of:

A T Bell FRICS (Chairman); G Fairbrass FRICS; H Hay FRICS; G H Hughes OBE FRICS; H Knight FRICS FIArb; E F March ARICS; A L Moseley FRICS; V S Renauden FRICS; J A Sneden FRICS; C J Vickers FRICS.

Acknowledgement is also made to the following who assisted in the specific areas indicated: B Frost — Bituminous Work; A V Davies — Roadworks; S Favel — Tunnelling; K Lawson — Plant; J L Milverton — Sewage Treatment; A G Shallcross — Airfield Construction and Compliance control of concrete; J Snedon — Dredging and earthworks; A S West — Piling; Dr J G Gibb — Explosives; J Lewis for his helpful comments on Chapters 1 and 2 and A Bond for the cover design for the First Edition.

I would also like to express my gratitude to a number of others; to Hugh Knight without whose expertise and guidance it would have been difficult to achieve the aims of the working party and who contributed much to the technical content and was responsible for the liaison between the author and the many experts or companies in the field of civil engineering; to Leonard Moseley who gave much helpful advice and was responsbile for piloting this ambitious project through the College as well as for lettering the sketches; to John Armstrong and his staff in the printing division of the College of Estate Management for their patient labour in preparing the final work; to my colleague D I Chappell for the painstaking way in which he read the whole draft, making helpful suggestions where corrections were necessary and finally the two ladies who were greatly involved in the work, my typist Doreen Highnam, who patiently transcribed the original manuscript and my wife, Margaret, who assisted with the proof reading and was a source of great encouragement during the long period of writing.

AKD Engineering; Asphalt and Coated Macadam Association; Aveling-Barford Limited; Balfour Beatty & Co. Limited; Barber-Greene Company Ltd.; F E Beaumont Ltd.; Benford Limited; Alfred Booth & Company Limited; Bovis Civil Engineering Limited; British Airports Authority; British Lift Slab Limited; British Rail; British Ready Mixed Concrete Association; British Standards Institution; British Steel Corporation; British Visqueen Ltd.; BSP International Foundation Limited; Building Research Establishment; Butyl Products Limited; Caledonian Mining Co. Ltd.; Cawoods Concrete Products Ltd.; Cement and Concrete Association; Cementation Ground Engineering Ltd.; Cementation Piling and Foundations Ltd.; CCL Systems Limited; Central Electricity Generating Board; CET (Plant) Limited; Chemical Building Products Ltd.; Chemidus Wavin Ltd.; Christiani & Nielsen Limited; CJB Developments Limited; Clarke Chapman-John Thompson Ltd.; Compriband (Gt. Britain) Ltd.; Richard Costain Limited; Deilmann-Haniel GMBH; R M Douglas Construction Limited; Dosco Overseas Engineering Limited; Dow Mac Concrete Ltd.; C Evans & Sons Limited; Federation of Piling Specialists; F C Precast Concrete Ltd.; Foraky Limited; Foundation Publications Limited; Frankipile Limited; General Tire International Company; GKN Foundations Limited; GKN (South Wales) Limited; Gleeson Civil Engineering Ltd.; Greater London Council; W R Grace Ltd.; Ground Anchors Limited; Ground Engineering; Ground Water Services Limited; Hepworth-Polva Plastics Ltd.; John Howard & Company Ltd.; Icos (Great Britain) Ltd.; Imperial Chemical Industries Limited; International Harvester Company of Great Britain Limited; Intrusion Prepakt (UK) Ltd.; A Johnson Construction Company Ltd.; Johnson & Nephew (Abergate) Limited; Kwikform Limited; John Laing and Son Limited; Mackley Ace Limited; J T Mackley & Co. Ltd.; Mark-Thomsen Limited; G Maunsell & Partners (Consulting Engineers); M & H Tunnelling and Civil Engineering Limited; Millars Wellpoint International Ltd.; Mono Concrete Limited; National Research Development Corporation; National-Standard Company Limited; Norwest Holst Group Administration Limited; Edmund Nuttall Limited; Nuttall Bachy & Co. Ltd.; Pandroll Limited; Frederick Parker Limited; Permanite Limited; Preload Limited; Robert L Priestley Ltd.; P.S.C. Equipment Limited; Pynford Design Limited; Raymond Concrete Pile Co. Ltd.; Rees Hough Limited; E G Reeve & Sons Ltd.; R F D - GQ Limited; River and Sea Gabions (London) Ltd; Rock Fall Company Limited; Ruston-Bucyrus Limited; William R Selwood Ltd.; Soil Mechanics Limited; Soletanche Co (UK) Ltd.; Stanton and Staveley (British Steel Corporation); Stelcom Ltd.; Stelmo Ltd.; Henry Sykes Ltd.; Tarmac Roadstone Holdings Limited; Taylor Woodrow Construction Limited; The Cement-Gun Company Limited; The Dredging & Construction Co. Ltd.; The National Federation of Demolition Contractors; The Kaybore Thermic Lancing Co. Ltd.; The Phoenix Engineering Company Limited; The Ruberoid Company Limited; T H I Group Services Ltd.; Transline Units Limited; Transport and Road Research Laboratory; William Tribe Limited; Universal Anchorage Co. Ltd.; A Waddington & Son Ltd.; West's Piling and Construction Company Limited; Westfalia Lunen; Wickham Engineering Co. Ltd.; Extracts from British Standard Codes of Practice are reproduced by permission of the British Standards Institution, 2 Park Street, London W1A 2BS.

R H

Contents

Chapter 1   **General Considerations in Civil Engineering**   *Page*

   1.1   **SITE INVESTIGATION**
   1.1.1   Objects of investigation 1
   1.1.2   Classification of rocks and soils 1
   1.1.3   Types of investigation 3
   1.1.4   General enquiries and preliminary work 5
   1.1.5   Procedure for investigation 7
   1.1.6   Methods of site exploration 9
   1.1.7   Insitu testing 15
   1.1.8   Laboratory testing 18
   1.1.9   Geophysical surveys and other techniques 22
   1.1.10   Special information and costs 26

   1.2   **SITE ORGANISATION AND TEMPORARY SERVICES**
   1.2.1   Introduction 29
   1.2.2   General organisation and site clearance 29
   1.2.3   Demolition 30
   1.2.4   Site offices and general accommodation 33
   1.2.5   Material storage and compounds 35
   1.2.6   Temporary services 36
   1.2.7   Setting out 37
   1.2.8   Safety 42

   1.3   **MATERIALS**
   1.3.1   Materials in general use 47
   1.3.2   Materials for bulk filling 50
   1.3.3   Explosives 51

   1.4   **TEMPORARY WORKS** 54

Chapter 2   **Contractors' Plant**

   2.1   **MANAGEMENT OF PLANT** 55

   2.2   **EARTHMOVING PLANT** 57
   2.2.1   Construction methods and selection of plant 57
   2.2.2.   Excavating plant 58
   2.2.3   Transporting plant 63
   2.2.4   Compaction plant 65
   2.2.5   Performance and outputs of earthmoving plant 66

   2.3   **CONCRETING PLANT**
   2.3.1   Methods and selection of plant 70
   2.3.2   Concrete mixing plant 70
   2.3.3   Concrete distribution plant 71

   2.4   **PILE DRIVING PLANT**
   2.4.1   General considerations 78
   2.4.2   Methods of driving piles 78
   2.4.3   Pile-driving hammers 80
   2.4.4   Pile extractors 82
   2.4.5   Winches and other equipment 82

   2.5   **CRANES AND HOISTS**
   2.5.1   General considerations 83
   2.5.2   Mobile cranes 83
   2.5.3   Derrick cranes 85
   2.5.4   Tower cranes 87
   2.5.5   Hoists for men and materials 89

   2.6   **COMPRESSED AIR PLANT**
   2.6.1   General considerations 90

2.6.2	Air compressors	.	90
2.6.3	Pneumatic tools and equipment	.	91
2.7	**BITUMINOUS MIXING AND LAYING PLANT**		
2.7.1	General considerations	.	92
2.7.2	Heaters and boilers	.	92
2.7.3	Binder distributors	.	93
2.7.4	High speed road-surfacing units	.	93
2.7.5	Asphalt and bituminous mixing plant	.	94
2.7.6	Spreading and finishing machines	.	95
2.8	**PUMPS AND DEWATERING EQUIPMENT**		
2.8.1	General considerations	.	95
2.8.2	Pumps — types	.	96
2.8.3	Dewatering equipment	.	98

Chapter 3 **Earthworks**

3.1	**GENERAL CONSIDERATIONS AND PLANNING**		
3.1.1	Site considerations	.	99
3.1.2	Ground conditions	.	100
3.1.3	Contract duration and weather prospects	.	101
3.1.4	Economic aspects of earthwork design	.	101
3.2	**EXCAVATIONS**		
3.2.1	Bulk excavation	.	102
3.2.2	Rock excavation	.	103
3.2.3	Trench excavation	.	106
3.2.4	Support of excavations	.	107
3.2.5	Embankments	.	112
3.3	**CONTROL OF GROUND WATER**		
3.3.1	Pumping systems	.	116
3.3.2	Electro-osmosis	.	127
3.3.3	Freezing methods	.	127
3.3.4	Compressed air	.	132
3.3.5	Grouting methods	.	133
3.3.6	Comparison of methods and costs	.	134

Chapter 4 **Piling, Diaphragm and Retaining Wall Systems**

4.1	**SHEET PILING**		136
4.1.1	Types of piles	.	136
4.1.2	Methods of driving	.	142
4.1.3	Corrosion and protection	.	145
4.1.4	Selection and use of sheet piling	.	147
4.2	**BEARING PILES**		
4.2.1	General considerations	.	147
4.2.2	Types of bearing piles	.	149
4.2.3	Methods of driving	.	163
4.2.4	Caps and capping beams	.	166
4.2.5	Testing for load-bearing capacity	.	168
4.2.6	Economics and selection	.	169
4.3	**VIBRO-FLOTATION AND VIBRO-REPLACEMENT**		
4.3.1	Introduction	.	177
4.3.2	Methods and materials	.	177
4.3.3	Economic considerations	.	177
4.4	**DIAPHRAGM WALLING**		
4.4.1	Introduction	.	178
4.4.2	Methods of construction	.	179
4.4.3	Plant and equipment	.	186
4.4.4	Economic factors	.	187

4.5	**RETAINING WALLS**		
4.5.1	Types of walls	.	194
4.5.2	Methods of construction	.	194
4.5.3	Waterproofing	.	198

Chapter 5   **Tunnelling and Underpinning**

5.1	**TUNNELLING**		
5.1.1	General considerations	.	199
5.1.2	Methods of tunnelling	.	200
5.1.3	Tunnelling in rock	.	207
5.1.4	Tunnelling in soft ground	.	210
5.1.5	Use of compressed air	.	213
5.1.6	Safety aspects	.	213
5.1.7	Ventilation and lighting	.	214
5.2	**UNDERPINNING**		
5.2.1	General considerations	.	215
5.2.2	Methods of underpinning	.	216

Chapter 6   **Marine and Other Works Associated with River or Groundwater Environments**

6.1	**COFFERDAMS**		
6.1.1	Introduction	.	223
6.1.2	Types of cofferdams and methods of construction	.	224
6.1.3	Economic factors	.	231
6.2	**CAISSONS**		
6.2.1	Introduction	.	232
6.2.2	Caisson types and forms of construction	.	232
6.2.3	Positioning and sinking of caissons	.	235
6.2.4	Sealing and filling caissons	.	238
6.3	**UNDERWATER FOUNDATION CONSTRUCTION**		
6.3.1	General considerations	.	239
6.3.2	Excavation	.	239
6.3.3	Formwork	.	239
6.3.4	Underwater concreting	.	239
6.4	**SEA WALLS, DOCKS, JETTIES AND OTHER MARINE STRUCTURES**		
6.4.1	Methods of construction	.	242
6.4.2	Other marine structures	.	246
6.5	**DREDGING AND RECLAMATION**		
6.5.1	General considerations	.	247
6.5.2	Plant and equipment	.	249
6.5.3	Construction and materials	.	252
6.6	**CANALS AND RIVER WORKS**		
6.6.1	Introduction	.	255
6.6.2	River-bank protection	.	256
6.7	**RESERVOIRS AND LIQUID-RETAINING TANKS**		
6.7.1	General considerations	.	261
6.7.2	Construction	.	261
6.7.3	Waterproofing	.	264
6.7.4	Special linings	.	266

Chapter 7   **Roadworks, Bridges, Subways and Airfield Construction**

7.1	**ROADWORKS**		
7.1.1	Earthworks	.	267
7.1.2	Flexible pavements	.	270
7.1.3	Rigid pavements	.	271
7.1.4	Composite pavements	.	277

	7.1.5	Surface water drainage	278
	7.1.6	Hard shoulders, kerbs, footpaths and verges	279
	7.2	**BRIDGES**	
	7.2.1	Types of construction	280
	7.2.2	Foundation techniques and bridge construction	284
	7.2.3	Bridge bearings and expansion joints	289
	7.2.4	Waterproofing and surfacing of bridge decks	291
	7.3	**SUBWAYS**	
	7.3.1	Methods of construction	292
	7.3.2	Methods of waterproofing	295
	7.3.3	Lighting, finishes and drainage	295
	7.4	**AIRFIELD CONSTRUCTION**	
	7.4.1	Introduction to pavement design	296
	7.4.2	Foundation considerations	296
	7.4.3	Pavement construction	296
Chapter 8		**Concrete and Steelwork**	
	8.1	**CONCRETE**	
	8.1.1	Materials	299
	8.1.2	Concrete mixing and placing	300
	8.1.3	Formwork and reinforcement	305
	8.1.4	Jointing in concrete structures	310
	8.1.5	Pre-stressed concrete	312
	8.1.6	Special concreting systems	317
	8.1.7	Cutting and demolition of concreting	320
	8.2	**STEELWORK**	
	8.2.1	Types of structure	322
	8.2.2	Erection of buildings and bridges	324
	8.2.3	Bolting, riveting and welding	328
Chapter 9		**Services**	
	9.1	**PIPELINES FOR WATER, GAS AND SEWAGE**	
	9.1.1	Introduction	331
	9.1.2	Pipe materials	331
	9.1.3	Jointing of pipes	334
	9.1.4	Construction methods	335
	9.1.5	Coatings and linings	339
	9.2	**SEWAGE TREATMENT**	
	9.2.1	General considerations	342
	9.2.2	Methods of treatment	343
Chapter 10		**Railway Trackwork, Chimneys and Cooling Towers**	
	10.1	**RAILWAY TRACKWORK**	
	10.1.1	Introduction	351
	10.1.2	The Permanent Way	351
	10.1.3	Switches and crossings	356
	10.2	**CHIMNEYS AND COOLING TOWERS**	
	10.2.1	Chimney construction	358
	10.2.2	Liners and insulation	362
	10.2.3	Demolition of tall chimneys	365
	10.2.4	Cooling towers	365
Index			371

Chapter 1

General Considerations in Civil Engineering

1.1 SITE INVESTIGATION

1.1.1 Objects of investigation

Civil engineering works and building structures are alike in having some form of foundation which is supported by the ground. The interaction between a structure and the soil beneath it is complex, and therefore knowledge of site and soil conditions is an essential prerequisite to sound design. This has not always been appreciated or exemplified in practice — understandably perhaps before the turn of the century, when studies first began to be made of soil conditions and soil behaviour. The earliest indication of this, with the advent of tall buildings, was the construction of three buildings in Chicago during the period 1880 to 1894, which were founded successfully on steel grillage bases and large rudimentary piles formed by filling wells with concrete. There are many other instances where the construction of buildings and engineering structures was not so successful and where monumental failures have, in some cases, become notable tourist attractions. The first published data giving comprehensive methods for the analysis of soil was not available until 1925, when Terzaghi's classic work 'Erdbaumechanik', was eventually written. It is now standard practice to examine any site on which a structure is intended to be erected, in order to determine

the suitability of the site for the proposed works

an adequate and economic foundation design

the difficulties that may arise during the construction period

the occurrence or cause of all changes in site conditions.

The practical outcome of such investigation depends upon the nature and magnitude of the proposed works together with the availability of reliable sources of information concerning the site or area. In some cases the area may have been investigated several times and data may be available relating to substrata details. Such data will enable the engineers to determine the extent to which further investigation may be warranted.

If the proposed work is not directly connected with the erection of new structures, there may be other factors to be considered, some of which are discussed in 1.1.3 (Types of Investigation).

1.1.2 Classification of rocks and soils

Rocks and soils are classified so that a systematic and concise record of their characteristics can be kept to provide engineers and others with basic information for design and other purposes. The classification offers a basic comparison against other similar materials.

The simplest classification of geological deposits falls generally into two major classes

'rock' which refers mainly to a hard rigid and strongly cemented deposit, and

'soil' which refers to the soft, or loose and uncemented deposits.

When using such definitions it must be appreciated that many deposits fall between these extremes which are difficult to define.

Rock types

The geological classification of 'rocks' is very complex, but from an engineering point of view they can be simply classified either by method of excavation, i.e. whether blasting is required or not, or by load bearing qualities and other physical properties.

A typical specification from a quantity surveyor's point of view would be as follows

For the purpose of measurement, rock shall mean solid rock found in ledges or masses in its original position which can only be removed after blasting or breaking by compressed air tools, hydraulic bursting appliances or wedges and sledge hammers; it shall also mean any solid boulders or detached pieces of rock exceeding 1.0 cubic metre in volume which may be encountered in the excavations.

Solid rocks normally provide excellent foundation support; they exhibit high load bearing capacities and negligible settlement.

Rock can be placed into one or other of three basic categories: Sedimentary, Metamorphic and Igneous.

Sedimentary includes sandstone, limestone and some shales. The quality of sedimentary rock depends on the angle of stratification and cementation (Fig 1.1) together with their behaviour in wet conditions. Deep fissures and swallow holes (swallow holes are cavities formed at some time by the passage of water through soft rock) (Fig 1.2) are common in limestone and are difficult to detect during site investigation.

Slope in rock formation may be subject to slip

Fig 1.1

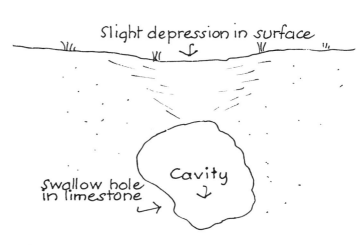

Slight depression in surface

Swallow hole in limestone

Cavity

Fig 1.2

Metamorphic includes slates, schists, gneisses and some shales. These rocks include any sedimentary deposit or igneous rock which, after consolidation, has become altered by heat or pressure eg limestone may become completely re-crystallised into marble. With few exceptions the metamorphic rocks are hard but are subject to faults which allow movements. This is found in tunnelling where overbreak is high ('overbreak' refers to the amount of extra rock excavation beyond the neat lines of tunnel excavation).

Igneous includes granites, dolerites and basalt, and they are formed by solidification of molten material which has ascended towards the surface from the hot lower levels of the earth's crust. Their bearing capacity is very high, in some cases three times greater than that of hard sedimentary rocks and forty times greater than that of alluvial clays and sands.

The loadbearing capacity of all rocks is greatly reduced if they are not in a sound condition. Unsound conditions are created by weathering where the rock becomes decomposed, by shattering caused by earth movements and by having steeply dipping bed joints. Some sedimentary rocks have low bearing capacity due to the presence of soft clayey material in the bed joints.

Soil types

Soils include materials of various origins, such as residual soils (topsoil), detrital sediments (sands, gravel, silts), organic deposits (peat), calcarious deposits (shell, coral) and pyroclastics (uncemented volcanic dust).

These soils are identified by two essential characteristics, firstly the size and nature of the soil particles and secondly by the density and structural properties. Basic soil types and their characteristics are shown in Table 1.1.

The particle size is particularly important when considering pumping operations since silts are difficult or impossible to drain, whereas sands drain readily.

Where soils are used in the actual construction works (e.g. roadworks and earth dams), the particle arrangement and moisture content of the soil may alter drastically and for this to be foreseen accurate preliminary classification is essential. Classification and testing of soils should be subject to BS 1377:1975.

1.1.3   Types of investigation

As indicated in 1.1.1 site investigation is carried out in most cases as a preliminary to new works; however, there are other reasons for site investigation and they are given below

investigation of defects or failure of existing works

investigation as to the safety of existing works

investigation relating to the suitability and availability of materials for constructional purposes.

Firms may specialise in any one or more of these types of investigation.

Investigation of sites for new works

This type of investigation has broader implications and a much wider scope than the other types of investigation above, due to the amount of information required and the economic solutions involved. Considering excavation methods, the investigation will reveal such things as

ground water condition and implications such as the necessity of ground water lowering

whether excavation of the soil will be difficult

whether the sides of the excavation will be stable if unsupported.

On the design side test samples and insitu tests when analysed will indicate such things as the bearing capacity of foundations, the amount of settlement likely to occur and the stability of cuttings and embankments. It is particularly important, in the case of new works, to consider the least favourable site conditions encountered when designing the proposed works — this will take into account the possible variations in strata.

Such information on sub-surface conditions is especially valuable in the case of virgin sites particularly where there is evidence of failure or distortion in similar structures in the locality. Special precautions are necessary where it is known that underground cavities, such as mine working and swallow holes, are likely to exist.

The data obtained will require careful recording and plotting, the extent of which will depend on the nature of the site. Sites may be classified into two broad groups

Field identification and description of soils

TABLE 1.1

BS 5930 : 1981

Basic soil type	Particle size, mm	Visual identification	Particle nature and plasticity	Composite soil types (mixtures of basic soil types)	Compactness/strength — Term	Compactness/strength — Field test	Structure — Term	Structure — Field identification
BOULDERS	over 200	Only seen complete in pits or exposures.	Particle shape: Angular, Subangular, Subrounded, Rounded, Flat, Elongate	**Scale of secondary constituents with coarse soils** — Term | % of clay or silt	Loose	By inspection of voids and particle packing.	Homogeneous	Deposit consists essentially of one type.
COBBLES	200 to 60	Often difficult to recover from boreholes.		slightly clayey / slightly silty { GRAVEL or SAND } — under 5	Dense		Inter-stratified	Alternating layers of varying types or with bands or lenses of other materials. Interval scale for bedding spacing may be used.
GRAVELS (coarse 60–20, medium 20–6, fine 6–2)	coarse 60, medium 20, fine 6	Easily visible to naked eye; particle shape can be described; grading can be described. Well graded: wide range of grain sizes, well distributed. Poorly graded: not well graded. (May be uniform: size of most particles lies between narrow limits; or gap graded: an intermediate size of particle is markedly under-represented.)	Texture: Rough, Smooth, Polished	clayey / silty { GRAVEL or SAND } — 5 to 15	Loose	Can be excavated with a spade; 50 mm wooden peg can be easily driven.	Heterogeneous	A mixture of types.
SANDS (coarse 2–0.6, medium 0.6–0.2, fine 0.2–0.06)	coarse 2, medium 0.6, fine 0.2 / 0.06	Visible to naked eye; very little or no cohesion when dry; grading can be described. Well graded: wide range of grain sizes, well distributed. Poorly graded: not well graded. (May be uniform: size of most particles lies between narrow limits; or gap graded: an intermediate size of particle is markedly under-represented.)		very clayey / very silty { GRAVEL or SAND } — 15 to 35. Sandy GRAVEL / Gravelly SAND — Sand or gravel and important second constituent of the coarse fraction. (See 41.3.2.2) For composite types described as: clayey: fines are plastic, cohesive; silty: fines non-plastic or of low plasticity	Dense; Slightly cemented	Requires pick for excavation; 50 mm wooden peg hard to drive. / Visual examination; pick removes soil in lumps which can be abraded.	Weathered	Particles may be weakened and may show concentric layering.
SILTS (coarse 0.06–0.02, medium 0.02–0.006, fine 0.006–0.002)	coarse 0.06, medium 0.02, fine 0.006 / 0.002	Only coarse silt barely visible to naked eye; exhibits little plasticity and marked dilatancy; slightly granular or silky to the touch. Disintegrates in water; lumps dry quickly; possess cohesion but can be powdered easily between fingers.	Non-plastic or low plasticity	**Scale of secondary constituents with fine soils** — Term | % of sand or gravel. sandy / gravelly { CLAY or SILT } — 35 to 65. – CLAY:SILT – under 35.	Soft or loose; Firm or dense	Easily moulded or crushed in the fingers. / Can be moulded or crushed by strong pressure in the fingers.	Fissured; Intact	Break into polyhedral fragments along fissures. Interval scale for spacing of discontinuities may be used. / No fissures.
CLAYS	under 0.002	Dry lumps can be broken but not powdered between the fingers; they also disintegrate under water but more slowly than silt; smooth to the touch; exhibits plasticity but no dilatancy; sticks to the fingers and dries slowly; shrinks appreciable on drying usually showing cracks. Intermediate and high plasticity clays show these properties to a moderate and high degree, respectively.	Intermediate plasticity (Lean clay); High plasticity (Fat clay)	**Examples of composite types** (Indicating preferred order for description): "Loose, brown, subangular very sandy, fine to coarse GRAVEL with small pockets of soft grey clay"; "Medium dense, light brown, clayey, fine and medium SAND"; "Stiff, orange brown, fissured sandy CLAY"; "Firm, brown, thinly laminated SILT and CLAY"; "Plastic, brown, amorphous PEAT"	Very soft; Soft; Firm; Stiff; Very stiff	Exudes between fingers when squeezed in hand. / Moulded by light finger pressure. / Can be moulded by strong finger pressure. / Cannot be moulded by fingers. Can be indented by thumb. / Can be indented by thumb nail.	Homogeneous; Inter-stratified; Weathered	Deposit consists essentially of one type. / Alternating layers of varying types. Interval scale for thickness of layers may be used. / Usually has crumb or columnar structure.
ORGANIC CLAY, SILT or SAND	Varies	Contains substantial amounts of organic vegetable matter.			Firm	Fibres already compressed together.	Fibrous	Plant remains recognizable and retain some strength.
PEATS	Varies	Predominantly plant remains usually dark brown or black in colour, often with distinctive smell; low bulk density.			Spongy; Plastic	Very compressible and open structure. / Can be moulded in hand, and smears fingers.	Amorphous	Recognizable plant remains absent.

Left-margin groupings:
- Very coarse soils
- Coarse soils (over 65 % sand and gravel sizes)
- Fine soils (over 35 % silt and clay sizes)
- Organic soils

Interval scales

Scale of bedding spacing

Term	Mean spacing, mm
Very thickly bedded	over 2000
Thickly bedded	2000 to 600
Medium bedded	600 to 200
Thinly bedded	200 to 60
Very thinly bedded	60 to 20
Thickly laminated	20 to 6
Thinly laminated	under 6

Scale of spacing of other discontinuities

Term	Mean spacing, mm
Very widely spaced	over 2000
Widely spaced	2000 to 600
Medium spaced	600 to 200
Closely spaced	200 to 60
Very closely spaced	60 to 20
Extremely closely spaced	under 20

Colour

Red, Pink, Yellow, Brown
Olive, Green, Blue, White, Grey, Black, etc.
Supplemented as necessary with:
Light, Dark, Mottled, etc.
and
Pinkish, Reddish, Yellowish, Brownish, etc.

(Reproduced by permission of HMSO)

compact sites such as those to contain buildings, bridges, dams, docks and airfields. (Reference 1.1.5 see page 7).

extended sites covering a long narrow strip of land required for roads, railways, tunnels, sewers, pipe and transmission lines and coastal defence.

The type of site and site works determine the extent of the investigation to be made and the number of records and plans to be established.

In many cases the construction of new works affects adjacent properties or interests and therefore a desirable factor in the investigation is that of making a record of existing works. This will usually involve a photographic record in addition to the normal survey.

Investigation of defects or failure of existing works

This type of investigation is necessary to establish the cause of the failure and to provide information indicative of a remedy. Measurements and observations of the structure in question are taken to indicate whether or not the ground conditions are involved; if so then soil investigation should take place. This investigation will reveal the level of ground water and the true state of sub-strata. Faults can often be traced to a weakness in a particular stratum of soil.

Investigation as to the safety of existing works

When proposed new works are planned it may be necessary to investigate existing works to decide whether the latter will be adversely affected by changes in ground conditions brought about by the new works. Existing works may be affected by the following

excavations which may reduce ground support

tunnelling or mining which may cause subsidence

vibrations (eg.from piling operations) which may cause fractures

extra load created by new works may overload stratum supporting existing works

soil movement due to heat or freezing induced by proximity to plant installations

ground water lowering may cause settlement

disturbed drainage path may cause flooding and instability of slopes.

All these factors have to be considered if danger is to be avoided from the construction of new works.

Investigation as to the suitability and availability of material for construction

There are two quite different problems with the mass movement of earth; the first is disposal e.g. in the case of spoil from cuts and the second acquisition e.g. for large fill projects such as reclaimation. In both cases however, investigation is necessary to establish the quantity and suitability of the soil for the purpose for which it is to be used. In some cases the suitability of the material can be established by visual inspection and the main problem is the sheer volume involved and this normally requires investigation to establish the quantity available. In other cases the quantity is not in question but detailed testing of the quality is necessary.

It should now be appreciated that the type of investigation could greatly affect the cost of works at design stage.

1.1.4   General enquiries and preliminary work

Before the work can start certain general enquiries should be made; these include a check of information from local authorities, libraries, museums and other relevant sources. These checks may reveal records of previous or nearby soil investigations. Geological data, aerial photographs, historical information and local knowledge will help to establish the existence of particular problems. In some cases the general enquiries will give enough information to obviate the need of further detailed investigation (e.g. in the case of structures with minimal loadings). However, where loadings are high and substrata investigation is necessary, reference should be made to the County

Geological Survey. This will show the main strata and any superficial deposits. The Geological Survey Office also keep records of boreholes, which are available for perusal.

In mining areas the National Coal Board keep records of active works and details of some abandoned workings are recorded and filed in the Mining Records Office.

Aerial photography is a valuable means of obtaining topographical maps, especially of extended sites. This work is undertaken by specialist firms and the photographs can be geologically interpreted so as to highlight areas for detailed investigations.

Where, however, detailed information is not available then a preliminary reconnaissance should be carried out by engineers. This reconnaissance, normally carried out by walking over the area, will reveal many local conditions which can be inspected in detail. The general topography will often be indicative of the soil conditions below which will require further investigation: typical examples of this are: stepped ground, which may be caused by geological faults; broken or terraced ground which may indicate landslip; depressions in a limestone area may indicate the existence of swallow holes and the nature of the vegetation may give some indication of the moisture and acidity characteristics of the soil.

If the site has been used in earlier years it is important to establish the use it has had and the position and type of foundation if any. It is important also to obtain further details of sites which have been previously used as pits, quarries, coal mines or for brine-pumping. A particular problem is that where depressions have been subsequently filled in with waste, such fill areas are not only subject to excessive settlement, but can also be subject to spontaneous combustion and harmful chemical content.

These preliminary investigations can save a great deal of time and money in the planning and development stages of a contract, as well as being the essential background to positive soil investigation.

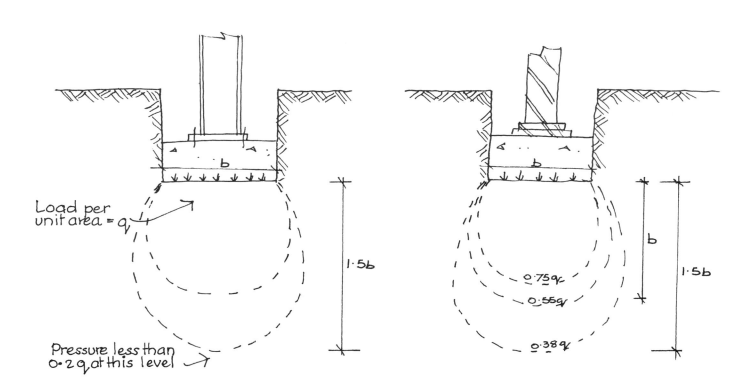

Fig 1.3   *Bulb pressure under a pad foundation showing distribution of load*

Fig 1.4   *Bulb pressure under strip foundation showing distribution of load*

1.1.5   Procedure for investigation

Compact sites

In the case of compact sites for buildings, bridges, dams, reservoirs, docks, etc the investigation will require deep and closely spaced borings. The actual number and position of borings depends on the type of structure and nature of site. However, the number of bore holes should be such as to give a clear picture of all significant variations in the soil over the site, and the depth of such bore holes should be such as to reach all strata likely to influence the stability of the works. Particular attention should be given to soil at or just below the proposed foundation level because weak strata below the foundation level may fail even though only subject to reduced 'bulb pressure' (see Fig 1.3 and Fig 1.4).

It will be noticed that the pressure bulb below strip foundations is greater than that underneath pad foundations; this is due to the plan continuity of the foundation. Pressure bulbs of less than 20 per cent of the original loading at foundation level can be ignored when considering the effects of loading on various strata. Where two foundations are near to each other the overlap in stresses may call for further investigation of lower strata (see Fig 1.5).

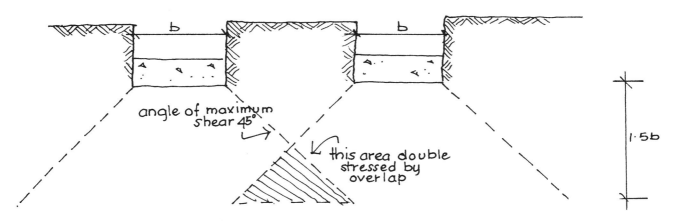

Fig 1.5   *Showing overlapping of foundation stresses*

Extended Sites

The detailed work of exploring such sites will vary according to nature and complexity of the proposed works. A preliminary survey is of particular importance in such cases because the evidence thus gained will assist in planning the bore hole frequencies and patterns. In the main, shallow borings will suffice to reveal ground water conditions and the nature of upper strata. Borings are often made by means of hand or machine augers, the latter often mounted on a small mobile vehicle.

In all cases the 'extent' of the borings will be determined by reference to site conditions revealed by reconnaissance. The first few borings will indicate the amount of horizontal variation and hence will suggest a suitable pattern of boring. All borings should be spaced sufficiently close together to prevent false deductions concerning the uniformity of horizontal strata. The 'depth' of boring will be determined by the type of loading involved but account must be taken of any slope in the strata and variations in their thickness. In particular when boring through glacial deposits, care must be exercised to ensure that boulders are not mistaken for bedrock. There are three main factors which govern the depth of exploration

the depth to which the soil is to be significantly stressed

the depth to which weathering is likely to affect the soil

the depth at which impermeable strata occur.

The first factor depends on the type of structure, the intensity of loading and the shape and size of the foundation structure. Where large foundation areas are stressed the bulb pressures are far-reaching, therefore raft foundations may carry loads which will stress weak areas below normal good load bearing strata (Fig 1.6).

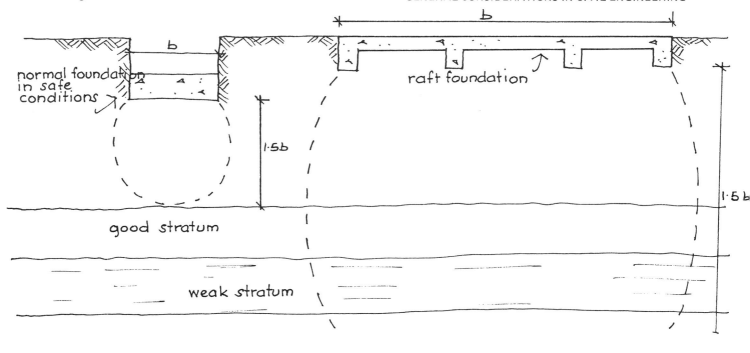

Fig 1.6   *Showing bulb pressure below raft going through weak stratum*

It is necessary therefore to know the characteristics of soil at a depth of up to 1.5 times the breadth of foundation. For such works as roads and airfields the depth of exploration is normally taken as a minimum of 1.5 metres.

The second factor deals with seasonal changes in moisture content and this has been known to affect some soils down to depths of 1.5 metres. In extreme cases on the continent this depth may be even as much as 4 to 5 metres. Frost is unlikely to affect soil more than 0.75 metres below ground level unless industrial equipment such as freezing plant is installed.

The third factor will apply to water conserving structures such as reservoirs where an impermeable stratum is essential and must be located.

The seasonal presence of waterlogged ground may render the site unsuitable for the proposed works and the contours of the water table should therefore be found in order to decide whether this can be overcome. This type of survey will also be necessary as a preliminary to design of intercepting lines of drainage to prevent the influx of ground water from higher levels (Fig 1.7).

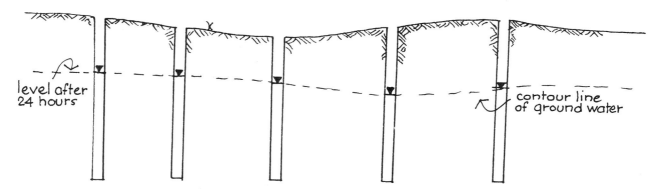

Fig 1.7   *Ground water level in bore holes*

The ground water should be tested for the presence of harmful substances such as sulphates, which might adversely affect the strength of concrete, steel or other materials used in the development.

Soil movements other than those due to loading

So far, the procedure for investigation has dealt with normal considerations in soil investigation, but it must be stated that not all soil movement is due to loading from new works, or to the collapse of underground cavities. Movements may be caused by any or all of the following:

drying and shrinking of soils

frost heave

artesian pressure

seismic phenomena

Perhaps the most common is the first, where clays are found. The clay loses water in certain climatic conditions or where vegetation is excessive. Trees and shrubs can cause permanent drying to depths of up to 5 metres during summer and normal vegetation can cause drying out up to 2 metres deep. Vertical movements of the soil up to 100 mm have been recorded in the vicinity of large trees. These factors should be borne in mind when the investigation takes place.

1.1.6 Methods of site exploration

When discussing the procedure for investigation, reference was made to borings as a means of investigation. This is perhaps the most common method of site exploration, but certainly not the only one. Considering new works, from the very small to the very large contracts, a general guide to exploration would be as follows:

small works — trial pits up to 3 m deep

medium to large scale works — borings up to 30 m deep

very large scale works (e.g. dams, power stations) — a combination of deep boring, pits and insitu examinations from headings and shafts.

It must be noted that the above is only a guide: the detailed methods of exploration would depend on the type of construction and site involved.

Trial pits

This is the cheapest form of exploration in shallow depths (e.g. up to 3m); above 3 metres deep the cost increases rapidly compared with boring. The main advantage is that soils and rocks can be exposed and examined insitu. This method shows changes in strata much more clearly than by borings. The pits are dug out either by local labour or by a small tractor-mounted excavator. The plan size of a pit depends on method of excavation but approximately 1.2 x 1.2 m and should be dug at distances 20 metres apart in either direction. Holes should be kept well clear of the position of actual foundations, but should be in the vicinity of important structures such as heavily-loaded walls or columns. Problems occur in water-bearing soils, particularly sands, and therefore the economies of shoring and pumping pits may outweigh the savings gained against specialist borings. In dry conditions these pits are particularly valuable since they allow hand-cut samples to be taken, thereby minimising the disturbance of the sample and maximising the conditions for accurate testing. Deeper trial pits may be used for the investigation of rock fissures or to explore layers of weak rock which cannot be removed intact in normal boring operations. Such deep pits are costly to construct and would be used only in large scale exploration. Trial pits are the best method of exploring back filled areas and sites overlain by variable natural deposits.

Borings

This type of exploration can be achieved by various methods:

Hand or mechanical auger borings are relatively cheap methods of sub-surface exploration for soils which will stand unsupported. Holes can be sunk to depths up to 3 metres provided there are no obstructions such as boulders. The diameter of the bore hole is usually 150 or 200 mm: this allows soil sampling tubes to be used without difficulty. The mechanical auger is used in gravelly soil, which involves the use of a casing to prevent collapse of the boring.

Shell and auger boring is a method which can be carried out in all types of soils, because the bore hole is lined with a thick-walled steel casing. The boring is achieved by augers or open ended shells in cohesive soils (fig 1.8) and shells in the case of non-cohesive soils (Fig 1.9).

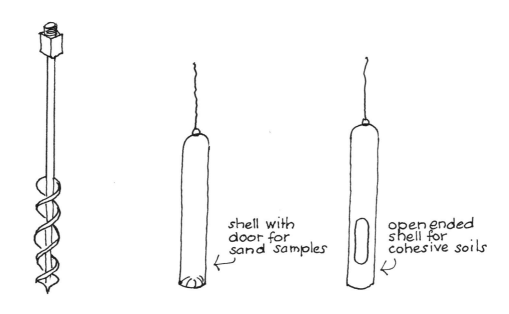

shell with door for sand samples

open ended shell for cohesive soils

Fig 1.8   *Auger*   Fig 1.9   *Sampling shells*

Other tools consist of chisel bits for breaking up boulders. All the tools and sampling tubes are attached to sectioned rods.

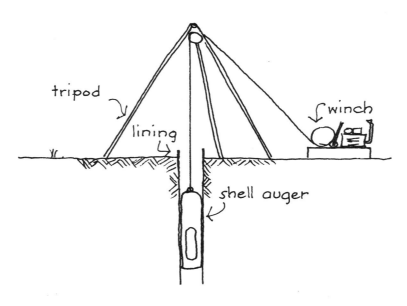

tripod

lining

winch

shell auger

Fig 1.10a   *Boring rig*

The borehole is lined as the hole is bored and the section linings screwed together and driven as the hole deepens (Fig 1.10a).

Percussion boring is the oldest method of boring, in which the formation is broken up by repeated blows from a bit or chisel. Water is added to the hole as the work proceeds and the resulting debris is removed at intervals by shell auger or pressure washing. Samples from this type of boring are inevitably disturbed and some engineers seriously question their value and reliability.

Fig 1.10b *Investigator rig for penetrating soils and weak rocks. (Soil Mechanics Limited)*

Fig 1.10c *The Boyles rig which penetrates rocks by diamond drilling. (Soil Mechanics Limited)*

Wash borings (Fig 1.11): the soil is loosened and removed from the bore hole by means of a strong jet of water or drilling mud. The liquid is jetted through a steel tube which is worked up and down the hole. The liquid disintegrates the soil and carries it up the annular space between the tube and casing. Wash boring has the advantage that the soil is not disturbed by blows of a tool or shell, but it is limited to soils which do not contain boulders or large gravels. Mud, such as bentonite allows borings to be carried out without linings in non-cohesive soils . The soil in its settled out state can be dried and used for identification purposes.

Rotary borings: this method, which is used for the exploration of rocks, can be divided into three categories:

mud-rotary drilling

core drilling

shot drilling

In mud-rotary drilling a mud-laden fluid is pumped in a continuous stream down hollow drilling rods to the rotating bit. The bit is kept in contact with the face of the boring and the fluid carries the debris up the annular space between the rods and the sides of the hole. A steel casing to the hole is not necessary. The cores are obtained by the use of coring tools.

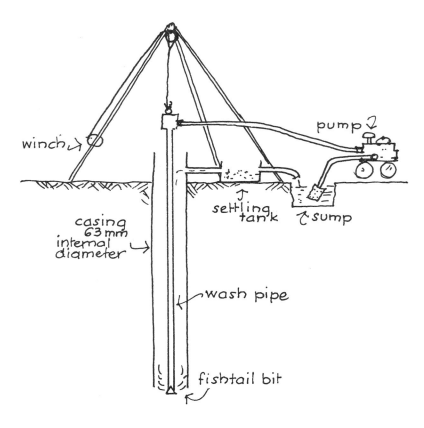

Fig 1.11   *Wash boring*

Core drilling is a process designed to recover continuous cores of rock. Water or compressed air is jetted down the hole through hollow rods and returns up the annular space carrying rock cuttings when the rock is friable. For hard rock cores, the crown of the drill is usually tipped with industrial diamonds. The continuous cores are laid in wooden core boxes in depth order.

Shot drilling differs from the other two types of core drilling in that the drilling head consists of chilled steel shot being fed down the bore as an abrasive in place of the normal drilling head. Another feature is that the coarse cuttings do not flow to the surface but are accumulated in a special cup above the cutting head. This method of drilling is used for holes in excess of 150 mm diameter.

Headings and shafts

Headings are employed to explore steeply dipping strata. Headings are also used in the form of a pilot tunnel, in anticipation of the driving of larger tunnels later. They have an advantage over pits in that they can be drained easily and also allow easy removal of spoil. Shafts approximately one metre diameter can be bored using large power-driven augers. The sides of the shafts are supported to protect personnel engaged in soil inspection.

Choice of method

The choice between these various methods of exploration will normally depend on the following factors:

Topography: although there are exceptions, in general terms hilly country offers the choice between pits and headings whilst low-lying marshy areas are best explored by borings.

Nature of ground: where rock is expected, borings of various types should be used unless a number of pits would prove more economical. Large diameter borings in fissured rock will allow photographs to be taken by a remote-controlled borehole camera (Fig 1.12 'a' and 'b'). In soils the normal method of exploration is by boring holes unless the loads expected are small; then shallow pits will provide adequate samples for testing.

Cost: this subject is discussed more fully in Section 1.1.10 but as a general rule deep exploration by boring is more economic than pits, whereas shallow exploration may be more economical using pits. The final decision will depend on the number of holes and the amount of information required.

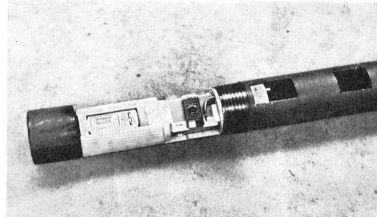

Figs 1.12a and 1.12b   *The camera and flash-gun assembled in a 1.5m length of HX core barrel*   (Ground Engineering)

Fig 1.12c   *Borehole camera photograph of a 40 year old timbered heading to a sewer some 9 metres below a trunk road*   (Ground Engineering)

Types of samples

These are two types of samples:

Disturbed samples: these are samples removed from boreholes with augers or other equipment which interfere with the natural structure of the material. Such samples are useful for visual grading and determining moisture content, and in some cases for laboratory testing. Samples are placed in airtight jars with identifying labels.

Undisturbed samples: these are samples removed by methods which preserve, so far as practicable, the natural structure and properties of the material. Samples in this category are easily obtained in rock and clay, but difficult in certain other soils. Table 1.2 below shows the method employed for obtaining samples. The graph in Fig 1.13 shows the comparative strength of various samples of the same soil strata.

TABLE 1.2

SAMPLING METHODS		
Soil	Disturbed	Hand samples Auger samples Shell samples
	Undisturbed	Hand samples Core samples
Rocks	Disturbed	Sludge samples from percussion or rotary drills
	Undisturbed	Hand samples Cores

(a) Remoulded sample
(b) Sample obtained by normal methods
(c) Sample taken out by hand from a trench

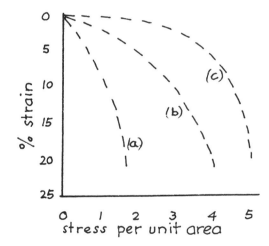

Fig 1.13   *Comparative strengths of soil samples from the same strata*

The method used to obtain samples in cohesive soils is that using 100 mm diameter sampling tubes. The tube, shown in Fig 1.14, is screwed on to a set of rods and pushed down or driven into the soil. The cutting edge of the tube is a detachable threaded ring in metal or plastic which cleaves the soil 1 mm under the internal tube diameter. This prevents consolidation of the soil during the overdrive so that further consolidation is avoided. The tube, when removed, is sealed at both ends with wax or rubber caps and after being suitably marked is sent to the laboratory for the testing of its contents. On arrival at the laboratory the sample may be carefully extruded into a 100 mm plastic pipe (normally ordinary PVC soil vent pipe), thus reducing the cost of storing valuable steel sampling tubes.

1.1.7 Insitu testing

Tests to obtain the density or shear strength of soils insitu are very valuable since they can be carried out without disturbing the soil. Such tests are particularly valuable in sands and silts. The main tests are:

standard penetration

vane

unconfined compression

plate bearing

California bearing ratio (CBR).

Standard penetration test (BS 1377 Test 19)

As with all penetration tests this consists of measuring the resistance of the soil to penetration under static or dynamic loading. This particular test is made by driving a 35 mm (internal diameter) split-barrel sampler into the soil at the bottom of a bore hole (Fig 1.14b). The sampler, suspended on rods, is first driven 150 mm into the soil by a falling standard weight (65 kg falling through a distance of 760 mm). The sampler is then driven a further 300 mm and the number of blows required to effect each 75 mm of penetration is recorded. The test is used to establish the relative density of soil. Tables No 1.3 and 1.4 overleaf give some indication of the results of such tests, but the data shown is only approximate and would require expert interpretation before being used.

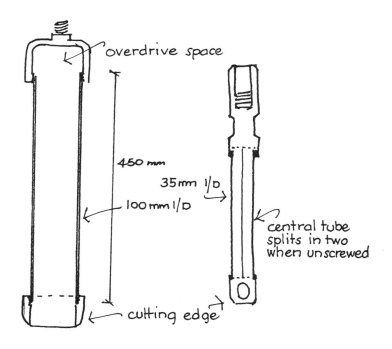

Fig 1.14a   *Standard sampling tube*   Fig 1.14b   *Split-barrel sampler*

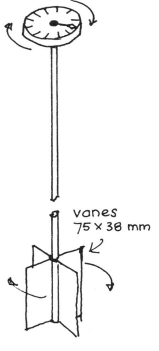

Fig 1.15   *'Pilcon' hand vane test equipment*

TABLE 1.3   **TABLE 1.4**

SANDS			CLAYS		
No. of Blows	Relative Density	Notes	No. of Blows	Consistency	Compressive Strength in kN/m^2
0 — 4	Very loose	Can behave like a liquid	0 — 2	Very soft	0 — 24
4 — 10	Loose		2 — 4	Soft	24 — 49
10 — 30	Medium		4 — 8	Medium	49 — 98
30 — 50	Dense		8 — 15	Stiff	98 — 196
Over 50	Very Dense	Withstands heavy loads	15 — 30	Very stiff	196 — 392
			Over 30	Hard	Over 392

Vane test (BS 1377 Test 18)

This test measures the shear strength of soft cohesive soils insitu. The vane (Fig 1.15) is pushed into the soft clay and rotated by hand at a constant rate. The amount of torque necessary for rotation is measured by some type of spring balance on top of the rods and the shear strength of the soil is calculated. In some Scandinavian countries the vane test is also regarded as a reliable means of determining the shear strength of fissured clays.

Unconfined compression test (BS 1377 Test 20)

This test can be used either in the site laboratory or in the field since the apparatus is very portable; this method is therefore particularly useful where a large number of samples are required to be tested. Samples 76 mm long and 38 mm diameter are placed in the apparatus and a load applied. The sample is sheared under load and the shear stress is automatically recorded on a chart fixed to the apparatus (Fig 1.16).

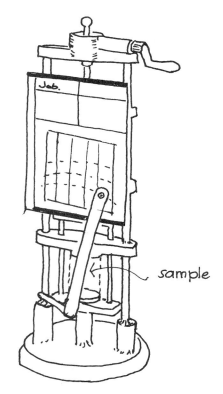

Fig 1.16   *Apparatus for unconfined compresssion test*

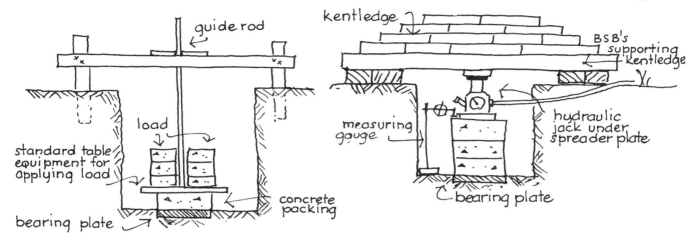

Fig 1.17   *Plate test using loading table*   Fig 1.18   *Plate test using hydraulic jack*

Plate bearing test

This type of test was once very popular and is still used on large engineering projects, such as power stations, as a means of providing insitu data on the behaviour of soils at foundation level. The procedure consists of excavating a pit to the level of the proposed foundation and then loading a steel or cast iron plate (usually 600 x 600 mm in size) on the bottom of the pit. The load can be applied in either of two ways; the first by loading it with increments of kentledge (concrete blocks or steel billets) (Fig 1.17) or by means of a hydraulic jack bearing against a heavily loaded beam (Fig 1.18).

The load is applied in increments and the settlement after each increment is recorded and plotted on a time graph. A typical increment of loading would be from approximately 1/5th of the proposed design load up to failure point, which should be not less than approximately 3 times design load. Each increment should be added at 24 hourly intervals depending on the type of soil to allow settlement to cease, and measurements of this should be taken about every 6 hours. Failure is assumed when the settlement reaches a depth equal to 10% (some engineers say 15%) of the breadth of the loading plate. The safe load (qs) should be taken as one-third of that load which causes failure. One disadvantage of this test is the lack of simulation of 'bulb pressure'. The bulb pressure from a test of this nature is usually far smaller than the bulb pressure from the actual foundation (Fig 1.19). This could lead to error in detecting settlement of a weak stratum.

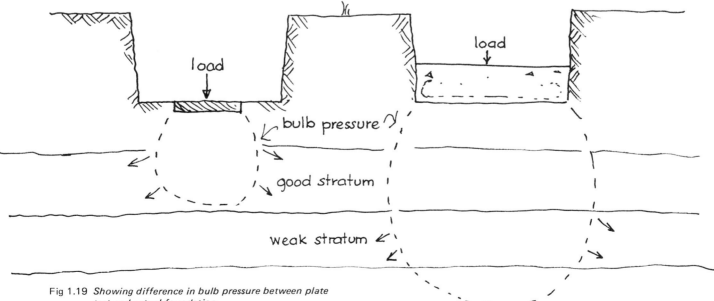

Fig 1.19 *Showing difference in bulb pressure between plate test and actual foundation*

California bearing ratio test (CBR Test — BS 1377 Test 16)

This test is used in the design of flexible pavements and can be carried out on site. The test was first designed by the California Division of Highways, as a result of an extensive investigation into the causes of pavement failure in 1928—9. The test shows the load-penetration of soils relative to standard crushed stone sample. The test is carried out using a lorry to obtain the necessary reaction load through a screw jack. The test is normally carried out on soil at least 1 metre below ground level (i.e. below the level of any seasonal moisture fluctuation). The test can also be simulated in a soils laboratory by forcing a cylindrical plunger, of a known cross-sectional area, into soil at a given rate.

Other insitu tests include permeability tests, ground water level observations and ground water pressure. These tests are described in BS 5930:1981. Geophysical testing is described in Section 1.1.9.

1.1.8   Laboratory testing

Laboratory testing is undertaken to establish the following characteristics of soils:

identification and classification

measurement of their engineering properties

chemical content

Identification and classification

This analysis involves a number of individual tests, such as:

visual examination

moisture content

liquid and plastic limits

particle size distribution

Visual examinations are made to note the colour, texture and consistency of disturbed and undisturbed samples, these being used later to describe the soil in the engineer's reports.

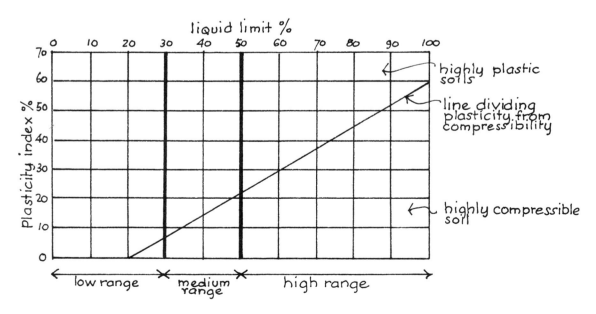

Fig 1.20   *Plasticity chart*

The moisture content is important in all soil samples, since it helps to arrange a programme of testing (by relating samples to liquid and plastic limits) so that no doubtful sample will be overlooked. The higher the natural moisture content of the soil the greater will be its compressibility. Clays in London have an average moisture content of 25% whilst those under Mexico City are about 250%, this accounting for the excessive settlement in the city.

Liquid and plastic limit tests are made on cohesive soils for classification purposes and for assessing their compressibility. The liquid limit (LL) (BS 1377 Test 2) determines the amount of moisture content necessary to cause the material to flow or move readily under a given number of vibrations, whereas the plastic limit (PL) is determined by rolling out a 3 mm diameter thread of soil and noting the moisture content which will allow the thread to be rolled out still further until it breaks up due to drying. When both liquid and plastic limits are known, the Plasticity Index can be established (Plasticity Index = LL − PL).

Reference to a standard chart, such as Fig 1.20, will indicate likely soil properties in further tests.

Particle size distribution is of particular importance when assessing problems of excavation in permeable soils below the water table. It is also useful for assessing the value of non-cohesive soils for use as aggregates. The first part of the test is achieved by sifting dried samples through BS 410 sieves. In the case of cohesive soils a wet analysis is used, employing a hydrometer. The range of particle sizes is compared with a standard chart.

Measurement of their engineering properties

The foregoing tests give some indication of the engineering properties of a soil but there are also specific tests which yield more definite information relating to, for example:

bulk density of soil

shear strength of soil

consolidation of soil

The bulk density of material is the weight of that material per unit volume. It includes the weight of air or water in its voids. This information is essential in the design of retaining works, where the weight of a stratum is an important factor (e.g. stablity of slopes, formation of earth dams, earth pressure of retaining walls etc). Dry density (weight of solids per unit volume) is used for the determination of optimum compaction in earth dams, embankments and other soil structures.

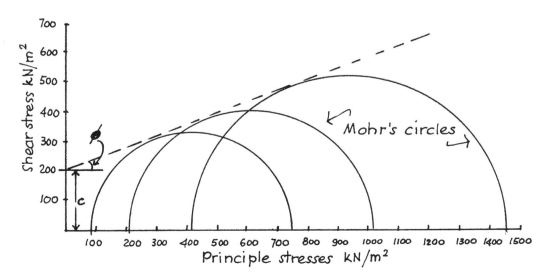

Fig 1.21   *Test on stiff clay plotted on Mohr's circles*

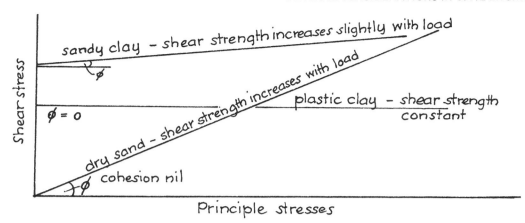

Fig 1.22   *Showing results of triaxial tests for various types of soil*

Shear strength of soil

The shear strength of a soil can be used directly to calculate its bearing capacity and also to calculate the pressure on supports in excavations. There are several tests available for ascertaining shear strength, but the most popular is the Triaxial Compression Test. This test can be carried out using any of three different methods

undrained

consolidated undrained

drained

In principle the test consists of subjecting a cylindrical sample of undisturbed soil (75 mm long x 38 mm diameter) to lateral hydraulic pressure in addition to a vertical load. This is achieved by placing the sample in a plastic cylinder which is subsequently filled with water. Both loads can be increased as required. Measurement of the forces needed to shear the sample is used in the calculation of bearing capacity. In the undrained triaxial test (often referred to as the quick test) the sample, encased in a rubber sheath, is capped with non-porous end plates to prevent the pore water escaping and allow axial loading of the ends. Three tests are carried out one on each of three samples (all cut from the same large sample), each being subjected to a higher hydraulic pressure before axial loading is applied. The results are then plotted in the form of Mohr's circles (Fig 1.21 and 1.22). The consolidated undrained triaxial test allows the sample to drain while applying the hydraulic pressure, thereby allowing the sample to consolidate. After consolidation the sample is stressed without further drainage. In the drained test the axial load is applied so slowly that the pore water can drain off without building up any pressure in the sample; the drainage continues throughout the test and the amount of water drained off is measured. In both cases where drainage is achieved, the water passes through porous discs at the ends of the sample and then through ducts in the apparatus. The consolidated undrained test and the drained test have particular application to the behaviour of soil in earth dams and embankments, and also to stability problems in general. Triaxial compression tests are suitable for cohesive soils only. Where non-cohesive soils have to be tested the Shear Box test is used (Fig 1.23a). A sample of soil is subjected to a standard load, under which a horizontal force is applied to the lower half of the box until the sample shears.

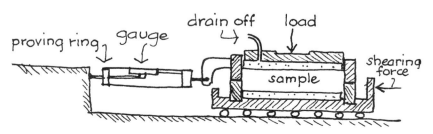

Fig 1.23a   *Shear box test*

Fig 1.23b   *General view of the main Soil Mechanics laboratory showing:- Oedometer presses. Three in the foreground.*

(Soil Mechanics Limited)

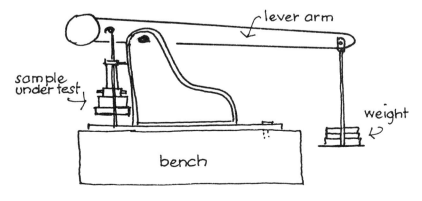

Fig 1.24   *Oedometer*

Consolidation of Soil

The consolidation test provides results which are used to calculate the magnitude and rate of consolidation of a particular soil. This is very important in calculating the movement of soil under foundations. The apparatus used is called an 'Oedometer' (Fig 1.24). The test consists of placing a cylindrical sample (75 mm diameter x 18 mm thick) in a metal ring and capping with porous discs. The sample is placed in a water-filled tray and subjected to load. The load is increased every 24 hours and a time-settlement curve is plotted.

Chemical Content

A chemical analysis of soils and ground water is carried out to assess the effects, if any, which their composition might have on any materials to be used in the proposed works. The tests mainly cover sulphate content and pH value, although bacteriological analysis may also be required for works in tidal mud flats.

1.1.9   Geophysical surveys and other techniques

This type of investigation is useful for extended sites where conditions are generally favourable. Favourable conditions include vast areas of land or water, beneath which a layer of rock may have to be surveyed for thickness and extent by a rapid and inexpensive method. The main contribution is to detect and locate any changes in material or stratification of material in the earth's crust so that the number of borings can be reduced to a minimum. Readings are taken between widely-spaced borings (to ensure continuity or otherwise), allowing rapid coverage of large areas at very low cost. The methods most commonly used are:

electrical resistivity

seismic refraction and reflection

magnetic

Electrical resistivity is based on the difference in electrical resistance between one rock or soil type and another. The method uses four electrodes (an outer pair and an inner pair), a current being passed through the ground via the outer electrodes and the drop in potential being measured at the inner electrodes (Fig 1.25). The electrodes are spaced equally in a straight line and by varying the centres of the electrodes the depth of penetration can be varied. The results allow mathematical and graphical analysis to be made to establish the thicknesses and depths of the various sub-strata. Problems can occur if unsuspected conductors are present e.g. pipes and cables; such conductors can render the results unreliable.

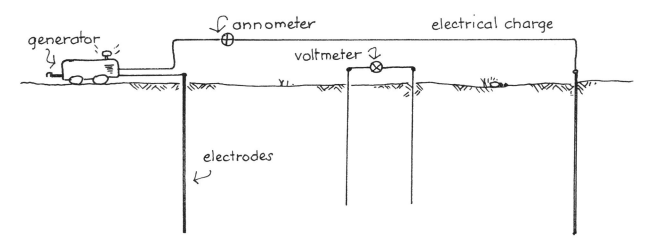

Fig 1.25   *Showing electrodes in position for measuring resistivity*

Seismic methods involve setting up vibrations, normally by explosions, and measuring the time taken by the shock waves and the distance covered (Fig 1.26). The refraction method is suitable for shallow exploration; in this method seismometers are spaced at increasing distances from the source of vibration and the shock waves are recorded and plotted graphically against a time scale. Vibration for this method can be produced by a 6.5 kg hammer. The Reflection method is limited to depths of exploration greater than 150 metres.

Both methods are particularly useful in surveying sites for tunnels, dams and harbour works.

Magnetic methods of investigation are based on measuring the variations in intensity and direction of the earth's magnetic field. The most important application is that of tracing underground cavities such as mine shafts and swallow holes.

Geophysical surveys are still very much in the experimental stage and should be considered complimentary to established methods of exploration rather than an alternative means of obtaining accurate information.

Pumping test

This is a test used to determine a permeability and storage coefficient of the soil where excavations are to be taken down below natural water level. The test involves the construction of a deep well or a ring of well points. A number of observation wells are dug around the pumping point and a check kept on the levels of water in these as pumping continues. The data thus obtained assists in the design of ground water-lowering systems as well as drainage and irrigation systems.

Off-shore investigation

In many cases investigation has to be made in seas and rivers for information concerning future tunnels, jetties, barrages and similar marine works. Drilling is often carried out from the deck of a floating pontoon (Fig 1.27), or alternatively from a Jack-up or spudded pontoon (Fig 1.28), but the most modern and versatile drilling platform for off-shore investigation is the "Mackace" Hover Platform (Fig 1.29). The hover platform has many advantages over a conventional platform, including that of launching directly from a beach, and ease of working over mud trenches, sand banks and deep gullies.

TABLE 1.5

Cost index based on cost of test for moisture content	
Determination of moisture content	1.00
Test for liquid and plastic limits of one sample	6.25
Determination of particle size distribution (dry sieving)	6.25
Determination of particle size distribution (wet sieving)	6.25
Test for organic matter content	10.00
Test for soluble sulphate content of soil or water	6.00
Test for pH value of soil or water	1.00
CBR test	12.50
Determination of compression strength by undrained triaxial compression test (set of 3 specimens)	9.50
Shear box test (6 cm square Quick Drained — set of 3)	21.00
Consolidation test	17.50
Compaction test (BS)	17.50
Unconfined compression test	4.00

Fig 1.26a   *Seismic survey in progress on*
             Cork Refinery site
             using refraction technique
                   (Soil Mechanics Limited)

Fig 1.26b   *Firing the explosives*
                   (Soil Mechanics Limited)

Fig 1.27 *Floating Pontoon* (Soil Mechanics Limited)

Fig 1.28 *Spudded Craft*
(Soil Mechanics Limited)

Fig 1.29 *Hover Platform* (J.T. Mackley & Co. Ltd)

In addition to the investigation for major engineering works, off-shore drilling is also used as a preparation for dredging. In this type of work the same platforms are used but with multi-drilling machines. The technique is known as 'drill and blast' in which rock is drilled and then blasted to a dredgeable size. The whole operation of drilling, placing of explosives and detonation is carried out without men having to leave the platform. This work is discussed further in Section 3.2.2.

1.1.10 Special information and costs

The cost of site investigation is likely to be in the region of only 1% - 2% of the total contract cost, although some contracts where only a limited amount of work is necessary (due to available data) the cost is likely to be less than 1%. This is a small price to pay to ensure the correct design of foundations and the stability of the works.

The cost of setting up drilling rigs on site varies from area to area depending on transportation costs. The cost of drilling and testing are indicated using an index number of 1.00 based on the cost of the test for moisture content and bulk density (Table 1.5).

Before an estimate can be established for site investigation work, the number of bore holes and types of test must be determined. The layouts given in Fig 1.30 give some guide to the number of bore holes required for multi-storey structures.

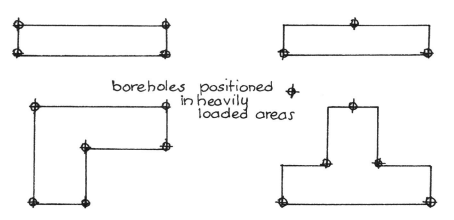

Fig 1.30   *Showing bore hole layout for varying plan shapes of multi-storey blocks*

The depth of boring will be determined by the engineer who carries out the drilling, and he will know by experience when he has reached a stratum capable of carrying the desired load.

The report

The site investigation report will include the following data:

preamble — giving client, job, terms of reference

general description of the site

general geology of the area

description of soil in bore holes — together with borehole sections

laboratory test results

discussion of results commenting on type of foundation, type of cement, etc if specified

conclusion and recommendation, if specified.

Specification for site investigation

In preparing a specification for work to be done on Site Investigation the Quantity Surveyor will have to consider two quite different situations in which investigation is undertaken. Firstly, 'Onshore Site Investigation', which forms the greater proportion of all site investigation and is therefore the one with which the Quantity Surveyor will have most contact; secondly, 'Intertidal and Offshore Investigation' which although not rare is of a specialised nature and therefore dealt with by a small number of Quantity Surveyors who are employed by very large Construction Development Organisations.

Onshore Site Investigation will be concerned firstly with general clauses which include the following:

Conditions of contract

Location of site

Scope of work — number of boreholes and testing

Drawings

Site access

Accommodation and storage areas

Site working conditions

Cleanness of roads

Existing services

Use of site — which includes care in moving plant; protection of boreholes and site clearance.

This will be followed by detailed specification on the following items:

Boring and drilling — which includes depths and diameters of boreholes; method of boring or plant to be used; use of linings; removal of obstructions.

Disturbed samples — frequency of obtaining such samples; method of storage and identification.

Undisturbed samples — size of sampling tube and frequency of obtaining samples; method of taking samples; method of protecting samples, particularly rock.

Samples of ground water — quantity and method of storage

Insitu tests — type of test with relevant BS; frequency or spacing of test; method of measuring results.

Guide references. These may be quoted for particular tests or methods of executing the investigation.

Borehole records — method of presentation; description of tests, soils and field work. (Normally covered by Provisional Sum.)

Setting out and supervision — datum levels.

Backfilling of boreholes — type of filling; extent of filling.

When costs are not proportional to the quantities of permanent works the tenderer has the option to define items and insert charges for such items. These charges are called method-related charges.

Items will include —

Plant and equipment — providing and bringing to site; erecting at first position; dismantling and moving from one position to another; removal from site.

Temporary works

Maintaining site facilities

These items are divided into two groups: those which are time-related and those which have a fixed charge.

Intertidal and offshore site investigation

In the general clauses the type of investigation involves such items as —

>   Clearly marking stagings or obstacles below high water mark
>
>   Removal of sunken plant
>
>   Protection of banks, roads etc.
>
>   Lighting, marking, buoying and watching
>
>   Life saving appliances

The general preamble will include depth of boreholes measured from a known datum level. The actual Bill items will be similar to 'On Shore' work but borings and corings will be measured in depth stages below the sea or river bed.

1.2   SITE ORGANISATION AND TEMPORARY SERVICES

1.2.1   Introduction

The nature of the site, its geology and subsoil conditions, the nature of the Works in relation to the site, considerations of access and strategic locations for stores, plant repair shops, supervisors' offices, mess rooms and the like, together with the Resident Engineer's accommodation, will all have been considered when preparing the tender. In jobs involving large volumes of earth transportation, such as airfields and roadworks, the broad plan for the movement of excavated material will also have been worked out. In many cases working drawings and diagrams will have been prepared for these preliminary planning considerations and in special cases even scale models may be constructed. There are two types of models. The first type is experimental and might be used in the solution of complex structures, hydraulics or other analytical problems. The second type is visual and might be used to give an impression of the physical appearance of the work or to identify problems which may arise in construction. The latter is of great importance in site organisation. Such models would be used in a 'method study' of the work to be achieved, and the alternative solutions would be subject to technical and economic assessment. In addition, working drawings of contractors' temporary works and falsework will have to be prepared.

These considerations generally lead to the preparation of a Master Programme, which should take into account such matters as rate of construction, timing of operations, type of plant and equipment. In most cases this will take the form of a bar chart but in some cases, including those where the specification may require it, a 'critical path' network will be produced. All such programmes should include sufficient 'float-time' to allow for circumstances likely to cause delay but for which the contractor will not be entitled to an extension of time.

1.2.2   General organisation and site clearance

On signing the contract the contractor will use the data from the preliminary planning stage to establish and set up an appropriate site organisation. This organisation will include the layout of the site, which will involve the siting of access roads, storage areas, hutting, spoil heaps, plant areas etc. Access roads may be aligned on permanent access roads or hard standings; this will allow grading to correct levels and the formation of a good base ready to receive final wearing coats later. Haulage roads, for taking materials within the site and off the site to tip and for bringing in fill material, must be planned and positioned to give economy and efficiency. In all cases, the roads will need to be considered in the light of the equipment and plant to be used, and the type of site being worked, i.e. Compact or Extended Site.

Where the site is compact the access roads are readily formed as stated above or use can be made of temporary hardwood mats, sleeper mats or inter-locking steel sheeting.

Hardwood mats consist of a number of hardwood strips each 1 m long and 150 x 40 mm in section. Ten such boards are strapped together with two 40 mm wide mild steel bands. The bands, which are bolted to each board, are looped at the ends of the mats to facilitate connection to each other.

Sleeper mats consist of standard railway sleepers held in position by metal dogs or bolted together four to a mat.

Pierced steel planking (P S P) forms a very rigid mat across soft ground but is difficult to dismantle and re-use, owing to distortion caused by load. (Fig 1.31).

Where the site is extensive some distinction will be drawn between access roads and haulage roads. On such sites, permanent access roads will be positioned to serve both the main administration area and the internal movement of plant and materials. The rest of the site will be served by rough access roads which require constant maintenance during wet weather to prevent break up of road surface and consequent damage to vehicles.

All the above organisation refers to normal sites on land, but some consideration must also be given to sites where access may be limited to water. This would include sites on or in a sea, lake or river. In such cases transport is normally undertaken by barges towed by diesel tugs, and organisation must allow for tides and bad weather. Temporary jetties will also be required for the loading of the barges. Other forms of transport which require a great deal of planning and organisation prior to installation are cableways, railways and conveyors (see Plant Section).

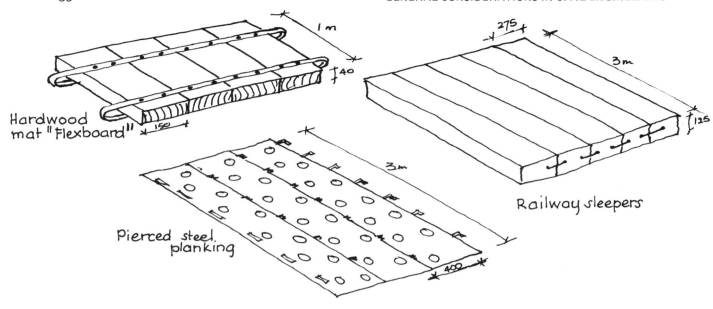

Fig 1.31 *Various forms of temporary roadways*

Site clearance

This should be undertaken as soon as the contractor gets on site, so as to permit the initial siting of access roads and site accommodation. The method of working will again depend on the type of site.

In the case of compact sites, trees and other growth might be removed by a specialist sub-contractor. This will be quickly followed by removal of the top soil, which will be deposited in spoil heaps ready for re-use in finishing off verges and similar features immediately prior to completion. The setting-out of site works will proceed *pari passu.* However, with an extensive site the problems are much greater. The clearance of such a site could involve diversion of sewers, drains, gas, power lines, GPO lines, and it might also involve phasing some or all of the work to facilitate harvesting of crops, all of these adding to costs and legal claims for compensation. In particular, the problem of site drainage may be involved. When large scale earth moving is involved it often interferes with natural drainage which either causes a waterlogged site or causes a movement of mud into water courses. Both have their own disadvantages, the former making the site difficult to work and the latter bringing complaints from other land owners and river authorities because of contamination.

It may be an advantage to cut a perimeter or cut-off drain around major excavation works to intercept water during a rainy season. The same principle can be employed on large scale road works, where a carriageway can be cut to just above finished formation level during the dry months to intercept and channel water in the wet months. This will assist general earth-moving work in inclement weather. In some cases site clearance necessitates the installation and operation of dewatering plant: this technique is described and explained in Chapter 3.

In a great many instances site clearance will also involve large or small scale demolition of existing works and buildings.

1.2.3   Demolition (Also see Chapter 8)

Before any demolition work is commenced a detailed survey of the property should be made. Photographs should be taken of the works to be demolished, together with any adjoining property; this will serve as valuable evidence in the event of claims being made against the contractor. A check must be made of any legal rights which may affect the demolition; these may include easements, questions of ownership, etc, as well as liability for damage and tresspass. Detailed survey of the buildings to be demolished should include the following:

Framed buildings — will unbalanced thrusts occur when members are removed?

Walls — loadbearing or non-loadbearing; stability of party walls if roof or floors removed.

Support required for all elements where stability is to be reduced.

Any cantilevered structure — nature of support.

(Pre-stressed concrete and other concrete structures are covered in Chapter 8 on Concrete).

Basements and voids — method of filling or protecting.

Underground storage tanks — position, size, contents of tanks.

Supplies and Services. These may include:

Drainage, gas, electricity, water, GPO, television or radio lines; hydraulic pressure mains; district heating mains.

Bench marks on buildings — inform the Ordnance Survey.

Insurance

On completion of the survey but before commencing work the contractor should ensure that he is adequately covered by insurance against all risks. The client or client's agents should check the insurance policy concerning collapse, subsidence, weakening of supports, use of plant, consequential damage and fire. In addition to being insured the owner, or his agent, should give notice to the Local Authority and Statutory Undertakers that demolition is due to commence. Special notice must be given in the Inner London Area and Scotland.

Work on site

The demolition contractor is required to appoint a competent foreman to supervise the work and a programme of proposed sequence of operations should be prepared. Particular attention should be given to the following —

Licences for hoarding, fencing, lighting etc.

Scaffolding for access purposes (consult BS 5973:1981)

Closing of roads — Special notice to LA

Access to site — may need special protection. Planning permission will be required if access leads directly on to a highway

Services — may require specialist treatment; diversion

Safety — (consult BS 6187:1982). Workmen must be protected at all times, see Statutory and Common Law Obligation

Uncontrolled Collapse — ascertain method of support shoring etc.

Methods of Demolition

There are numerous methods of demolition which the contractor may employ but the method chosen should suit both location of site and type of structure.

Hand Demolition

Use of Demolition Ball

Use of wire ropes

Use of Pushing Arm

Use of Explosives

Other methods

Hand demolition involves the progressive demolition of a structure by operatives using hand tools. Craneage is often used to lift out members once they have been released. Generally speaking, the order of demolition is the reverse to that of construction.

Demolition by swinging ball involves demolition by swinging a heavy steel ball suspended from the jib of a crane. It should not be used for buildings over 30 m in height and should be supplemented by hand demolition. In particular pitched roofs as well as floors should be removed by hand (providing sufficient members are left in position to provide lateral support).

Demolition by wire rope: only steel ropes with a circumference of 38 mm or more should be used for demolishing parts of the structure, and such ropes must, by law, be inspected frequently by a competent person to ensure that their strength has not been impaired by use. Care must be taken to ensure that there are no persons standing between the winch and the building being demolished or nearer than a distance equal to 75% of the distance between winch and structure on either side of the rope. Where the building fails to collapse during a pulling operation the work must continue using some other mechanical method. Hand methods must not be used since the structure may have been weakened. Wire rope pulling should not be used on masonry structures exceeding 21 m in height.

Demolition by pushing arm: since this method is limited in its operation by height, the structure must be reduced to a suitable height by one of the other methods. The method involves the use of a machine fitted with a pusher arm (normally hydraulic) which exerts a horizontal thrust. This method is more suited to small demolition work.

Demolition by explosives is normally used for tall structures such as chimneys and cooling towers. It allows the complete demolition where other methods could prove dangerous or slow. The work is usually carried out by specialist contractors.

Other methods

When site conditions preclude the use of explosives, the following methods may be used:

Gas expansion burster

Hydraulic burster

Thermal reaction

Thermic lance

These methods are discussed fully in Chapter 8, section 8.1.7.

Procedure for various types of structure

Before any major work commences the roof of a building should be removed as carefully as possible if it is to be salvaged, together with windows, doors, and their linings.

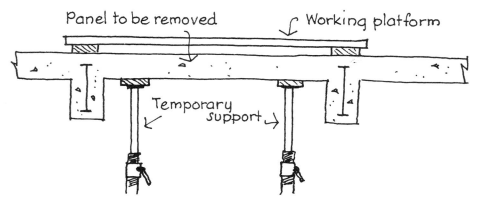

Fig 1.32 *Panel support during demolition*

Roof trusses: temporary bracing should be introduced to allow individual trusses to be removed. Where trusses support gable walls, the wall should be removed prior to dismantling of the truss.

Filler joists: when removing filler joists or any infilling materials such as concrete or blockwork, the operation should have a safe platform independent of the work being demolished.

The joists or panel being removed should be supported to allow cutting out, prior to lowering to ground level. (Fig 1.32).

Structural steel: the sequence of demolition should be arranged to maintain a stable structure. This will often involve the use of temporary bracing or steel ropes. Members should be lowered carefully to the ground thus preventing any increased load on other elements during demolition.

Pre-cast insitu and pre-stressed concrete — see Chapter 8.

Bridges: attention should be given to careful planning and organisation of such work. The work should be carried out in reverse order of erection, after first removing as much dead load as possible without affecting the stability of the bridge.

Guys and braces should be fixed to all main beams to prevent their slipping during dismantling operations. Temporary support to abutments may be necessary during the main lifting and removal operation owing to the lateral support being removed.

Where old brick and masonry arches are involved, these may require temporary centres (particularly over road and rail services) to prevent total collapse and consequential damage to the work below.

Independent chimneys: where the chimney is in good condition, demolition can be carried out by a steeple-jack, but alternatively it may be felled by the use of explosives. Where part of the chimney is pulled out at the base to cause deliberate collapse, there should be a clear space of 1½ times the height of the chimney (from its centre).

Steel and reinforced plastic chimneys should be dismantled from a safe platform provided by an external scaffolding. The steel lining may be cut into manageable sizes and lowered to the ground and debris allowed to fall into the chimney.

Petroleum tanks and the like: before work commences on the demolition and removal of tanks which have held inflammable liquids, they should be made safe by one of the following methods:

Filling with water

Filling with an inert gas, ie Nitrogen

Use of dry ice (4 kg per 2,000 litres capacity)

In the last method, operatives should wear gloves and the tank should be left for 12 hours after the addition of the ice.

Further comment and details can be found in BS 6187:1982 — Demolition.

1.2.4   Site offices and general accommodation

Accommodation for sites covers two types of structure: small mobile transportable units and sectional pre-fabricated buildings. Both types are popular since they both fulfil specific requirements depending on site, space required etc. On small, short-duration contracts the mobile unit is economical and adaptable to site organ-isation and conditions. The sectional structure, however, is preferable on large contracts, allowing better co-ordination and control by providing many offices under one roof.

Fig 1.32a   *'Jack-leg' accommodation*   (Transline Units Limited)

The main factors which govern the choice of site accommodation are location and duration of the contract concerned, together with the factor of space on compact sites. In some cases, where the contract is long term involving a large labour force, the accommodation may equate to a small township catering for living, sleeping, feeding and recreational facilities which may not exist locally. Where this is necessary a more permanent type of structure, such as pre-fabricated concrete office buildings, may be required. For most sites however, the offices consist of pre-fabricated timber buildings, normally single storey, but adaptable for two storey layout (Fig 1.32a).

Mobile units play a very important part in site accommodation and new developments have been introduced to satisfy site conditions. The older wheeled chassis unit has largely been superseded by 'skid mounted' and 'jack-leg' designs. Although the new designs are less manoeuvrable on site they are just as quick to transport and are not so restricted in size as the wheeled chassis. The 'jack-leg' units have the advantage that they can be levelled easily on sloping sites and can be stacked on top of each other to form a double storey. One particular mobile unit 'Portakabin' has a floor area of 56 square metres, which can be linked or double stacked, ready for use in one day. These units can be delivered to site containing complete catering facilities or toilet facilities and therefore have much to commend them.

The amount of office accommodation needed will be determined by the type of organisation and amount of staff required for controlling the contract. Fig 1.33 shows a schematic organisation for a large contract. From this chart the amount of office space needed can be assessed, allowance being made for conference rooms to cater for site meetings.

The amount of general accommodation for men can be calculated from a master programme which will show the labour force throughout the contract. Actual facilities, such as toilets, catering and first aid, must conform to the standards laid down in the Construction (Health & Welfare) Regulations 1966, which deals with facilities on site in broad terms. All hutments should be as centralised as possible and be near main access roads. The time-keeper's office should be near the main gates together with the materials control office.

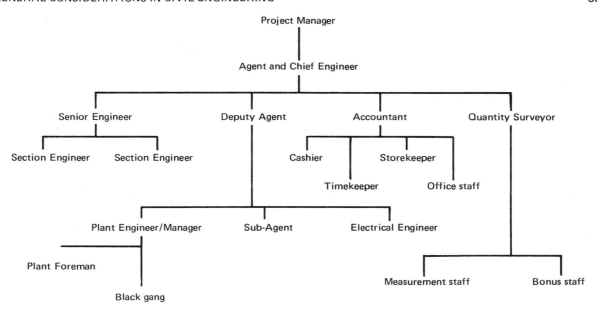

Fig 1.33   *Schematic chart showing typical organisation for civil engineering contract*

1.2.5   Material storage and compounds

Some form of hutting or more permanent buildings must be provided for storage of materials which are subject to pilfering, vandalism and deterioration from weather. Stores should be laid out in such a way that checking and issue of materials can be carried out easily.

Storage bins, cast in concrete, may be used for storage of bulk aggregates near central mixing plants whilst heavy materials such as steel reinforcement, concrete pipes etc., can be stored in the open. When materials are likely to be damaged by children or building operations they should be stored in a lock compound for safe keeping. Compounds will also be necessary for the safe keeping of plant and equipment.

The storage of liquids such as oil and petrol are subject to the following regulations:

Petrol

Any storage within 6 metres of a building is governed by the petroleum regulations and the associated fire regulations. These regulations include wired glass windows, sliding doorways and limiting devices for volume. Where the fuel is stored within a building, containers must have screw tops and not exceed 9 litres each in capacity, and the maximum number of containers allowed in any store is two.

The type of tank used for fuel storage is governed by local regulations which specify gauge of metal, concrete shrouding and position below ground.

Derv and gas oil

These oils must not be stored in close proximity to petrol but can be stored in suitable containers above ground. Each container must be clearly marked showing the contents.

Cement

The storage of cement on large contracts is best achieved by the use of a silo which allows free delivery with minimum waste.

1.2.6   Temporary services

Every site, whether large or small, requires some temporary services. On the small site the requirements may be limited to electric power, water, telephone and sewer connections. On the larger construction site they will include compressed air, heat supply, forced ventilation, catering services and possibly a properly equipped medical centre. There is no set formula for establishing the type and range of services for a site; each site must be considered on its own merits and the services designed to fit the specific needs of the contract. Factors that affect the selection and design of temporary services are —

Specific needs

Number of working shifts per day (e.g. whether continuous working would demand trouble-free equipment)

Job location

Safety

Cost.

This selection does not describe in detail the design and installation of temporary services, which is a speciality, but lists, rather, some factors which merit consideration when planning the installation of such services.

Electricity

Where electricity can be supplied by the local undertaking the following factors must be considered —

Capacity of existing system

Demand of site including type of supply (single or three phase)

Cost of installing transmission line to central sub-station

Alternative methods and cost of producing equivalent power supply.

Where the local undertaking cannot readily supply the site, then other additional factors must be considered —

Design and position of generating house

Type or quantity of generating equipment

Method of earthing and distributing power on site

Safety — see Section 1.2.8.

One of the common failings when considering a supply is to underestimate the lighting requirement on site, particularly in winter working, when daylight fails quickly.

Water supply

The water supply to a large construction site may be divided into two types (i) industrial water and (ii) drinking water. The latter, which must be potable, is required for work areas, offices, mess rooms, shops etc. The former is required for rock drilling, feed water for boiler plant, moisture control of dam fill, transporting materials by sluice or dredge pipelines.

In both cases certain factors must be considered at the detailed planning stage; these include —

Available sources

Quality and treatment

Water storage

Pumping requirements

Protection during winter period

Distribution

Fire fighting requirements.

Heating

Every site requires some form of heating for offices and mess rooms and the form of heating ranges from calor gas heaters to steam generating plants which circulate steam through pipes to every work and rest area.

High pressure steam lines can also be used for heating domestic water and defrosting material or steam-curing of concrete. Factors for consideration are —

Size of contract — amount of hutting

Availability of equipment

Availability of fuel supply

Economics of system.

Compressed air service

Most large sites are involved with the generation of compressed air since it has become a power source for hand tools, rock drilling, hammers and a means of transporting materials in pipes, i.e. concrete. It is also used for sand blasting, placing gunite, and pressure grouting. The multiplicity of uses is a very important factor to consider when planning the services requirements. Other factors include:

Type of equipment (e.g. central or local)

Method of generation (layout for power house)

Distribution lines and air receivers

Air losses

Safety.

Ventilation

In certain work areas, e.g. tunnels, a system of forced ventilation may be necessary. The clearance of blasting by this method requires a great volume of air over a short period of time. This can be achieved by a system of fans placed at intervals along the tunnel route. Consideration must be given to the following:

Size of fan

Time lapse requirement for achieving clean air conditions

Type of power required; e.g. electrical demand is very high when using large fans and therefore consideration should be given to other forms of power.

Gas supply

In most cases gas supplies to sites are in the form of cylinders or main storage tanks on site. All such requirements must be subject to strict adherence to the regulations on storage and fire risk. Consideration must be given to —

Type of gas e.g. methane, propane, oxygen, acteylene

Quantities in store

Position of storage in relation to work areas

Fire fighting facilities

Safety in respect of explosion.

1.2.7   Setting out

The contractor is normally made responsible for setting out all works and therefore must employ quali-fied engineers to deal with this work. The Resident Engineer may have the right, under the contract, to check the setting out but this does not diminish the contractor's responsibility for any errors which may not be detected.

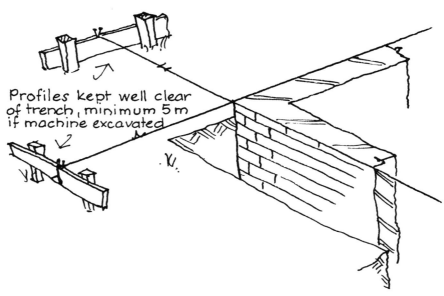

Fig 1.34   *Use of profiles in setting out*

Setting out of small and medium sized works

This is best achieved by using profiles and wire or string lines. In the case of brickwork and other masonry the setting out line will normally be taken to the outer face of the walls (Fig 1.34).
Where steel or concrete columns are used the setting out line will be taken to the centre lines of the columns. (Fig 1.35). This will assist in the positioning of holding down bolts for column fixings.

In both methods all the profiles should be kept at the same level; this keeps the lines in the same plane and thereby assists in measuring all horizontal distances and the checking of the diagonals.
All profiles should be set well back from the actual works to allow access for machines and excavators. Profiles at the corner of trenches are totally impracticable and whilst appearing in this form in many text books, serve only to lead the reader into problems.

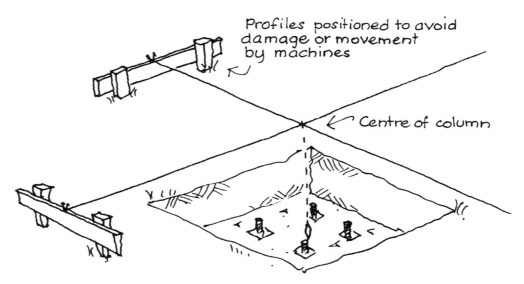

Fig 1.35   *Setting out for columns*

Whether the setting out is for walls or columns, the basic procedure is the same, and is as follows (Fig 1.36) —

Establish a base line — usually the face of the building or a centre line of columns.

Establish a fixed point on the base line — usually a corner or centre of the end column.

From the fixed point set out a line at right angles to the base line. This is achieved with a theodolite, or by the 3.4.5 method using steel tapes.

Establish parallel lines to the base line and adjacent right angle, giving a rectangle to enclose the building, ignoring all offsets. When measuring across sloping terrain it will be necessary to calculate the slope length in relation to the true horizontal length.

Check the diagonals to establish whether the building is square, having first calculated the diagonal mathematically. The latter calculation will serve as a check on all horizontal measurements since the correct diagonal can only be achieved by correct setting out.

On achieving an accurate enclosing rectangle, establish other profiles for offset walls and columns, using the established setting out as a base.

When the setting-out lines have been established a plumb bob is used to transfer critical points vertically.

Accuracy in setting-out will depend on the time of year and prevailing conditions as well as on the quality of instruments used; but it should be within ± 5 mm in 30 metres. Any error greater than this warrants a further check on the setting-out.

Setting out large and complicated works

This should always be undertaken by experienced engineers using one or more theodolites. The basic principles apply as before, namely establishing a base line and then establishing lines or points along and at right angles to that base line. The base line need not be the edge of a building or centre line as in the case of smaller works; it may best be set out down the centre of a road or edge of the site, well away from the actual works.

Fig 1.36 *Basic procedure for setting out rectangular structures*

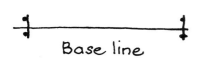

Base line

Fixed point

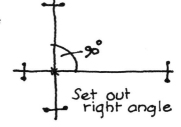

Set out right angle

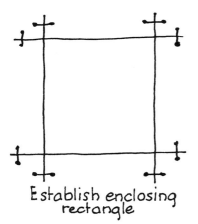

Establish enclosing rectangle

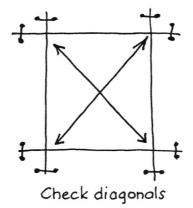

Check diagonals

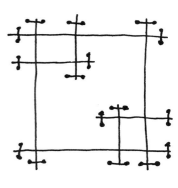

Complete offsets

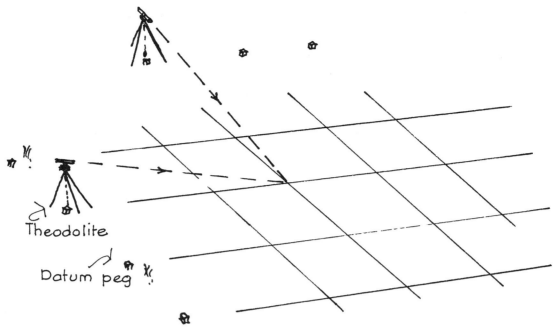

Fig 1.37   *Datum pegs from which grid can be re-aligned*

The base line should be accurately measured out by steel tape (using a standard pull by spring balance), allowance being made for temperature. From this base line all other points may be fixed by triangulation with a theodolite.

Having established positions of columns, walls etc., the engineer should then set-up 'stations', well out of the way of traffic and plant, from which he can, if need be, quickly re-align the positions determined (Fig 1.37). In some cases a setting out drawing is prepared giving numerous co-ordinates for the positioning of key points. These co-ordinates form the basis for further setting out (Fig 1.38) and will be established from a grid of pre-determined size.

For example, co-ordinate A would be 100 North, 000 East and co-ordinate D would be 130 North, 180 East. For a large industrial complex, reference can be made to the triangulation stations on the national grid, which is based on 19 km squares. Permission should be obtained from landowners or tenants before establishing and using a station on private land.

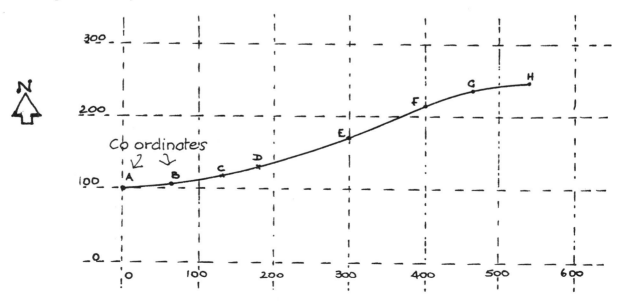

Fig 1.38   *Basic grid for positioning co-ordinates*

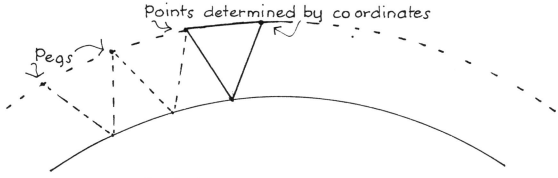

Fig 1.39 *Setting out curved work using triangular template*

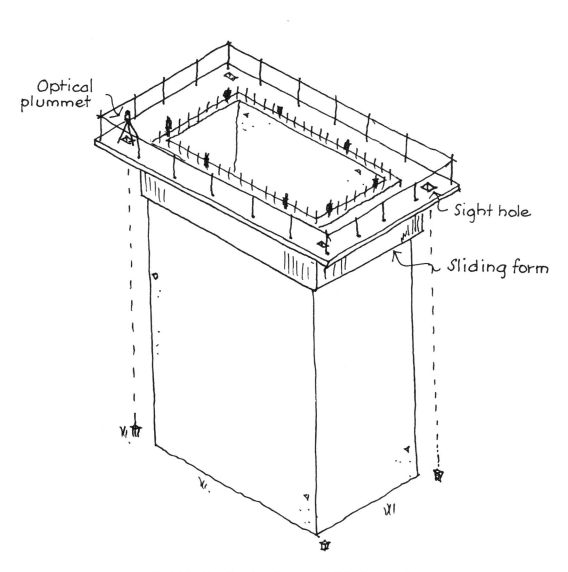

Fig 1.40 *Use of optical plummet on sliding form work*

Curved work

Where setting-out includes a curved section of work the profile method is inappropriate. Small radius curves can be established by trammel or template, whereas large radius curves can be set out from pre-determined pegs by means of a triangular template (Fig 1.39).

The pegs are positioned by theodolite and steel tape or by co-ordinates from a known grid.

Vertical work

The increase in high rise structures has brought about a need for more accurate methods of establishing vertical alignment. The most popular instrument for this accurate work is the optical plummet. This instrument is screwed to the tripod of a theodolite or level and when positioned over a reference point, projects a very accurate vertical sight line. Several optical plummets incorporate semi-automatic levelling devices and project a line upwards as well as downwards. If the instrument is to be used from a height, e.g. on sliding formwork, then a platform must be constructed with a sighting hole to carry the instrument (Fig 1.40).

The limits of accuracy in all setting out should be stated in the Specification or the Bills of Quantities. For vertical alignment the limits should be within ± 10 mm per 30 m rise, and horizontal measurements within ± 5 mm per 30 m.

Site surveys

It is necessary to mention the use of site surveys in this section since their setting out should be done accurately and recorded for further reference. Their main use is to establish existing ground levels, prior to excavation and filling operations (Fig 1.41).

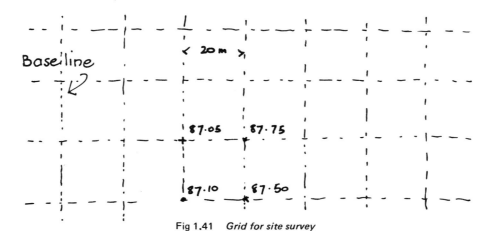

Fig 1.41   *Grid for site survey*

A grid, the size of which is dependent on the irregularity of the ground, is established from two base lines at right angles to each other. Providing the ground is smoothly contoured the levels on the grid will give an accurate record of soil moved or filled.

Where the contours change rapidly it may be necessary to reduce the survey to a smaller grid. The grid levels are then established for each intersection against some known datum, usually an ordnance datum.

1.2.8   Safety

The change in attitude to safety measures over the last ten years has led to the development of complex and costly solutions in the civil engineering field. The Quantity Surveyor must be aware of the requirements which the contractor has to meet and for that reason this section is covered in some detail.

Site safety must be considered by the contractor during the early planning stages of the contract so that requirements and procedure can be established. The items for consideration include —

Design and construction of temporary works

Site access and egress

Offices and compounds

Temporary Power Houses & Services

Plant

Working in compressed air

Dangerous atmospheres

Design and construction of temporary works

All such works must be designed by competent personnel and constructed by competent men. These structures require examination and maintenance on a regular basis so that the structure does not deteriorate and become a safety hazard. This is particularly applicable to support systems such as shoring, scaffolding, trench sheeting, gantries, falsework etc., where conditions may vary considerably during the contract period. In the case of falsework (formwork) special consideration must be given to live loads which are imposed during the pouring of the concrete. These loads are created by plant, men and flow of concrete.

Piling

Piling frames must be designed to withstand not only driving stresses but also wind loading.

All platforms on the piling frame must be fully decked and ladders provided for the full height. The capacity of the piling winch should include a margin of safety above the weight of the maximum weight of pile. In addition the weight of the driving hammer and helmet must be considered. Heavy concrete piles may require craneage and this will involve design of slings for inclined and eccentric loading.

Shafts

These are covered under the Construction (General Provision) Regulations 1961. Access to and from the working surface for men may be achieved by means of a skip raised and lowered by a crane. The skip must be constructed for this use alone and include a device to prevent overturning. Where ladders are used they must be screened from the operation of hoists or cranes and be well lit. Support material, to be used during sinking, should be available for securing the excavation, and one operative should be detailed to supervise the lowering of objects and materials into the shaft. The tops of the shafts at ground level must be protected with some form of guard rail or extended shaft lining to a height of 1 metre.

Tunnels

Ventilation by artificial means is necessary in tunnelling by mechanical shields, where the rate of heat dispersal is high and where humidity is troublesome. Where explosives are used some form of artifical ventilation will be necessary to reduce the fumes.

For electrical supplies in tunnels, the supply should be either 110 V single phase or three-phase with centre points earthed and the installation completely watertight. Conductors carrying a voltage to earth of between 25 and 65 V must have rubber insulation. For voltage to earth exceeding 65 V the cable must be enclosed in a continuous earthing metallic shield. All trailing cables must be armoured and handlamps reduced to 25V. Portable tools must not be used at a voltage exceeding 110 V.

In compressed air tunnelling, where there is a risk of sudden flooding due to water breaking through the face, an elevated escape way must be provided which includes watertight plates across the upper sector of the tunnel to provide air pockets.

Site access and egress

The layout of site roads and haulage roads must be considered in the light of speed and volume of traffic. Where possible, a one-way system is advisable when moving large quantities of materials by wheeled transport. The layout should provide good visibility or alternatively incorporate warning and control systems to prevent collision. All junctions and hidden access points should be clearly signposted. Special consideration must be given to sites where public 'through ways' have to be maintained. The last factor may involve the use of hoardings and fans to protect the public, permission to erect these structures being obtained from the Local Authority.

Offices and compounds

Office buildings must be sited to minimise the fire risk and allow adequate means of escape. Where offices are raised above ground level the area below must be enclosed to prevent storage of materials or accumulation of rubbish. Methods of heating and cooking in buildings must be carefully considered and naked flame heaters should be avoided. Full cylinders of gas and empty bottles should be stored in racks outside the buildings.

Where compounds contain workshops a number of factors should be considered:

Hand operated electrically driven tools should be 110 V supply

Lifting devices must be tested

Machinery should be positioned to deal with long units

Fire extinguishers of the right type must be located in strategic positions

Lighting must be adequate for work being undertaken

First aid equipment must be readily available

Storage of inflammable materials, such as timber, must be kept 6 m clear of buildings, all stacks being separated by adequate fire breaks.

Temporary power houses & services

This section includes compressed air and electrical installations. All electrical installations must be laid out by an experienced engineer who understands the dangers of short circuits, and who can advise on the safest method of earthing the system. Where diesel installations are used for generation of power, there is some fire risk due to spillage of fuel on hot exhaust systems. In no case should large quantities of fuel be stored in the generating house. All cables must be protected and positioned so that working plant cannot foul them.

Compressed air and the generation of air are both controlled by regulations, but factors to be taken into consideration are:

No unauthorised person allowed access to the compressor and receivers; one man to be responsible for the control and maintenance of the whole installation

The compressor should be contained in a building with a receiver of matching capacity

Where possible it is good policy to run a central air main to workshops

All joints in power lines should be flanged and spring-clipped rather than screwed

Water traps should be provided

Valves for blowing out water should be installed

Other aspects are discussed in Section 2.6.

Services

Whilst services to the site include gas, electricity, water, telephones, sewers, etc. care must be exercised in the diversion and installation of such work. The temporary service which requires greatest consideration is that of electricity.

The temporary supply will be provided by either the local Electricity Board or, in the case of remote sites, the contractor's own generators. In either case, the main problem is a matter of earthing. Where the supply is provided by the Electricity Board by underground cable, it is possible to obtain earther facilities by connection to the metallic sheath of the supply cable. This method is highly recommended. Where the supply is brought in by overhead line or distributed from power houses over the site, then some form of earth electrode must be used. A metallic water main may be used after consultation with the Water Board. Another method of earthing is one where the contractor provides his own earth electrode by burying suitable conductors in the ground. Such conductors require expert supervision and testing for earth resistance on installation and at intervals during use. All apparatus and equipment must be efficiently earthed.

Where it is difficult to obtain a low resistance earth path, use should be made of an earth-leakage circuit breaker unit. These units can be either voltage operated or current operated; both are available in single phase or three phase forms. The voltage operated device has its operating coil connected between earth and the frame of the apparatus. If the voltage in the apparatus rises higher than a certain level above earth, the current through the coil trips the circuit breaker and disconnects the supply. The time of operation for these circuit breakers is very low thereby giving a very high degree of safety. In the current operated circuit breaker the incoming and outgoing currents are compared and any difference, which represents a leak, is used to operate a trip switch.

Whatever the supply, the main switchboard will normally provide for an outgoing 415 V three phase supply. Such a supply will be necessary for items of plant such as cranes, hoists, pumps, and concrete batchers. The switchboard will also supply current to step-down transformers which operate at 110 V for hand-operated tools and lighting equipment. This step down transformer should have its centre point connected to earth thereby reducing the risk of shock to a maximum of 55 V to earth. In some cases, especially working in wet conditions, 50 V transformers may be used, thus reducing the shock potential to 25 V.

Where plant is provided with 415 V three phase supply the cable should be protected with metal armour, preferably of the steel wire type and either buried or surfaced laid on a clearly marked route. Overhead lines should follow the perimeter of the site and never in the vicinity of areas used by high vehicles.

Travelling cranes requiring electrical supplies should have supplementary earthing though the wheels and rails. This means that rail joints must be bonded and rails effectively earthed. For moving plant an electronic device can be fitted to the machine, e.g. on a crane jib, which will detect a live supply line and give an audible alarm signal in the cab of the machine. These devices are particularly useful on craneage where the operator is concerned with watching the load.

Plant

Safety can be greatly increased by adherence to the Construction (Lifting Operations) Regulations 1962 which cover two very accident prone pieces of plant, namely Hoists and Cranes.

The former may be used for goods or passengers and the regulations cover such points as:

Enclosing the hoistway

Securing the hoist tower to the structure

Gates fitted at every landing

Hoist level indicators on goods hoists when over 15 m high

All hoists to be inspected weekly

These and many other regulations apply to hoists and reference should be made to the Regulations. Cranes are similarly dealt with by the Construction Regulations, which include factors such as:

Proper calibration of radius and load indicators

Audible and visual indicators

Test certificate for the machine and equipment

Examination of machine and equipment

Systems of signalling (normally that which is recommended by the Federation of Civil Engineering Contractors)

Lifting hooks must be tested to twice the maximum load

Warning lights for low flying aircraft

Working in compressed air

The use of compressed air to achieve working conditions in water bearing strata may cause men to suffer from Compressed Air illness. This illness is caused by incorrect decompression of the body which results in limb pains (known as ''the bends') or paralysis or problems with sight, hearing and breathing (in some cases bone damage). The situation is created in the first place by the blood absorbing air proportionately to the pressure exerted on it and distributing it in solution to all parts of the anatomy. During the reverse process (decompression), the oxygen element in the inhaled air is used up in the tissues and nitrogen accumulates in the form of bubbles in the tissues of joints and muscles. These bubbles of nitrogen must be recompressed back into solution in the blood (where illness occurs) and a method of decompression is employed to let the excess nitrogen leave the body via the lungs.

The principal means of curing compressed air illness is the medical air-lock, which allows medical attention without interrupting any recompression process.

Regulations concerning 'Work in Compressed Air' give no guidance concerning the treatment of 'sickness'; however, these regulations have been amplified by the Medical Code of Practice for Work in Compressed Air.* This Code of Practice contains the 'Blackpool' decompression tables which give the times and rates of decompression to minimise sickness. The Code also includes procedures for dealing with illness after decompression.

Prevention of decompression sickness depends upon two factors —

Careful examination of each worker prior to admission to the pressurised atmosphere, rejecting the unfit.

Strict observance of rates of decompression.

In the case of caisson sinking, an alternative method of decompression may be used called 'decanting'. By this method persons are rapidly decompressed in the man-lock to atmospheric pressure, followed promtly by rapid recompression in a separate chamber and subsequent gradual decompression in accordance with the Blackpool tables. In this method the total time spent between the start of the primary decompression in the man-lock and the completion of recompression in the separate chamber should not exceed five minutes. See also Chapter 2 on compressed air plant and Chapter 5, section 5.1.5.

Dangerous atmospheres

In certain works such as shafts, headings and underground works where machinery is being used, there is a risk of men being overcome by dangerous fumes.

Carbon Dioxide (CO_2) is the asphyxiating gas most likely to be encountered in the course of well or shaft sinking. It is likely to occur especially in chalk, limestone or greensands and in all cases where acids or solid carbon dioxide are being employed. Since the gas is heavier than air it tends to accumulate at low levels. Detection can be achieved by means of a flame, which will be extinguished by the pressure of the gas (where oxygen is reduced in the atmosphere by 20 - 25 per cent).

Carbon Monoxide (C O) is introduced into working areas by internal combustion engines, welding or brazier fumes. It is slightly lighter than air and is extremely dangerous; even 0.01 per cent may be harmful. The capacity of this gas for combining with the blood is more than 200 times greater than that of oxygen; resulting in headaches, loss of breath, dizziness or vomiting to collapse followed by death in a matter of moments. Affected persons should be taken into the fresh air with urgency and kept as warm as possible with blankets and hot water bottles. If available, oxygen should be given freely.

Methane (Firedamp) (C H 4) is found near the roof of headings. It is lighter than air and although not poisonous its presence in excess leads to a diminution of oxygen with a consequent danger of suffocation. Explosions can occur if as little as five per cent of this gas is present and this should be regarded as the principal risk. Detection is best achieved by means of a flame safety-lamp of approved design.

Published by Construction Industry Research and Information Association (Report No 44).

Nitrous Fumes may occur during the process of well construction as a result of the use of explosives, particularly in consequence of incomplete detonation. Their effect on the body is usually delayed and symptoms of coughing and shortness of breath may not appear for some hours. The gas should be regarded as dangerous and medical help should be sought immediately.

1.3 MATERIALS

1.3.1 Materials in general use

Since many of the basic materials in use in the Construction Industry are examined in detail in other books, this section is limited to a brief description of certain materials specifically used in civil engineering works.

Steel

Although a large proportion of the world's steel is still produced by the open-hearth process, there is an increasing amount being produced by the L.D. converter process. In the L.D. process, which was developed in the Austrian steelworks at Linz and Donawitz in the 1950s, pure oxygen is blown through a lance into the molten iron at the top of the converter. This process combines good scrap-consuming capacity and a high rate of production at low cost.

Steel can be classified by the degree of carbon content as follows:

Low carbon steel; up to 0.15 per cent carbon, suitable for tin-plate and wire.

Mild steel; 0.15 to 0.25 per cent carbon, suitable for standard sections, e.g. universal beams, channels, angles.

Medium carbon steel; 0.20 to 0.50 per cent carbon, suitable for general engineering work; e.g. high tensile steel reinforcement and high tensile sections.

High carbon steel; 0.50 to 1.50 per cent carbon, suitable for tool making and heavy castings.

Weathering steel is a term given to steels which contain a proportion of copper, e.g. 'Cor-ten' steel. In some cases the copper content is sufficient to produce a steel which requires no protection against corrosion; the additional copper provides a natural oxide protection when subject to normal weathering. This form of steel is sometimes specified for sheet piling in coastal and river bank protection.

Extras and allowances

In addition to having a basic knowledge of steel the Quantity Surveyor should also be aware of the extras and allowances that may be incurred by quality and specification. The carbon content has already been mentioned, the amount of carbon in the steel affecting the price. Other quality steels include: Manganese, re-sulphurised, niobium, copper, killed steels and tensile and impact properties. Specification extras include structural and shipbuilding steels, pressure vessel steels, cold flanging, normalising, brand name steels, and the finishing and treatment of steel, e.g. cambering, shot-blasting, pickling, oiling and priming.

Cements and concrete

Cement has been produced since 1824 and uses clay and limestone as the main constituents; little more needs to be said about this material in a text on civil engineering, apart from reminding the reader that certain cements are of particular value in the civil engineering field. One such cement is an ultra-high early-strength Portland cement. The cement reaches the equivalent 3-day strength of rapid hardening cement in 16 hours and the 7-day strength in 24 hours. This makes the product very suitable for concreting in cold weather and in situations where rapid turn round of formwork is necessary.

Low-heat cement is of particular value in the construction of mass concrete bases and dam construction where hydration could create problems of expansion and cracking. However, the extent to which these cements are used is very limited when compared with ordinary Portland cement.

Concrete

This material is discussed fully in Chapter 8, but it should be noted at this juncture that it is advisable to specify concrete by its strength and aggregate size, reference being made to CP 110: 1972, CP 114: 1969, and CP 115: 1969. Where concrete is to be used for roads and bridges, reference should be made to 'Specification for Road and Bridge Works' HMSO 1976.

Bricks

There are numerous types of bricks used in civil engineering work, and although BS 3921:1974 classifies bricks in only three qualities (internal, ordinary and special qualities) the reader will be aware of a much broader classification, namely variety. The main varieties are:

Engineering bricks, Class A are the densest, hardest and heaviest bricks used; trade names include Staffordshire Blues and Southwater Reds. They absorb no moisture of any consequence and can thus resist great extremes of weather. They are used in bridge abutments, boiler bases, culverts etc. Cost per thousand delivered to site is approximately four times the cost of common bricks.

Engineering bricks, Class B are slightly less dense than Class A, having a minimum strength of 48.5 N/mm^2 compared with 69 N/mm^2 for Class A. They are used in manhole construction and in work below ground level. Cost per thousand delivered to site is approximately three times the cost of common bricks.

'Calulon' bricks are a proprietary brick, specifically made for highly stressed walls. These bricks are made in three strength grades A10, B7.5 and C5, having strengths of 69 N/mm^2, 52 N/mm^2 and 34.5 N/mm^2 respectively. Tests show a 30% increase in the speed of laying and 40% reduction in the quantity of mortar used compared with solid brick walling. They are suitable for load-bearing structures above ground level. Cost per thousand is about the same as Class A engineering bricks.

Common bricks; this is a broad term applied to bricks which are suitable for internal work. 'Commons' may vary in different localities so it is essential to state the type of common bricks to BS 3921:1974 e.g. London stocks, flettons, Sand Lime.

Facing bricks; although almost any bricks can be used as a facing, this term is generally applied only to better quality bricks which possess an aesthetically pleasing texture. Engineering bricks can be used as facings, e.g. in retaining walls.

Fire bricks, as the name suggests, are made to withstand high temperature. Refractory bricks, e.g. Armitage, are used in furnace work and in flues operating at high temperatures. Fossosil bricks, made from diatomaceous earth, are used for flues operating at more moderate temperatures. Common bricks are quite suitable for flues having low temperatures, e.g. factory chimney, but the top 2 m of upper linings of the chimney which are particularly prone to damages by frost and water vapour, should be constructed in Class A engineering bricks.

Timber

Timber used in civil engineering is mainly confined to temporary works such as strutting, formwork and gantries. With this in mind the details given in this section will be limited to the strength aspect of timber.

Timber has a high strength both in tension and compression and it is elastic. The strength of timber increases with density and varies greatly between species. CP 112 deals with the structural use of timber and contains the basic stresses for specimen pieces of timber free from all visible defects. The Code of Practice defines grades of timber in four categories; 75, 65, 50 and 40 grade. These grades are determined by the visible defects such as 'slope of grain', size of knot and wane in proportion to width of timber, size of fissures. It is now possible to obtain machine-graded timber which is graded as it passes through a series of rollers under stress.

Softwoods are the most common timber used in construction work; they have a density of between 450 and 550 kg/m^3 and have basic tension stresses (parallel to the grain) of 11 to 14 N/mm^2 depending on species. The most suitable timber for civil engineering work is Douglas fir (Pseudotsuga taxifolia) known to some as Oregan pine or British Columbian pine. The principal source of this timber is the North West coast of North America, particularly British Columbia. The trees are large in diameter (600 to 1200 mm) and over 30 metres high, thus allowing very large section timbers to be produced for piling and shoring work. It has a very high basic strength in tension which, when seasoned, approaches 18 N/mm^2, and it is in this respect far superior to any other softwood. After use as a temporary support every piece of timber should be examined for flaws or faults which may have developed in use.

Timber that is to remain as part of permanent work must be protected from attack by fungi, insects and marine borers. The most common treatment is achieved by pressure impregnation, using tar oil (Coal tar creosote BS 144: 1973). The process is described in BS 913: 1973 — Wood preservation by means of pressure creosoting.

Plywoods are graded in accordance with BS 1455 which cover three grades:

Grade 1 is a smooth cut veneer used for high class work

Grade 2 is normally used where the surface is to be painted, and it has a surface free from defects

Grade 3 is used for formwork and may contain defects which would otherwise exclude it from other grades.

For good quality finishes to concrete it is usual to use Grade 2 Douglas fir ply, coated with an epoxy resin; this can be used many times before deterioration. For rough concreting and for formwork panels which require decorative finishes — normally achieved by a secondary lining — it is possible to obtain and use an inferior grade of ply known as 'shuttering quality'. This ply has all the normal strength qualities but has defects on one or both faces such as split laminates or missing knot infills. In all cases the plywood should be treated against the effects of contact with cement by coating with a vegetable oil before every use. Plywood permanently exposed to weather must be marine quality, having a waterproof glue as its bonding agent, and be painted or treated for protection against the elements.

Stones

Stones fall into three geological classes: Igneous, Sedimentary and Metamorphic.

Igneous stones, which contain crystalline silicates, are best known for the granite group of stones. Granites have a very high compressive strength as well as a highly decorative finish. They are highly resistant to chemical attack and are virtually impervious. Pink and grey granite can be obtained from Scotland and light grey from Cornwall.

Sedimentary stones include sandstones, consisting of fine or coarse particles of quartz with mica or felspar bound together in a natural cement. Limestones consist mainly of calcium carbonate in the form of calcite and vary in hardness. Limestone from the Pennines is very hard and therefore suitable for road works and concreting. Sandstone can be obtained from many parts of the country but Yorkshire and Derbyshire stones are among the best. Limestones for walling purposes are mainly obtained in a belt from Dorset to the Wash, the best known examples being Bath and Portland Stones.

Metamorphic stones include slates and marbles which have been produced by tremendous heat and pressure. Slates come from Cornwall, the Lake District, and Wales and vary in colour with each area. Thin roofing slates are confined to the Welsh quarries and riven slate panels to the quarries in the Lake District.

Stone for road works, often called 'road-metal', can be obtained from numerous quarries in all counties, but wherever possible a local stone should be specified to avoid high transport costs.

1.3.2 Materials for bulk filling

Bulk filling materials in civil engineering include soil, rock and aggregates, and pulverised fuel ash (PFA).

Soil

This is used for the formation of embankments and other areas which require fill. Such soil may be brought to the site from other contracts but in the main forms part of the earth transportation on site. It is usual to 'cut' soil from the high points of the site and place the soil in layers in lower areas; this method, known as 'cut and fill', is the standard procedure for dealing with 'the mass transfer of soil' since it greatly reduces the cost of removal to spoil heaps with consequent additional spreading. However, soil used for bulk filling must be suitable for this purpose and the Quantity Surveyor should specify, having first consulted a competent engineer, what is meant by 'unsuitable material'. Unsuitable material includes the following:

Material from swamps, bogs and marshes

Perishable material such as peat, logs and stumps

Materials prone to spontaneous combustion

Frozen materials

Materials having a liquid limit exceeding 80 and/or a plasticity index exceeding 55.

Suitable materials for bulk filling should be grouped as follows:

'Cohesive soil' which includes clays and marls with a moisture content not less than the plastic limit minus 4. This soil may contain up to 20% of gravel or it may consist of chalk having a moisture content of 20% or greater.

'Well graded granular and dry cohesive soil' includes clays and marls with more than 20% gravel content and having a moisture content less than the plastic limit minus 4; well graded sands and gravels with a uniformity co-efficient of 10 or more; chalk having a moisture content within the range of 15–20%; and all shales and clinker ash.

'Uniformly graded material' includes sands and gravels with a uniformity co-efficient of 10 or less; and all silts and pulverised fuel ash.

Compaction of filled areas should comply with the Specification for Roads and Bridges, HMSO 1976 which clearly specifies the methods and requirements of compaction.

Rock and aggregates

Rock fill consists of hard material of suitable size for compaction and may include crushed stone, hard brick, concrete or other hard inert material. The predominant supply of such hard fill comes from quarries where the rock is crushed to a suitable size. The crushed stone is transported either by road or rail; most quarries of any size have a direct link to the major railways. Large aggregates and crushed stones may be used providing that no boulder exceeding 0.015 m^3 in size is placed within 600 mm of formation level.

Formation of embankments in rock fill is covered by the Specification of Roads and Bridges, HMSO 1976.

Pulverised Fuel Ash

This is a material obtained from coal fired power stations. Coal is pulverised and blown into the combustion chamber by a jet of air. After burning, the resultant ash is extracted by cyclone collectors or electrostatic precipitators. This ash is known as Pulverised Fuel Ash (PFA). PFA can be supplied in the following ways for use as a bulk fill.

Conditioned PFA — in which water is added to the material to bring it to the correct moisture content for compaction

Lagoon PFA — which consists of PFA with a percentage of furnace bottom ash which has been pumped hydraulically into lagoons to drain and dry out

Stock-pile PFA — which consists of PFA plus furnace bottom ash, all of which has been stock-piled after drainage in lagoons.

The material is transported to site in lorries or by rail, depending on accessibility. It is easily handled and compacted on site, is much lighter than conventional fill materials, and has a much higher shear strength than rock and soil fills. One of the greatest advantages is the absence of settlement when compacted correctly. To achieve good results the following specification should be adopted:

Once PFA is spread it must be compacted immediately.

Compaction should be in layers not exceeding 150 mm in thickness.

The minimum dry density after compaction should be 90% of the mean of the maximum dry densities obtained from a number of samples.

In certain classes of work on waterlogged or impermeable ground it is advisable to provide a drainage layer at the base of the PFA fill. This layer should be at least 300 mm thick. If PFA is to be used within 450 mm of the road finish, it must be stabilised against frost by using 10% (by weight) cement. PFA, if wet, creates great problems by turning to slurry; for that reason it is not very popular with contractors.

1.3.3   Explosives

Blasting explosives can be divided into two groups, high explosives and low explosives. The former detonate with a rapid production of gas, while the latter deflagrate and produce gas slowly.

High explosives can be further divided into three main classes, Gelatines, Powders and Slurries.

Gelatinous explosives have a good resistance to moisture both in use and in storage. The maximum storage life varies with conditions and climate but is in the order of one or two years. This type of high explosive is suitable for use in boreholes containing water. Some of the more popular gelatinous explosives are:

Submarine Blasting Gelatine, the strongest commercial explosive available. This is a nitro-glycerine gelatine explosive, specially formulated for use under the high hydrostatic pressures met with in underwater work.

Special Gelatine 90% is a high strength gelatinous explosive containing nitro-glycerine and ammonium nitrate. It has high density, good water resistance, and is recommended for use wherever a powerful shattering explosive is required.

Opencast Gelignite is a gelatinous explosive, slightly less powerful than Special Gelatine 90% but similar in other properties. It was originally designed for blasting the overburden for opencast coal mining but it is now widely used for quarrying and excavation.

Special Gelatine 80% is slightly weaker than the preceding explosives, but is of the same basic type and has similar density and water resistance characteristics. Special Gelatine 80% is classified as a medium strength nitro-glycerine and one which gives good fragmentation. It is referred to as an 'all purpose' explosive and is suitable for all types of blasting.

Powders

Polar Rockite is a lower density nitro-glycerine-based explosive which is not resistant to water. It is suitable for blasting medium and soft rock where there is no water problem.

TNT (Trinitrotoluene) Ammonium Nitrate is an explosive in which TNT replaces nitroglycerine as the sensitiser. It has low density and less resistance to water than gelatine explosives. It is suitable for quarrying and civil engineering work where conditions are dry. It is manufactured by ICI under the trade name of 'Trimonite'. Since powder type explosives are susceptible to dampness, they must be fired soon after charging in wet conditions.

Slurries

Slurry explosives contain no nitroglycerine or TNT and are very much less sensitive to accidental initiation by impact or friction than either gelatines or powder explosives. Operators cannot suffer nitro-glycerine headaches when handling slurry explosives. They are completely waterproof both in storage and use. Slurry explosives can therefore be used in wet boreholes. The maximum storage life varies with conditions and climate but is generally at least six months. There are various types of slurry explosive, two of the most popular types in the UK being Iregel slurries and Supergex slurries.

Iregel slurries are composed on a thickened and gelled aqueous solution of oxidiser salts, eg ammonium nitrate, sensitised by aluminium. None of the raw materials are explosive in their own right. The range comprises 'Iregel 335C', 'Iregel 385D', 'Iregel 445D', and 'Iregel 455D' in ascending power and density. They can all be initiated by 'Cordtex' detonating cord or No 8 star strength detonators.

'Iregel 445D' and '455D' are generally used as base charges in hard rocks where a well fragmented rock-pile is required. 'Iregal 385D' is usually employed as a base charge in easier conditions, as a column charge in harder rocks and for blasting the overburden in opencast mining. 'Iregel 335C' is generally used as a replacement for ANFO (Ammonium Nitrate Fuel Oil) in wet conditions.

Supergex slurries are basically thickened and gelled ammonium nitrate slurries sensitised by isopropyl nitrate (IPN). Their power is varied by the aluminium content. The Supergexes are not sensitive to initiation by detonators or 'Cordtex' detonating cord. Satisfactory initiation can be achieved using 'Superflex' detonating cord or 'Powerprime' primers etc. Supergex is a high density, high strength explosive suitable for most hard rock blasting operations. 'Premium Supergex', with an even higher strength and density than Supergex, is capable of dealing with the toughest conditions and is especially well suited for toe charges.

Low explosives

The only low explosive in common use is black powder, also known as Black Blasting Powder or Gunpowder. It is the oldest known explosive and has a heaving action instead of the shattering effect of high explosives. It is ignited by means of a safety fuse or electric powder fuse and should not be used in wet conditions. The low strength explosion is suitable for splitting stone beds in quarries when stone is required for building.

AN/FO (Ammonium Nitrate/Fuel Oil)

This type of explosive is available in several forms, the most common of which is a mixture of explosive-grade ammonium nitrate 'prills' (small globules) and diesel oil. The mixture is poured directly into shot holes and initiated by a primer or Superflex detonating cord. This explosive is cheaper than pre-packed explosive and is widely used in quarries and bulk excavations. A more powerful explosive mixture can be obtained by using crushed prills with fuel oil; this provides better explosive characteristics and a higher loading density.

Low density AN/FO can be used for controlled blasting in areas where normal blasting would be prohibited. A proportion of the ammonium nitrate is replaced by a lightweight, inert material such as polystyrene balls. This mixture has explosive properties which are quite weak and is therefore suitable when vibration and shock waves are to be restricted.

Blasting accessories

Plain detonators for use with a safety fuse are supplied in No. 6 strength or No. 8 strength in boxes of 100. A No. 6 strength detonator is adequate and gives efficient detonation with gelatines and powders. Slurry explosives cannot be reliably initiated using only a plain detonator and safety fuse.

Electric detonators are suitable for firing single or a number of shots simultaneously in a round. They are manufactured in two types:

Instantaneous in No. 6 strength

Delay and Short delay in No. 8 star strength when a delay is necessary.

Delay and Short delay detonators have standard time delays depending on the type used. Delay detonators are made in thirteen types from 0–12; No. 0 gives instantaneous explosion and the remainder have a delay of 0.5 seconds between each number.

Short delay detonators have a delay of either 0.025 seconds or 0.03 seconds between successive numbers. Each detonator has a fuse head assembly fitted with insulated leading wires sealed in position with a neoprene plug.

'Magnadet' electric detonators

For improved safety and speed of connecting up, 'Magnadet' electric detonators are available. 'Magnadet' electrically isolate the detonator from outside influences by coupling each detonator via its own transformer to a special exploder. The transformer used is a ferrite ring or toroid and is attached to the lead wires of the detonator. The toroid exployed is such that it is frequency selective and can only be activated by high frequency AC power — 15 000 Hz or greater. This means that the detonator is immune to DC energy and to standard 50 or 60 Hertz mains supply frequency.

'Magnadets' are simply and easily coupled by passing the primary circuit wire once through the centre of the toroid protector cover, giving a uniquely quick method of connecting up.

Compared with normal electric detonators, 'Magnadets' offer:

Improved protection against stray currents from both DC and normal AC power

Improved protection against static hazards

Improved protection against radio-frequency radiation

Virtual immunity from problems of current leakage.

The 'Magnadet' concept has been incorporated into the 'Magna' primer, which comprises a cast pentolite charge within a specifically designed plastic housing and can accommodate two 'Magnadet' electric detonators. The detonators are easily located in the 'Magna' primer so that the centre of the toroids or transformers are co-axial with an aperture cast in the main body of the pentolite charge and plastic housing. This allows the primary circuit wire to be threaded through the primer and through the toroids of the detonators, forming an inductive coupling.

'Magna' primers are used in both surface and underground blasting operations employing large diameter blastholes to initiate either primer sensitive explosives or different decks of explosives within the same shothole on different delay periods. Such an in-hole delay system enables the maximum charge weight of explosive per delay to be reduced, thus limiting the intensity of airblast, noise and ground vibrations caused by blasting.

'Magnadet' electric detonators are manufactured in No. 8 star strength. The delay range comprises a series of twelve detonators, numbered 1–12. There is a standard time interval of a half-second between each number. Short delay detonators in a series numbered 1–30 are also available. The range has a nominal delay interval of 25 milliseconds from Nos 1 to 12, increasing to 30 milliseconds from Nos 13 to 30.

Safety fuse is used for setting off plain detonators or for initiating black powder, wrapped in layers of textile yarn or tape with waterproof coverings. The burning speed must not vary by more than 9.5 seconds above or 12.5 seconds below 100 seconds per metre.

Capped fuses consist of lengths of safety fuse with plain detonators crimped on to the ends. They are supplied in lengths of 750 mm to 1750 mm in boxes of fifty.

'Cordtex' and the stronger superflex are detonating cords consisting of a core of pentaerythritol tetrantrate (PETN) enclosed in a tape, which is wrapped with yarn and completely enclosed in a white plastic cover. This gives a strong flexible waterproof cord. They have a high velocity of detonation (76 800 m/sec) and characteristics which ensure the initiation of all commercial explosives. Both types are very safe to handle and if crushed and spilled would require a further blow before detonation could occur. Detonating relays can be fitted anywhere along the cordtex to enable any special blasting sequence to be arranged.

'Plastic Igniter Cord' is an incendiary cord used for lighting a number of safety fuses in series. Three types are available with nominal burning speeds of 3.5 secs/m, 33 secs/m, and 50 secs/m. Beanhole connectors are used to ensure the transmission of the flame to the safety fuse in all circumstances.

Electric powder fuses consist of an electric fusehead assembly sealed into a cardboard tube containing a charge of black powder. They are used to ignite black powder.

Exploders: firing shots electrically can be done either with exploders or mains connection, but the most common method is by the use of an exploder. Various exploders can be obtained which fire from one shot up to 1000 shots in series. A popular exploder in civil engineering work is the Beethoven exploder which has a capacity for firing 100 shots in series. A circuit tester should be used to test for open and short circuits before linking the wires to the exploder.

Cables and connecting wire: firing cables, either single or twin core type, are available in different grades to suit the type of work involved. It can be obtained with a tough rubber sheath for use under water. Connecting wire is used to connect the cable to the round of shots and thus prevent damage to the cable by blasting.

Handling and storage of explosives

The handling and conveyance of explosives is covered by the Explosives Acts of 1875 and 1923 as well as by subsequent Statutory Instruments, such as The Conveyance of Explosives Byelaw 1958. Before any explosive is conveyed by road transport it must be packed in accordance with the Packing of Explosives for Conveyance Rules 1951 or a Special Packing Authority issued by HM Inspector of Explosives.

If carried in a petrol or diesel drive vehicle, the maximum permitted load is 3628 kg. Two men must accompany the vehicle at all times and the vehicle must be provided with a fire screen between cab and body. The interior of the vehicle body must be lined with asbestos or other non-inflammable material.

Storage regulations vary according to the quantity of explosive to be stored and fall into five categories:

Private use: limited to 5 kg of explosives or 13.6 kg of black powder to be kept in a locked box marked 'Explosives'. Detonators should be kept in a separate box. Since a Police Certificate or licence is necessary the storage arrangements will have to satisfy the Chief Constable.

Registered premises: Mode A, which consists of a substantial brick-built building with steel doors, can be used for storing 30 kg of explosive or 900 kg of black powder only. Mode B, which may consist of a fireproof safe of other substantial receptacle, can be used for storing up to 7 kg of explosive or 25 kg of black powder only.

Multiple registered premises consist of substantial buildings, as those in Mode A, but with facilities for distributing explosive substances to shift workers such as miners without having to issue direct from the bulk store. Instead explosives are taken daily from the bulk store and placed in explosive compartments ready for the out-going shot firers.

Stores: under the Stores for Explosives Order 1951, there are five divisions of stores, A, B, C, D and E, classified according to their distances from other buildings and works. Division A can be used for storing 75 kg of explosives and Division E for storing 1814 kg of explosives. The other divisions are graded in measurements of 136 kg, 453 kg and 907 kg respectively.

Magazines are used for storing quantities of explosives over 1814 kg and can only be constructed under a Magazine licence obtained from HM Inspector of Explosives.

1.4 TEMPORARY WORKS

On many civil engineering projects the cost and design of temporary works forms a very high proportion of the total contract. Therefore care in design and planning is essential. Each temporary structure must be considered on its merits in relation to the importance of the contract and especially the consequences of failure. If under-design could lead to failure in operating conditions, then the cost of delay, together with loss of valuable plant and equipment (not to mention injury to persons) would far outweigh the saving in design. Therefore, it is important to design all structures to take the full working load envisaged. Allowance must be made for site conditions and human error in the erection of such structures in bad weather. Supervision in the erection, removal and maintenance of all these structures is paramount. Where materials are used more than once, e.g. as in the case of falsework, they should be checked to ensure that they have not been weakened by their initial uses. Second-hand materials should be subject to careful scrutiny before being used in situations where the design was based on new materials. Typical examples of temporary works are:

Piling

Dewatering systems

Ground support, e.g. Cofferdams, timbering, underpinning and shoring

Access Bridges

Gantries and Scaffolding

Track work for cranes and trains

Specialised topics are dealt with in detail in subsequent chapters of the book. Safety aspects have already been dealt with in Section 1.2.8.

Chapter 2

Contractors' Plant

2.1 MANAGEMENT OF PLANT

Plant is one of the most important resources in civil engineering; without it massive construction work and soil movements would be difficult to achieve in this country, which is not highly labour intensified. Plant will generally save time, manpower, cost, and produces a better finish to the work. It must be stressed, however, that costs are only reduced by good management of plant. Such management involves factors such as:

Outputs

Method appraisal

Continuity of work

Training of operatives

Organisation of plant work

Maintenance and repair of plant

Economic selection of plant.

Once a contract has been signed, the contractors' plant department will be responsible for the provision of the requisite plant and equipment for the site. This will have to be brought from the owner's depot, other contracts, bought in new or hired from specialists. Alternatively, the contractor may sub-let certain works which include heavy plant, e.g. earthworks, and be involved only in planning the continuity and progress of work.

The plant manager will assist in the preparation of programmes (Fig 2.1) and in the selection of plant for the work in hand. He will also prepare maintenance programmes and install a record system for checking the performance of each piece of plant.

Fig 2.1

WEEKLY PLANT PROGRAMME						
Plant	Mon	Tues	Wed	Thurs	Fri	Sat
Crawler Tractor (1)	←——————— Clear site ———————→					
Ditto (2)	←—Remove Scrub —→✕ Form access road —→					
Scraper 8 m³	←——————— Reduced level work ———————→					
Ditto 8 m³	←——————— Reduced level work ———————→					
Truck 7 m³	←——————— Haul rubbish to tip ———————→					
Ditto 7 m³	←——————— Haul rubbish to tip ———————→					
Ditto 7 m³	←——————— Haul rubbish to tip ———————→					

In selecting plant and equipment the plant manager will consider the following factors:

The work load to be undertaken

The time allowed in the construction programme for the work

The capabilities of the machine or equipment

The various tasks which any one piece of plant could accomplish

The transportation costs involved

Maintenance facilities.

The cost, whether to hire, or buy; if bought the economics will be established by the following:

Capital cost, residual value, machine life, capital interest, maintenance costs,
terrain on which plant has to operate, weather conditions, availability of plant,
future utilisation potential.

As a general rule the large and expensive items of plant are best hired, if and as required, for short periods of time and high output of work. General items of plant which have a good utilisation factor are best owned. However, the duration of a contract and the amount of work involved might create a particular situation where it could be cheaper to buy all new plant to be disposed of afterwards when the contract is complete.

The maintenance of plant is a major factor in large plant departments and all maintenance should be planned to ensure high productivity with low breakdown time. Maintenance costs depend upon:

Age and condition of plant

Care of plant by the operator

Labour and overhead costs

Cost of spares

Cost of general maintenance which includes: lubricants, anti-freeze, batteries, tyres, tracks, hydraulics, replacement of ropes etc — all of which should be carefully planned

Availability of suitable facilities in relation to the contract operation.

2.2 EARTHMOVING PLANT

2.2.1 Construction methods and selection of plant

Before commencing earth moving, a plan should be produced showing all areas for excavation, tipping and filling. The quantities of excavated material and required fill should be shown on this plan, so as to facilitate the most economic movement of soil. When large quantities of soil have to be moved, a 'mass-haul' diagram should be prepared (Fig 2.2). Such a diagram shows the distances and direction of haul and gradients calculated to balance the cut and fill.

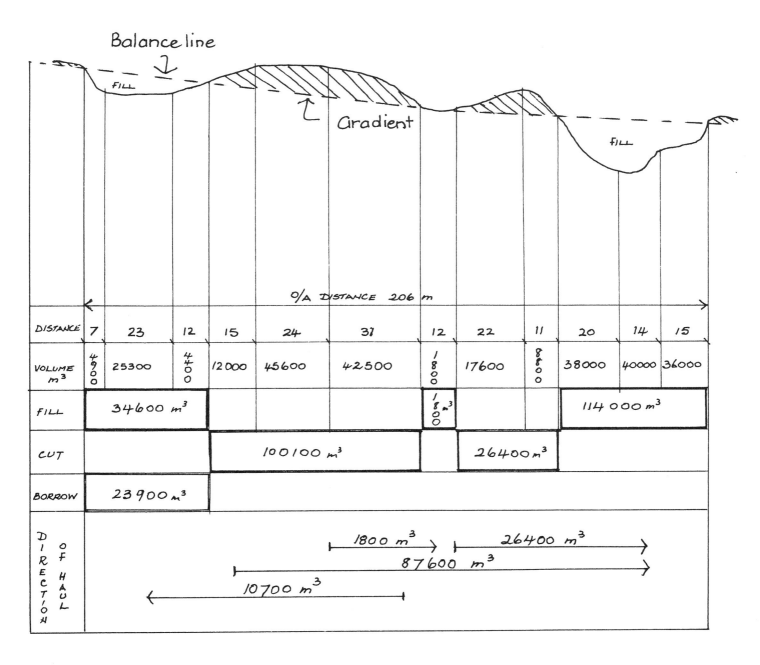

Fig 2.2   *Mass haul diagram*

If the excavated material is likely to be particularly variable some indication should be given of its method of disposal, i.e. whether to haul to spoil heap rather than fill areas. These factors are considered further in Chapter 3 — Earthworks.

Construction methods for smaller sites, eg basements, deep pits, trenches etc, will depend to a great extent on the following factors:

Type of soil or rock

Quantity of material to be moved

Presence of water

Depth of dig

Working space available

Whether excavated material can be left on site.

As a general rule, for large pits and basements, where space will allow, the excavation should be achieved by 'battering' the sides of the dig. This allows a clear working area, free from obstruction or shoring (Fig 2.3).

Selection of plant depends on the following factors:

Excavating Plant	—	quantities; type of soil; weather conditions; speed of removal; depth of dig; side cast or cart away
Transporting Plant	—	quantities; distance to be moved; condition of site; conditions of tip; speed of excavating; size of excavating bucket; turn-round time
Placing Plant	—	method of transporting and compacting; quantities involved; weather conditions; finish required
Compacting Plant	—	nature of material; nature of contract; depth of fill; weather conditions.

Selection will also take into consideration availability of plant and costs per estimated unit of soil moved or placed.

Setting out for earthmoving plant

This differs somewhat from the setting-out covered in Chapter 1, since a different degree of accuracy is required. On some projects, the speed of earthmoving is more important than the achievement of precise final levels, eg road construction in forward areas. On the other hand, as eg in airfield construction, precision of final levels may be as important as speed of construction. This difference in approach affects the setting-out procedure, which will vary from project to project. The normal procedure is to use timber pegs or stakes as guides and reference markers for earthwork operations. These stakes are used for centre lines, shoulder lines, batter and reference points. They are approximately 600 mm long x 75 x 25 mm in section and are marked according to purpose (Fig 2.4).

In Fig 2.4 the batter stake shows the depth of cut (C = 2.6 m) and its distance from the centre line 12 m. On the edge of the stake the slope (1 in 2) is marked as a fraction, and on the back face of the stake the distance along the centre line from the first station. After reducing the levels a series of final level pegs are positioned at the shoulder and centre line. This procedure can be used for almost any form of mass excavation.

2.2.2   Excavating Plant

Universal excavator (Fig 2.5) (hydraulic or rope operated)

This piece of plant is the best known item and probably the most common used in construction work. It can be fitted with different front or back acting equipment to carry out various jobs. Rope operated equipment can also be used as a dragline, grab or crane and, where they can be converted, for pile driving.

The standard equipment is for backacter operations, in which trenches, deep pits etc, may be excavated below ground level. The choice of plant depends on the depth of dig, the type of ground, the quantity to be moved

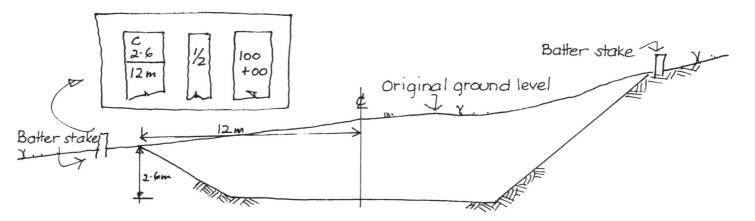

Fig 2.3   *Excavation with battered sides*

Fig 2.4   *Setting out for cuttings*

Fig 2.5   *Rope-operated backacter* (Ruston Bucyrus Limited)

Fig 2.6   *Dragline* (Ruston Bucyrus Limited)

and the speed of excavation required. A typical bucket size is approximately 0.75 m³ and the depth of the dig 6 - 7 m. Hydraulic machines can have extensions for greater depths.

Dragline equipment, seen in Fig 2.6, shows the rope controlled bucket to be swung far over, or deep into the excavation. It is suitable for a wide range of materials, but will not dig very hard ground or dig to fine limits. This equipment is suitable for large scale excavation, particularly in waterlogged ground or marine works. The long jib allows material to be dumped over a wide radius.

Grab (Fig 2.7): this is used for handling loose materials such as concreting aggregates or for digging pits which would prove difficult for the backacter. Hydraulic machines are being increasingly used as grabs. This piece of equipment is very suitable for marine works such as caisson sinking and dredging.

Face shovel (Fig 2.8): by adding a short jib to the centre of the jib on an excavator, this machine, with its upward digging action, is produced. It works in the bottom of the excavation digging upwards from the level on which it stands. It has a quick digging action and is very suitable for loading hard materials which have been reduced by blasting.

Trenching machines (Fig 2.9): this machine is suitable for excavating extremely long and narrow trenches, as for pipelines etc. They vary in size but will normally dig trenches from 0.25 m up to 1.5 m wide and down to 3 m deep. There are two basic types of trencher, one with buckets mounted on a wheel at the front of the machine and the other with buckets mounted on an endless chain which is carried by means of a jib. Both machines are self-emptying by means of conveyors which throw the soil clear on both sides of the machine. The wheel type is suitable for shallow (up to 3 m depth) trenches where high speed is required while the jib type is more suited for deeper trenches.

Tractor shovel-loader (Fig 2.10): the most common type of machine for reduced level dig on medium and small sites is the track-mounted loader with front-loading bucket. This bucket (known as a 4 in 1 because it can be used for four operations; dozing, loading, levelling and grabbing) is very suitable for stripping and loading the spoil on to lorries. It must be noted that tractor shovels can be fitted with backacting equipment. The disadvantage of tracked equipment is that it cannot travel between sites under its own power, every time the machine has to be moved a low loader unit has to be employed. This increases the overall hire cost of the machine. The advantage over the wheeled-type machine is that much more manoeuvrability is achieved on tracks over wet or poor ground conditions.

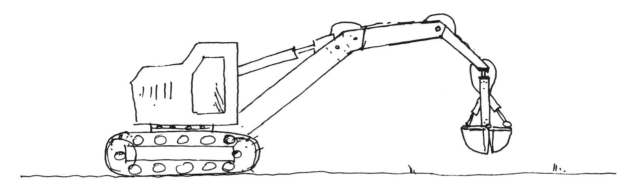

Fig 2.7   *Grab — hydraulically operated*

Fig 2.8   *Rope operated face shovel*

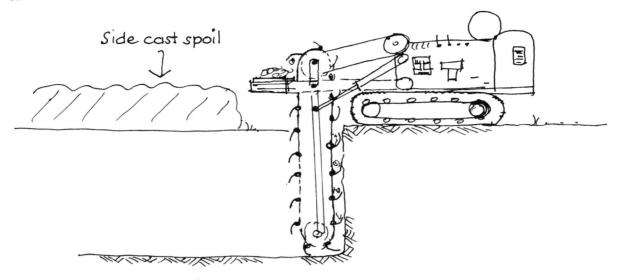

Fig 2.9   *Trenching machine*

Fig 2.10   *Tractor loader shovel with 4 in 1 bucket*

(International Harvester Company of Great Britain Limited)

2.2.3   Transporting plant

This section deals with plant which is involved in moving earth some distance from the point of excavation. The items of plant under this section include rubber-tyred vehicles, tractor-drawn equipment, track-mounted equipment and belt conveyors.

Rubber-tyred vehicles

This form of transport, namely tipper lorries and dump trucks, forms the largest section of earth moving plant. They vary in capacity from a basic 5 m³ lorry to a 30 m³ dump truck. Such vehicles have heavily plated bodies which are hydraulically operated to ensure quick clean tipping. The lorry is designed for working on reasonably level ground and for carrying evenly distributed loads, but under rough site conditions they are subject to axle and spring damage. For this reason, where large quantities of earth have to be removed or taken across rough ground, the dump truck is the best piece of equipment to be employed.

Tractor-drawn equipment

The most popular piece of equipment employed for moving large quantities of earth on extended sites is the scraper. The machine consists of a specially designed container on wheels which can be lowered at one end to pick up material while the machine is on the move. When full, the machine carries the earth to some other point and discharges its load by a similar principle. There are two main types of machine:

Crawler-drawn scraper

Motorised scraper.

The capacity of a scraper varies from 5 m³ to 50 m³ and the classification of a scraper is determined by its carrying capacity.

Crawler-drawn scrapers consist of a four-wheeled scraper unit being towed by a track-mounted machine. The scraper unit is connected to the crawler by a tow-bar and control cables (Fig 2.11). This type of equipment is slow in operation compared with other scrapers but is suitable for very rough ground.

Motorised two-axled wheel tractor scrapers consist of a unit mounted on four wheels — which are large diameter rubber-tyred. Over the front pair of wheels the power unit is mounted and in some models a rear power unit is employed to give a four wheel drive. These machines, unlike the other two types, are capable of self-loading without the aid of a pusher tractor. They are capable of high speeds over great distances and are therefore most suitable for road works (Fig 2.12).

Motorised three-axled wheel tractor scrapers consist of a unit mounted only on two rear wheels and towed by a special four-wheeled tractor. Both this machine and the crawler-drawn scraper require pusher assistance when excavating in hard ground. This pusher assistance is normally given by one bulldozer serving several scrapers. Special bulldozers with pushing pads or spring-mounted blades have been designed to deal with push loading work. The spring-mounted blade allows contact to be made while the machines are still moving, thereby reducing the duration of the working cylce. The three-axled wheel scraper, similar to the two-axled wheel scraper, is used for high speed earth moving but over medium distances, say 1 km.

Bulldozers

Crawler tractors include the bulldozer range of plant. It is used primarily for pushing earth from one point to another. It is quite normal for a bulldozer to excavate to a depth of 200 mm and then push the material 50 - 100

Fig 2.11   *Crawler-drawn scraper*

Fig 2.12 *Motorised scraper receiving pusher assistance*
(International Harvester Company of Great Britain Limited)

Fig 2.13 *Bulldozer with hydraulic tilt blade*
(International Harvester Company of Great Britain Limited)

metres for a spread and level operation. Angle and tilt dozers are another variation in the plant group where the blade is set at an angle to the machine for the purpose of pushing soil to one side instead of carrying it forward for levelling. Generally the normal bulldozer blade can be adjusted by hydraulic rams to function as an angle dozer; in other cases angle dozers are purposely designed for the angle dozing only (Fig 2.13). Dozers can also be fitted with winches for hauling and rippers for breaking up ground.

Conveyors

Belt conveyors are used for various operations and are therefore made in several forms; the most important ones are:

Independent units for the carriage of materials over considerable distances, eg sand and gravel

Units for moving materials in confined spaces

Track or wheel-mounted units — better known as portable units

Integral units, which form part of a large machine such as elevating graders or multi-bucket trenchers.

The advantages of a belt conveyor are:

They deliver a high ouput with a steady flow

They can deliver horizontally or on a limited incline

Movement is not affected by bad ground conditions

They can be used in situations where access for vehicles would create problems

They require minimal maintenance

Efficiency is high and power used is low.

The disadvantages are:

They are not as flexible in movement and re-arrangement as other forms of plant

The belts are subject to damage by sharp irregular materials, which if large may fall off.

Loading the belt should be achieved by one of the following methods:

Loading-hopper with restricted chute

Feeding device, such as a short conveyor.

On some earth-moving projects the elevator loader is used. This consists of a towing unit and a scraper with an elevator built in behind the scraper blade. The scraper is towed and the earth moves up the elevator and on to a second belt conveyor which fills a waiting haul unit.

Graders: something must be included about this piece of plant which is neither truly earth excavating nor earth moving. It is used to finish earth formations, such as roads and embankments, to a fine limit. The machine (Fig 2.14) is similar to a dozer, in that it carries a long slender blade which can be adjusted hydraulically. This long blade is normally slung under the centre of the machine (or to one side in the formation of slopes). There are two main types of grader:

Motorised — the most common one in use

Tractor-towed — usually a small grader, but rarely used.

2.2.4   Compaction plant

This section is limited to plant used on large earth-moving contracts and therefore does not cover items such as small vibrators.

Smooth-wheeled rollers such as those used in road works may be used for producing a smooth surface on top of embankments to facilitate the shedding of water, but other than that have a limited application to earthworks.

Sheepsfoot rollers (Fig 2.15) consist of a hollow steel cylinder on which are mounted rows of projecting studs (called feet). There are two types of foot, the taper foot and the club foot. For extra weight the roller is filled with water or sand; alternatively ballast boxes may be fitted to the roller. The sheepsfoot roller is towed by a tracked vehicle across a fill area until the roller has fully consolidated the material. On reaching consolidation the roller 'walks out', this meaning the feet no longer dig into the top of the fully compacted material.

Pneumatic-tyred rollers are designed to give a kneading action to the material. The roller has two lateral rows of wheels, the front row being out of line with the back row, so that no gaps are left in compacting. The wheels are mounted in pairs on separate axles, allowing each pair to follow the irregularities of the ground. This has given the name of 'wobbly-wheels' to the rollers. The load is applied by means of kentledge or sand and the roller is towed by a tractor or alternatively can be self-propelled.

Vibrating rollers are particularly effective for the consolidation of granular soils. The machine is smooth wheeled and is fitted with an engine-driven vibrating unit. It is towed by a tractor unit.

Fig 2.14 *Motor grader* *(Aveling-Barford Limited)*

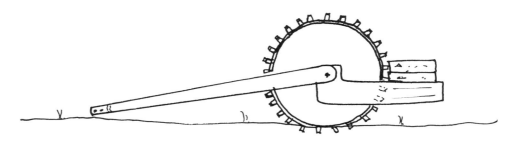

Fig 2.15 *Sheepsfoot roller*

2.2.5 Performance and outputs of earthmoving plant

The actual performance of earthmoving plant is very difficult to establish because no two sites are the same. The only way of arriving at a performance figure is by one of two methods:

Reference to output charts and tables, or

Detailed calculation.

In the first case output charts are produced either by the manufacturers, and must be treated with caution, or they are produced by a contractor's estimating department from information received from actual sites. The latter source is much more reliable since weather, quantities, time of year etc, can all be considered.

TABLE 2.1

TASK EFFICIENCY FACTORS FOR EXCAVATORS			
Equipment or machine	TASK	Task efficiency factors	
		When loading into vehicle	When side-casting
Backacter	Trenching		
	Bucket width	0.8	1.0
	more than bucket width	0.6	0.7
Dragline	Bulk excavation	0.8	1.0
	Wide open ditches	0.7	0.9
Trenching Machine	Continuous trenching	–	1.0
Face shovel	Excavating above track level		
	Little movement	0.65	0.8
	Much movement	0.45	0.6
	Moving shattered rock (delay due to blasting)	0.4	0.5
Scrapers and bulldozers	Cutting, hauling or pushing soil	–	1.0
Tractor shovel (Drott or similar)	Clearing site	0.8	1.0
	Reduced level dig	0.8	0.9
Grab (Hydraulic)	Excavating deep bases		
	Min obstruction	0.7	0.8
	Max obstruction (timbering)	0.5	0.6

Note: The above table must be used in conjunction with standard outputs which are shown in Table 2.2.

With detailed calculations it is necessary to assess the initial soil moving operations by means of a method study. This will take into consideration the actual site conditions and allow site management to base their decisions on accurate information.

It must be mentioned however that time for prime operations does not represent the optimum time for all operations since on every job there is a 'learning curve' and a job familiarisation factor to be considered.

If the plant has much moving to do during the task, the efficiency factor is greatly reduced. The above table (Table 2.1) shows typical efficiency factors for excavators.

For example a backacter trenching with a 1 m³ bucket will excavate and load 60 buckets per hour. 60 m³ x Efficiency factor of 0.8 = 48 m³ actual performance (allowance should be made for bulking).

These performance figures must be multiplied by the operator's efficiency factor which is normally 75 per cent. This allows for personal needs etc. during the working day. Taking the above example of 48 m³ actual performance of the backacter times the operator's efficiency factor gives the following overall performance figure for the machine — 48 m³ x 0.75 = 36 m³ per hour.

It can be seen from the above factors that outputs cannot be relief on from manufacturers' catalogues.

TABLE 2.2

PLANT OUTPUTS FOR CLAYEY SOIL		
Plant	Remarks	Output
Backacter	In confined conditions	Allow 30 buckets/hour (ie 30 x bucket size)
Backacter	In normal trenching	Allow 60 buckets/hour
Dragline	In open excavation	Allow 80 buckets/hour
Dragline	In restricted area	Allow 35 buckets/hour
Face shovel	In normal excavation	Allow 80 buckets/hour
Trenching machine	In normal trenching up to 1.5 m deep	Allow 2 metres/minute
Drott or similar	Reduce level dig	Allow 50 buckets/hour
Bulldozer	Haul = 30 m	Allow 60 m³/hour
	Haul = 60 m	Allow 20 m³/hour
Scraper 15 m³	Haul = 300 m	Allow 60 m³/hour
	Haul = 200 m	Allow 80 m³/hour
	Haul = 100 m	Allow 110 m³/hour
Grab	Normal conditions (bases)	Allow 40 buckets/hour

Note. In the majority of cases the above table shows outputs by number of buckets of earth which can be moved under normal conditions. The actual output, in cubic metres, can be calculated by multiplying the bucket size by the figure given in the output column.

The task efficiency for moving plant will depend on the length of each working 'pass' and speed of machine. Table 2.3 gives typical efficiency factors.

When considering earthmoving plant the output will depend on the haul distance and should be calculated as follows:

Estimate loading and discharge time

Calculate travelling time to and from discharge point.

These figures will give the cycle time.

Cycle time = Loading + discharge time + travelling time.

Output per hour = $\dfrac{\text{Capacity of machine} \times 60 \text{ minutes}}{\text{Cycle time}}$

Example for Scraper (30 m^3 capacity)

Loading time = 2 mins. Discharge time = 1 min.

Travelling time = 15 min. Therefore Cycle time = 3 + 15 = 18 mins.

Maximum Output per hour = $\dfrac{30 \text{ m}^3 \times 60 \text{ mins}}{18}$ = $\underline{100 \text{ m}^3 \text{ per hour}}$

(Note: Allowance should be made for bulking)

This figure must be multiplied by the operator's efficiency factor, i.e. 0.75, giving a basic output of 100 x 0.75 = 75 m^3 per hour. (Note: The task efficiency factor for a scraper is unity).

Soil types and site conditions affect the loading and spreading time as well as travelling time.

Where a number of vehicles are being filled by a loader the number of haulage vehicles required can be calculated as follows:

Haulage vehicles required = $1 + \dfrac{\text{Cycle time per vehicle}}{\text{Loading time of vehicle}}$

TABLE 2.3

TASK EFFICIENCY FACTORS FOR MOVING PLANT ON LARGE CONTRACTS						
Machine	Task	Task Efficiency Factor				
		Length of pass in metres				
		50	100	200	500	Over 500
Grader	Grading roads	0.4	0.6	0.8	0.9	1.0
	Spreading and shaping fill (brought by other machines)	0.4	0.5	0.7	0.8	–
Haulage plant	Carrying spoil to or from cut and fill area	0.7	0.75	0.8	0.9	1.0
	Carrying spoil over poor terrain (undulating)	0.5	0.6	0.7	0.75	0.8
Towed Rollers	Rolling fill areas	0.5	0.7	0.9	0.9	1.0
Rooters & Scarifiers	Breaking up ground	0.5	0.7	0.8	1.0	1.0
Mix in place stabilisers	Road works	0.5	0.6	0.7	0.7	0.7

2.3   CONCRETING PLANT

2.3.1   Methods and selection of plant

The production of a concrete structure involves three main stages, namely mixing, distribution and placing of the concrete. Each of these stages may be carried out in different ways and the best way for each operation must be determined for each site. The following factors must be taken into account when making the plant selection:

Topography of the site — boundaries, restrictions, noise, contours of land, soil conditions

The total volume of concrete required

The maximum amount of concrete required at any point at any one time

Availability of plant

Time of year in which concreting is to be carried out

Amount of space available for setting up plant

Quality of concrete required, ie specification, varying mixes

Cost of producing concrete by various methods.

From the above it can be seen that every site will have a set of conditions which require individual solutions for all three stages of the concreting operation. The best solution will depend on careful selection within each stage and on the inter-relationship of each stage in terms of speed and efficiency.

2.3.2   Concrete mixing plant

There are four main types of mixing plant:

Tilting-drum mixers (T)

Non-tilting drum mixers (NT)

Reverse drum mixers (R)

Paddle mixers (P).

The first type, tilting drum,is used mainly for mixing very small amounts of material on site and is normally used by a builder rather than by a Civil Engineer. It consists of a conical drum rotating on a movable axis. When the materials are mixed the drum is then tilted to discharge the mix.

However, larger output mixers are available for central mixing plants and these can produce up to 3 cubic metres per mix. The tilting action is controlled by hydraulic rams and batching is achieved by overhead weighbatch hoppers.

The second type, non-tilting drum, is suitable for larger outputs still of say 10 cubic metres per hour. It consists of a circular drum with a side outlet for loading (usually by means of a hopper), and an outlet on the opposite side for discharge, which occurs when the chute is inclined into the drum. The concrete falls on to the chute from the top of the drum. During mixing the chute is inclined to face the bottom of the drum thus preventing concrete from spilling out.

The third type, reverse drum mixer, is similar to the non-tilting mixer but it mixes when rotating in one direction and discharges in the reverse direction. Special baffles retain the concrete until the drum is reversed.

Paddle mixers consist of a stationary pan with rotating paddles. The paddles may be fixed or may themselves rotate as they go epicyclically round in the pan. This form of mixing unit gives very consistent mixes and is used for high-grade concrete. Since this type of mixer is not as portable as the others it tends to be used at a central mixing point or at locations where pre-cast units are made.

With all the types mentioned there are various sizes, giving outputs from as low as 200 litres to 4 cubic metres per cycle. In some cases a high level discharge is required and this can be achieved by setting a non-tilting mixer up on a steel frame. This allows discharge direct into large dumpers. Alternatively a skip-lift high discharger may be used. This equipment consists of a skip sliding up an inclined frame taking concrete from the ordinary discharge level up to a height of 2 metres.

.The selection of suitable plant for mixing will depend upon the following:

Amount of concrete required at any one time

Quality of mix required

Availability of plant

Amount of room for setting-up plant

Type of distribution plant.

In some cases it may be more economic to supplement the site output with ready-mixed concrete rather than set up another machine which will be under-employed most of the time.

Ready mix concrete has become increasingly popular over the last decade for the following reasons:

Congested city sites make it difficult to set up mixing plant

High-strength concrete is easily obtained thereby reducing expenditure on sophisticated mixing plant

Small quantities can be obtained.

However there are disadvantages, such as:

Delivery times are unreliable, due to traffic problems

Prices are considerably higher than the cost of site mixing

Large loads create difficulties in handling so much bulk quickly on the site

Access to site must be fit to carry the combined loads of delivery — vehicle and concrete

Washing down on site may create special problems.

Ready-mix concrete can be delivered in three different forms:

Dry-batched — in which water is added at the site and then mixed

Partially-mixed — during transit the drum revolves very slowly and the materials are completely remixed on arrival at site

Fully-mixed at the depot and agitated during transit.

The form to be used will depend greatly on the distance of the site from the mixing plant.

2.3.3   Concrete distribution plant

There are many ways in which concrete can be distributed on site, and the most common of these are:

Tipping barrows

Dumpers

Mono-rail

Hoists

Pumps

Placer units

Cranes with skips

Cableways

Conveyors

Tremie pipes, elephant trunking and chutes.

Hand operated tipping barrows (Dobbin barrows) have two wheels and are easy to handle and to discharge quickly. Powered barrows can be used to eliminate manual work; with this type of equipment the operator walks behind the machine controlling it by clutch and brakes.

Dumpers vary from small (500 litre) bowls to large (3 cubic metre) bowls. They can be either two-wheeled or four-wheeled drive and may be tipped by hand or by hydraulic mechanisms. In the hydraulic range there are various options, such as high discharge (Fig 2.16) units, discharge to both sides as well as the front, and a turntable unit which allows discharge through an arc of 180°.

Mono-rail equipment (Fig 2.17) consists of a power unit mounted on a single rail. The power unit has a side-tipping skip attached to it and it can also tow another unpowered truck behind it. The power unit can travel at 90 m per min. Trip-mounted rails provide automatic stopping and therefore eliminate the need for a driver. The power unit is capable of climbing slopes with a gradient of up to 1 in 8, and the capacities of the skips may vary from 300 to 500 litres. This method is particularly useful when working in areas of bad ground conditions, congested sites, heavily reinforced slabs etc.

Hoists have been developed for handling concrete economically. One such development is the 'Tip Skip' hoist in which a manually operated tipping skip replaces the platform of a normal hoist. The skip carries the concrete vertically and discharges it into receiving hoppers which are placed at each working level. The hoppers then feed barrows or other plant at each working level.

Another development is the static skip which discharges the concrete via a bottom door which is opened by pre-determined trip points (Fig 2.18). For large outputs twin skips can be used, one for filling while one is travelling. The skips travel on either side of a central hoist mast.

Fig 2.16 *High discharge skip on Benford Dumper* (Benford Limited)

Fig 2.17 *Mono-rail transporter mounted on scaffolding*
(Road Machines Limited)

Fig 2.18 *Centre slung hoist with automatic
discharge skip for handling concrete*
(Wickham Engineering Company Limited)

Pumps: there are two types of pumps available, namely mechanical and hydraulic. With the mechanical pump (Fig 2.19(a)) the concrete is forced along the pipes by a piston which is driven by a diesel engine. This type of equipment requires careful consideration when being set up because of its semi-permanent nature.

Hydraulic pumps which use either water or oil as a working fluid are more commonly used because there is much less work in setting-up (Fig 2.19(b)). They are self-contained in operation and are available as trailer units which can be towed into position on site and set up very quickly with the aid of jacking legs. Lorry-mounted hydraulic pumps with hydraulic booms to carry the delivery pipe to high levels are often used. This particular piece of equipment is often linked with ready-mixed concrete.

Both pumps are capable of straight line pumping for a distance of 300 metres horizontally and 30 metres vertically. Pipe lines are normally 110 or 150 mm in diameter.

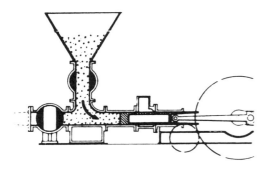

Pump cylinder and hopper
at the backward, or suction,
stroke of the piston.

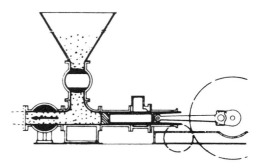

Pump cylinder and
hopper at the forward,
or driving, stroke of
the piston.

Fig 2.19(a)   *Mechanical concrete pump* (G.B. Davison)

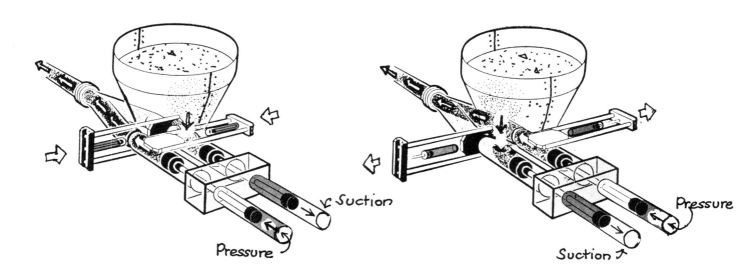

Fig 2.19(b)   *Hydraulic concrete pump* (G.B. Davison)

Placer units: in this method of distribution, concrete is fed into a hopper and then into an air-tight cylinder. Compressed air from an air receiver is admitted to the cylinder, causing the concrete to be driven along the pipe line at a predetermined speed. A special cone device prevents air from blowing a core through the batch of concrete, thus ensuring an even flow. The concrete is discharged at the delivery point through a special discharge box incorporating a vent for the compressed air (Fig 2.20).

Cranes are often employed in the distribution of concrete and little is required to explain their use. The type of crane varies with the type of job being executed. The main development in this form of distribution is the type of skip or bucket used. The two main types of skip are:

Roll-over
                              }   Fig 2.21
Constant attitude

The former is best suited to discharge into formwork, but the latter occupies less space under the crane hook. In both cases, where the bucket is capable of carrying large amounts of concrete, the method of controlling their discharge needs consideration. Discharge can be controlled by geared-gate mechanism, by air-operated mechanism or by hydraulic operation. Special buckets (Fig 2.22) are available for under-water placing, in which the concrete is protected while being lowered through the water.

Cableways (Fig 2.23) are used mainly for large civil engineering work, such as dams, where the concrete has to travel great distances over inaccessible ground. Cableways can be constructed in various ways such as:

Travelling

Radial Travelling

Luffing

Fixed

Travelling cableways have masts mounted on tracks thus enabling two dimensional coverage. Radial travelling cableways have one fixed mast and one travelling mast, thereby allowing the concrete to be distributed over a segmental area.

Luffing cableways have both masts mounted on pivots to allow some sideways movement from the base.

Fixed cableways, as the name suggests, have no tolerance in movement and these are therefore used only when concrete is to be placed in a straight line.

The output of cableways is very high, usually in the region of 8 to 60 cubic metres per hour. Travelling speeds of up to 350 m per minute are possible and spans can range from 300 to 600 metres.

Conveyors consist of a narrow continuous belt which runs over a series of rollers and carries a constant stream of concrete. The belt can travel at speeds of up to 150 m per minute, giving delivery of between 50 and 100 cubic metres of concrete per hour, depending on belt width (See Fig 8.3 — Chapter 8). The advantage of this type of equipment is one of full coverage, the conveyors being capable of easy removal and re-positioning for large slab areas. One type of conveyor — the bridge conveyor — is suitable for spanning over reinforcement and other obstacles. This particular conveyor can span distances of upwards of 30 m. Elevating units are also available for moving concrete to a higher level, the angle of elevation being restricted to approximately 25°.

Tremie pipes, elephant trunking and chutes are all pieces of non-mechanical equipment which are used for placing concrete in position below ground level (Fig 2.24). Such positions occur in piling, basements, diaphragm walling, etc, where segregation of the mix must be prevented. Tremie pipes consist of rigid tubes of metal or plastic, with a feed hopper at the head of the tube. As the concrete is placed the tube is shortened. Elephant trunking consists of PVC flexible tubing (which has superseded earlier metal versions) supported at intervals as it hangs into the area for concreting. The concrete is fed into the tubing by means of a hopper. The chute method of placing concrete has been used for many years and consists of an open metal channel or large diameter plastic tube (200 mm dia.), supported by scaffolding down into the area to be concreted (See Chapter 8). A hopper serves the chute at the top and a receiving hopper may be used at the bottom; alternatively the concrete can discharge directly into a dumper or other horizontal means of transport.

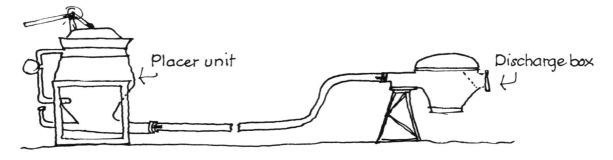

Fig 2.20   *Placer Unit*

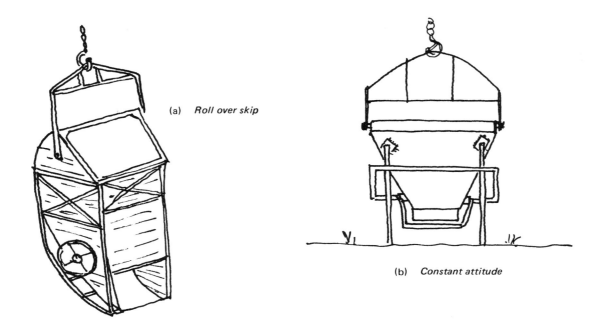

(a)   *Roll over skip*

(b)   *Constant attitude*

Fig 2.21 . *Concrete skips*

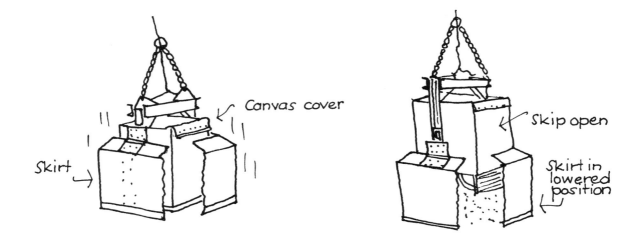

Fig 2.22 *Special 'underwater' skip*

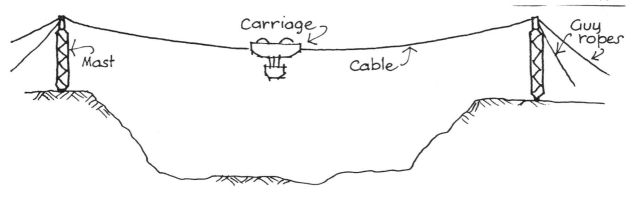

Fig 2.23   *Cableway*

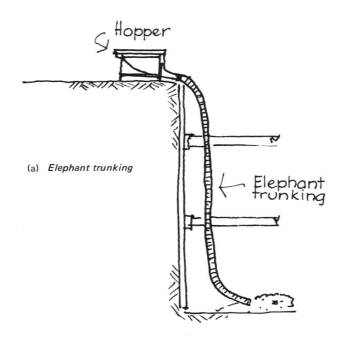

(a)   *Elephant trunking*

Fig 2.24   *Non-mechanical handling equipment*

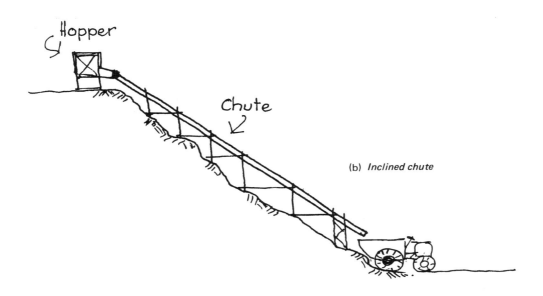

(b)   *Inclined chute*

Placing or finishing of concrete is achieved by vibrators and power floats (when a smooth finish is required). The vibrator used will depend on the location of the concrete. Where concrete is placed in columns, beams and walls, a poker vibrator or clamp vibrator is used. Surface vibrators, which can be attached to a tamping board, are used for consolidating slabs.

2.4 PILE DRIVING PLANT

2.4.1 General considerations

When selecting plant for piling operations it is necessary to establish the type of pile to be used. In the case of displacement piles, in which some form of pile or tubular casing is driven into the ground, consideration must be given to the support of the unit being driven. This normally takes the form of a pile frame or crane and leader, although latest developments use hydraulically operated telescopic back struts in lieu of a crane jib. In the case of replacement piles a hole is formed in the ground and then filled with reinforced concrete, the plant used varying with the size of hole formed. A tripod rig is used for small diameter holes (up to 600 mm). This rig is equipped with a winch for raising the cutting auger and the whole equipment weighs approximately 1.5 tonnes. For larger diameter holes the percussion equipment varies considerably; most systems use a crane and hammer grab for excavating the spoil inside the casings, but the method of inserting the casing varies. Some casings are placed with the use of oscillating machinery, which is part of the driving equipment; others are sunk by the use of a separate vibrator unit. Where large diameter auger holes are required the machinery is either purpose-built, or special attachments are mounted on standard craneage.

In each case consideration must be given to the height and manoeuvrability available on site, and whether vibration and noise would create problems to either adjoining buildings or residents. Further considerations include:

Type of sub-soil

Surface conditions, eg slope of site

Surface drainage eg waterlogged conditions

Obstructions e.g. old basements, existing services.

2.4.2 Methods of driving piles

Pile frames and leaders are used to locate and guide a pile during the initial stages of penetration as well as guiding and supporting the hammer. The leaders for guiding the hammer and pile extend the full height of the frame and consist of steel channels set some 150 mm apart. This space allows the lugs of drop hammers to be accommodated and facilitates the sliding of the hammer. A winch is used to lift the hammer in position and may also be used for positioning the pile. Pile frames may be vertical or raking and vary in height from 10 metres to 25 metres, adjustment for a raking frame being made by raking screw jacks. Stability is achieved by guy ropes from the head of the frame (Fig 2.25).

Cranes and leaders are commonly used instead of specialised piling frames. This equipment consists of a standard crane with a purpose-built leader unit attached to the crane at both top and bottom. These leaders can be obtained 30 metres high and are used on sites when normal piling frames would otherwise prove cumbersome. The crane can lift the leader unit and move easily across the site (Fig 2.26).

Pile driving rigs are similar in construction to the crane and leader unit but the crane jib is not used for lifting the leader. With this piece of equipment the leader is fixed to the crane with telescopic props from the rear of the crane, and the bottom of the leader is positioned by a hydraulic boom.

The actual 'driving' mechanism will depend on the type of pile, as set out below:

Driven steel casing: driven from the top by drop hammer or compressed air, diesel or steam hammer; by driving a mandrel and casing or by driving a shoe or plug of material by internal drop hammer. (See Chapter 4 for details).

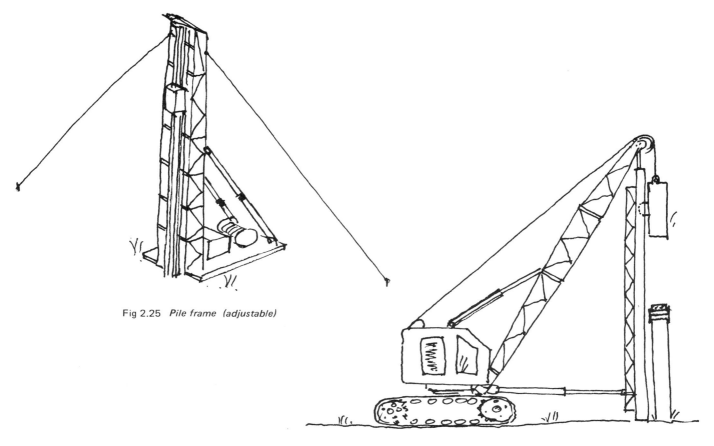

Fig 2.25 *Pile frame (adjustable)*

Fig 2.26 *Crane and Leader*

Pre-cast piles: all types of hammer are suitable but the hammer should weigh a minimum of half the weight of the pile being driven. The head of the pile must be protected against spalling; this is achieved by using a special helmet and dolly described below.

Special pre-formed steel piles: any type of hammer, but the heavier the hammer with reduced drop the less damage is done to the pile head.

Screw piles require a crane for pitching and some form of guide frame to hold the pile during its screwing operation.

Timber piles: drop hammers and single or double acting hammers are suitable. Where hard driving is anticipated the weight of the hammer should equal the weight of the pile.

Protection of concrete piles during driving is achieved by using a steel 'helmet' (Fig 2.27); the helmet is padded with a bed of sand on the top of the pile and the blow from the hammer is cushioned by a hardwood 'dolly'.

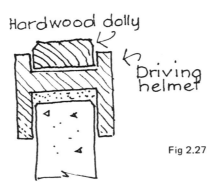

Fig 2.27

2.4.3   Pile-driving hammers

There are various types of hammer used in pile driving and the main types are as follows:

Percussion Type   —   Drop hammer
                        Diesel hammer
                        Single-acting hammer (steam or compressed air)
                        Double-acting hammer (steam or compressed air)

Hydraulic and
Vibratory   —   See Chaper 4 — Piling

Drop hammers consist of a shaped iron block, with lugs that locate in the leaders and a lifting eye for the winch rope. The hammer is lifted by the winch and slides down under its own weight, having been released on a free rope by means of a drum friction clutch. Alternatively the hammer can be released by trip mechanism. In the former method 15 to 20 blows per minute can be achieved; with the latter only 10 blows per minute.

The weight of the hammer is limited to the strain applied to the winch and hammers are manufactured in weights up to 4 tonnes each (Fig 2.28).

They are best suited for driving in marl, clay or compact sand, and particularly in driving past obstructions such as boulders.

Diesel hammers are self contained units which slide in leaders but do not require lifting as the drop hammer. The action is achieved by the falling cylinder of steel which is raised by the explosion of gas above the piston head (Fig 2.29). This cycle of operation is repeated continuously giving 60 blows per minute. The hammer is started by raising the ram in the leaders to the top of its stroke to fall freely. On falling the fuel is injected automatically, giving rise to an explosion for the continuous action. The weight of these hammers varies from 1 to 4 tonnes.

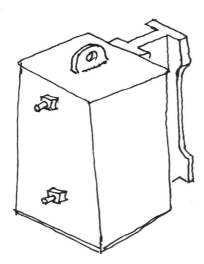

Fig 2.28   *Drop hammer*

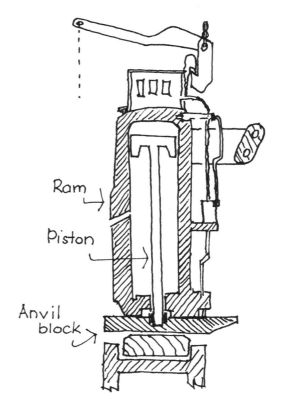

Fig 2.29   *Section through diesel hammer*

Single-acting hammers are similar in principle to the drop-hammer but are semi-automatic in action. The hammer is guided by leaders and the blow is provided by a heavy falling cylinder which is raised by means of steam or compressed air. The cylinder slides up and down a fixed piston (Fig 2.30). Steam or compressed air is admitted by a valve to raise the casing and exhausted through another valve to allow the casing to fall. Normal working speeds are 36 blows per minute up to a maximum of 45 blows per minute. Hammers of up to 6 tonnes are available. These hammers, like drop-hammers, are suitable for driving reinforced concrete piles.

Double-acting hammers are powered for both the upward and downward strokes, giving a rapid pattern of blows which keep the pile moving. This type of hammer is suitable for all driving with the exception of long, heavy piles. The force is less than that of a drop hammer or single-acting hammer but the number of blows per minute is greatly increased, varying from 95 to 500 blows per minute depending on the weight of the hammer. The cast iron cylinder (Fig 2.31) remains stationary and the blow is achieved by a piston moving at high speed. The double-acting hammer is suitable for use in situations where reduced head-room prohibits the use of a conventional hammer.

These hammers can be used for under-water driving controlled by compressed air and for driving steel sheet piling. The latter use can be achieved by suspending the hammer from a crane without the use of leaders, providing the piles themselves are in a guide frame.

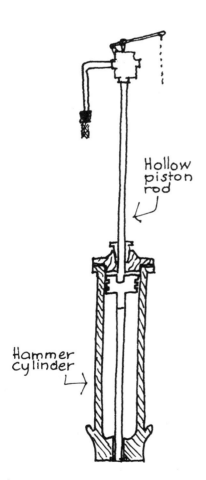

Fig 2.30   *Single-acting hammer*

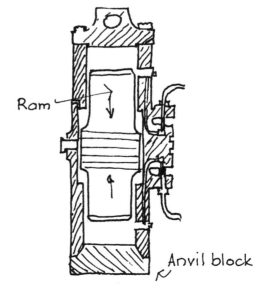

Fig 2.31   *Double-acting hammer*

2.4.4   Pile extractors

Pile extractors can either be specially designed for the sole purpose of extraction or they can be in the form of a double-acting hammer with extracting gear.

In the former type, a rapid number of blows in the upward direction causes the extracting jaws to grip and lift piles out of the ground (Fig 2.32). The specially designed equipment, which is similar in action to an inverted double-acting hammer, is more efficient and more compact than the double-acting hammer. The double-acting hammer has to be inverted for use and the extractor works on the principle of hitting the pile out of the ground. The extracting gear is fitted around the inverted hammer and a winch is used to exert an upward pull of 1 to 2 tonnes in excess of the weight of the extracting gear. The specially designed extractor can work at speeds of 350 - 500 strokes per minute.

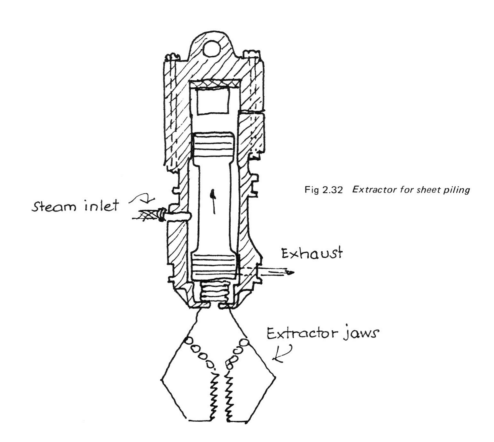

Fig 2.32 *Extractor for sheet piling*

2.4.5   Winches and other equipment

Winches are mounted on a base frame of steel construction which is long enough to accommodate the winch, a boiler and an engine or motor. The whole unit is usually mounted on wheels. The winch can be powered by steam, diesel, compressed air or electricity. They may be single, double or multiple-drums and can have reversing gear if necessary. The normal winch will be either single or double-drums with a slip-clutch mechanism to give positive release of the rope for the drop hammer. Winches vary in weight from 1.5 t to 4 t for single-drum and 2 t to 6 t for double-drum types. Each winch can be selected for a particular type of frame or driving situation. Boilers for use with pile-driving frames are normally fired by oil, the flow of oil to the pressure burners being controlled by a thermostat which automatically adjusts the fuel supply to suit the steam demand. The boiler unit and generator can be mounted on a wheeled base as a self-contained unit.

The steam generator, although designed for use with steam hammers and extractors, can also be used for other operations, such as steam lines for defrosting materials and concreting.

Further specialist equipment used in piling is discussed in Chapter 4 to which reference should be made.

2.5   CRANES AND HOISTS

2.5.1   General considerations

When selecting lifting plant there are many factors to be considered, such as:

Weight and size of load involved

Height of lift

Utilisation factor

Whether lifting operation can be static.

Such factors will help to decide whether to use a crane or a hoist. When selecting the type of crane further consideration must be given to the following:

Access — type of ground over which the crane may travel

Radius of swing

Amount of lateral movement

Whether 'luffing' will be required. (A luffing jib is a hinged jib which facilitates lateral movement without moving the complete jib)

Type of plant being used in conjunction with craneage, eg concreting plant.

To achieve the most economic cost of craneage, a programme showing the planned sequence of working is necessary. This can be checked against alternative methods of hoisting and selection is thereby made on an economic basis.

2.5.2   Mobile Cranes

Mobile cranes can be divided into four distinct groups; they are:

Mobile wheeled cranes

Truck-mounted cranes

Track-mounted cranes

Gantry cranes.

The mobile wheeled cranes consist of a simple crane on motorised wheels. Lifting capacities vary from 3 to 50 tonnes, but most standard mobiles have a capacity of up to 10 tonnes only (Fig 2.33). They need a hard level surface on which to run, and are used mainly in plant and goods yards for lifting moderately heavy loads. Telescopic jib cranes, the jib length of which can be altered at will, are tending to replace the conventional mobile crane. The development increases the mobility of the crane and provides a solution for lifting in difficult situations, e.g. where a fixed jib could not be raised.

Truck-mounted cranes consist of a crane mounted on a lorry or truck which has been specially designed to carry an increased load. The truck has its own conventional engine and controls for normal driving, plus an extra engine, cab and controls for the crane. A vertical frame extending above the driving cab carries the jib when the machine is travelling from one place to another. Once on site extra jib lengths can be achieved by bolting jib sections together; these sections are carried from job to job by separate transport. Fig 2.34 shows a typical truck-mounted crane. The capacity of these cranes is between 5 and 20 tonnes, but this can be increased by means of outriggers. The outriggers are incorporated in the crane chassis and jack down to timber bearers at ground level. Truck-mounted cranes are capable of travelling on the highway at 30 mph and are therefore suitable for short hire periods.

Track-mounted cranes (Fig 2.35) are basically the universal excavator (rope controlled) fitted with a long lattice mast and additional lifting ropes. The mast often incorporates a fly jib to obtain better coverage of the site, especially where physical restrictions, such as scaffolding, exist. The advantage of this type of crane is its multi-purpose utilisation — the basic machine can be used as a dragline or backacter or other similar item of plant and then quickly adapted for use as a crane. This is the only type of crane capable of operating on bad ground conditions and hire rates are much lower than for lorry-mounted and mobile types. They have a lifting capacity of between 5 and 30 tonnes, although normal lifting capacities are in the region of only 10 tonnes.

Gantry cranes, sometimes named portal cranes, are becoming increasingly popular in medium-rise as well as low-rise buildings, especially in Europe. A portal-frame type of structure straddles the work area and moves along two sets of rails, one on either side of the work area. The lifting gear is suspended from a horizontal frame which is capable of moving the full width of the portal (Fig 2.36).

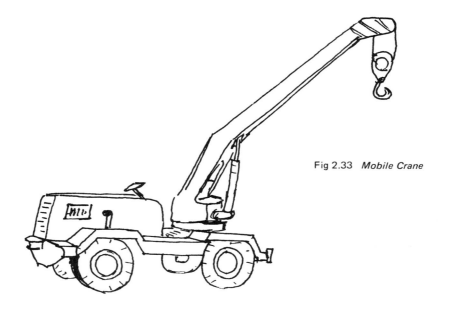

Fig 2.33   *Mobile Crane*

Fig 2.34   *Truck-mounted crane lifting bridge beams in College Road,
Birmingham in the construction of the M.6 Motorway.*

Courtesy: R.M. Douglas Construction Limited

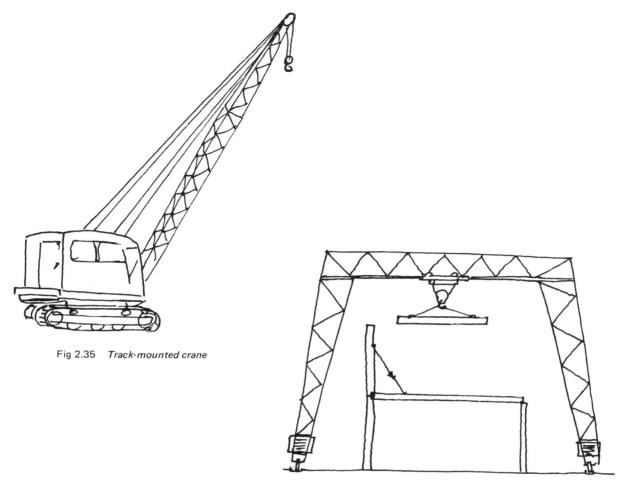

Fig 2.35   *Track-mounted crane*

Fig 2.36   *Gantry crane*

2.5.3   Derrick cranes

The derrick crane is widely used in civil engineering work because of its lifting capacity and wide reach. Such cranes are capable of lifting up to 30 tonnes and providing jib reaches of up to 45 m. The size of the crane and the fact that lengthy site assembly is necessary for each crane make this type of crane suitable only for heavy lifting or specialised construction, where the crane will be fully utilised over a long period of time.

There are three types of derrick crane:

Scotch or Stiff-leg derrick

Guy derrick

Monotowers.

The Scotch derrick (Fig 2.37) is the most commonly used derrick on civil engineering projects. It has a short vertical centre post, two rigid stays and a long jib (usually twice as long as the centre post). The crane is normally powered by an electric motor but diesel-driven models can be used in isolated locations where electric power is not available. The jib is fixed to the base of the centre post and, when slewing, the jib and centre post rotate together. Anchorage is provided by the three legs, onto which heavy kentledge, ie weights of iron or concrete, is loaded to prevent overturning. Alternatively, the legs may be bolted down to temporary concrete bases. This particular type of derrick can be either stationary or mobile. The travelling derrick can take one of two forms; either rail-mounted for work on shore; or floating, in which the derrick is mounted on some form of raft. Scotch derricks can be elevated by placing them on lattice steel towers (known as Gabbards). Such towers are braced together and either ballasted as stationary units or mounted on rails to give greater coverage. In all cases the Scotch derrick is limited in slewing to an arc of 270°, owing to the position of the rigid stays. Derricks are unwieldy

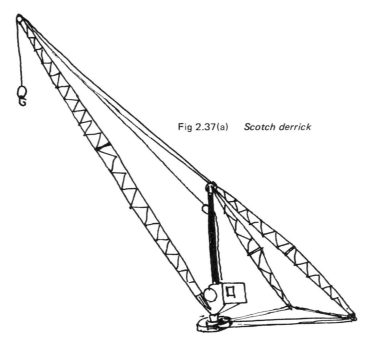

Fig 2.37(a)   *Scotch derrick*

Fig 2.37(b)   *Scotch derricks (rail-mounted) working on new lock entrance* (Edmund Nuttall Limited)

to move horizontally and so are moved only as the construction advances across the site; a bulldozer is used to tow the derrick along its rails.

Guy derricks (Fig 2.38) are used mainly in connection with steel erection. They are easily and quickly erected and dismantled and removed from one required position to another; this facility is often required on large, widespread steel frame erection, hence their popularity for such work. With this form of crane the vertical centre post is longer than the jib and is kept vertical by four wire ropes (guys), connected to a top plate. The jib and centre post both revolve on a base plate and because the jib is shorter than the centre post it can slew through the full 360°, clearing the guys by passing beneath them.

Monotowers (Fig 2.39) have developed from the elevated Scotch derrick. The Monotower consists of a braced tower up to 60 m high surmounted by a derrick crane. The centre mast of the derrick is pivoted well down inside the tower and the jib fixed near the centre of the mast. The whole mast, jib and operator's cab slews on a bearing plate on top of the tower. The jib is counterbalanced by a ballast counterweight. The derricking can either be controlled by ropes or hydraulic rams. Such cranes are capable of lifting 2 tonnes at a reach of 30 m.

2.5.4 Tower cranes

These may be of several types:

Static — self-supporting

Static — attached to the building framework

Rail-mounted or travelling tower

Climbing cranes

Static self-supporting cranes have their masts firmly anchored, at ground level, to massive concrete bases. Special base mast sections are provided which are cast into the foundation ready to receive the rest of the crane. Where poor ground conditions exist it may be necessary to use piles beneath the crane base; the pile foundation may then be utilised as part of the structure when lifting operations are complete. The crane should be positioned in front or to one side of the building under construction, thus preventing delay in completion of lower parts of the structure, such as might otherwise occur if the crane is situated within the building. These cranes are best used where the site does not allow room for a travelling crane.

Static, building-supported cranes, are similar in construction to self-supporting cranes, but are used for lifting to much greater heights. The crane is fixed to the building structure at intervals during construction of the building, since this type of crane induces stresses in the supporting structure, there may be extra cost incurred in designing and strengthening the structure.

Both the above cranes have static bases and static towers or masts (Fig 2.40) but it is possible to have a self-supporting crane with static base and slewing tower. In such a case the base of the mast is in two sections to permit slewing. A luffing jib would normally be used with the revolving mast.

Rail-mounted, or travelling, cranes are used on sites which cannot be served by static cranes. The crane is mounted on heavy wheeled bogeys travelling on a wide gauge rail track. The track is laid on sleepers and ballast, requiring great accuracy in level and gauge. In particular, the level of the track must be checked frequently for settlement, since a slight movement of the track could render the tower unstable. Any gradient for travelling cranes should be less than 1 in 200. Corners may be negotiated by radius rails or special turntables. Most travelling cranes are operated by an electric motor, and to prevent the cable trailing and becoming subject to damage the crane is equipped with a spring-loaded cable drum. This drum allows the cable to be paid out when the crane travels in one direction and draws it in when travelling in the reverse direction. The crane can also be used as a static crane by using stays, whenever loads and radius require greater stability.

Climbing cranes (Fig 2.41) are the best form of craneage for very high structures. The crane climbs with the structure, having a relatively short mast (20 m) and therefore occupying little space within the building. The crane is normally sited so that the jib has full coverage of the building, but should not be positioned in lift shafts since this could prevent preliminary lift installation work being carried out. The best position is one where little work is required to complete the structure after the crane has climbed beyond that point. Initially the crane is constructed on a foundation at ground level; when the first four floors of the building are in position, two special

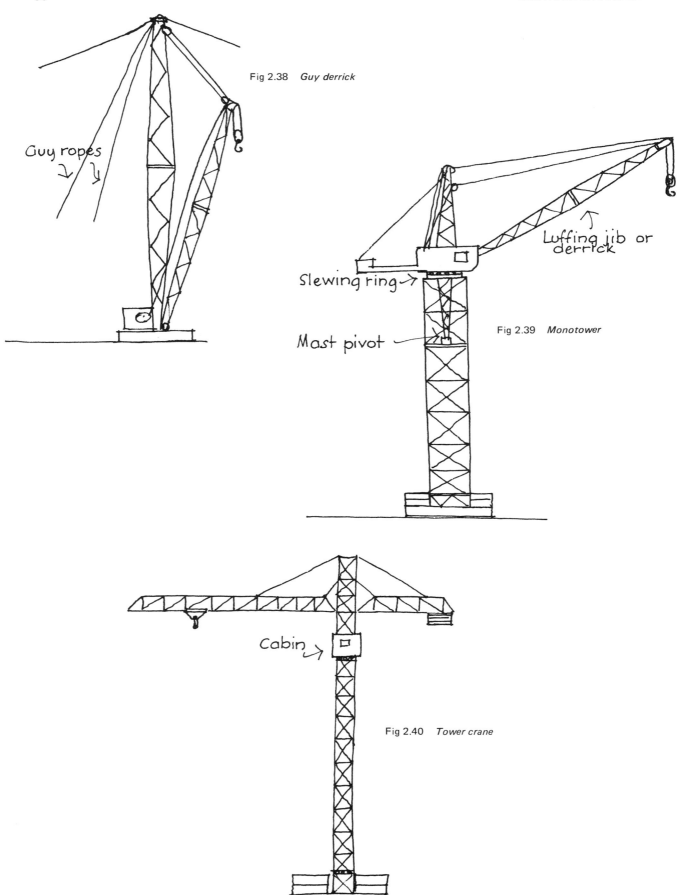

Fig 2.38 *Guy derrick*

Guy ropes

Slewing ring →

Luffing jib or derrick

Mast pivot

Fig 2.39 *Monotower*

Cabin →

Fig 2.40 *Tower crane*

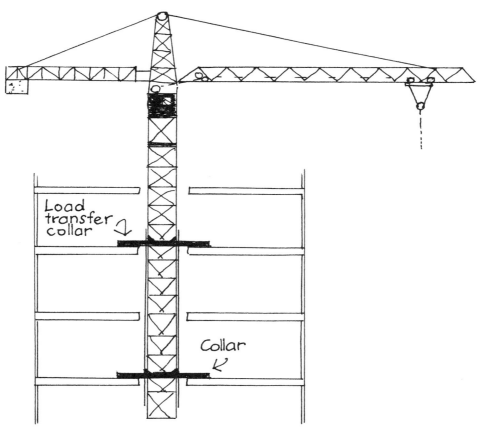

Fig 2.41 *Climbing crane*

frames or collars are fixed to the floor around the mast to transfer its load to the floors. A winch or jacking equipment is used to raise the mast to its new position and the mast is then bolted to the collar. This operation is repeated as necessary until the structure is completed, and the crane is finally dismantled into sections and lowered from roof level by means of a winch. The decision to use a climbing crane can only be made when the structure is capable of supporting the loads involved. The frames or collars must be designed to suit the particular structure.

Jibs: tower cranes use one of two types of jib, namely luffing jib or horizontal jib (sometimes called saddle jib). The luffing jib has a larger minimum working radius than horizontal jibs while the horizontal jib has a smaller maximum lifting capacity. The horizontal jib gives better and faster control in three directions. The masts of all horizontal jibs remain stationary while the jib revolves, this being either fitted on top of the mast or built on to a collar around the mast. The luffing jib has the advantage of reaching into corners which would be out of the reach of the horizontal jib.

2.5.5 Hoists for men and materials

The types of hoist vary from the small jib hoist, which can be fixed to tubular scaffolding, to large passenger hoists which are used for transporting men to heights of 450 m.

Mobile hoists are the most common type used and are capable of lifting light loads to a height of 30 m. The mast and winch unit is mounted on a wheeled chassis, the whole unit being adjusted for verticality by screw jacks. For movement between sites, the unit is lowered to a horizontal position and towed by a vehicle. Where such hoists are extended for use up to 30 m the mast is secured to the scaffolding or frame of the building.

Tower hoists are normally used for hoisting general materials to any height. The tower consists of a rectangular mast made in sections suitable for transportation. The mast is secured to the building or scaffolding throughout its full height and is provided with landing stages within the scaffolding at each floor or access level.

The platform for material hoists takes the form of a steel frame, covered with some form of durable decking such as plywood. The platform is normally interchangeable with hoppers or special carrying jigs to accommodate the lifting of special materials. One such jig might carry a monorail truck, thus allowing the truck to be lifted vertically to an elevated layout of track.

Passenger hoists differ from the general purpose hoists in that the platform must be fully enclosed to form a cage and must have additional safety devices to prevent over-run and free fall. They should also be controlled from within the cage.

Hoists are powered by diesel engines or electricity and may operate on the rack and pinion principle; the latter type can be used for non-vertical applications. All landings must have some form of guard, usually sliding gates, and the base of the hoist, where the winch is situated, must be fully guarded to prevent workmen being injured by moving parts.

2.6   COMPRESSED AIR PLANT

2.6.1   General considerations

Pneumatic tools are used extensively on civil engineering projects because the power source can be very mobile and the range of tools can easily be handled. By comparison with other forms of power the efficiency of compressed air is low, but the mobility of the power far outweighs this disadvantage. This mobility of power allows work to be carried out rapidly on isolated sites or in situations where access or work space may be confined. These advantages have resulted in the development of a wide range of tools for the following operations: concrete breaking, demolition, rock drilling, steel sharpening, woodworking, riveting, grinding, tamping and vibrating concrete, pumping, pile driving, winching and spraying, blowing fine debris out of formwork before concrete is poured.

The type of compressed air system will depend on the nature of the work involved, but will be either a local or a centralised system. In the case of local systems the compressor unit, with air receiving tank, is mounted on a four-wheeled chassis for towing around the site or on public highways. In some cases the compressor is lorry-mounted. These mobile units are powered by diesel, petrol or electric motors, the most common being diesel. The need for maintenance of local supplies is much greater than that of a centralised supply and the cost is also greater. The centralised supply of compressed air involves the installation of a larger semi-permanent plant. A central compressor house is then built to accommodate the plant and a network of air pipes is taken from the compressor house to a variety of outlet points. The range of such a supply will cope with most extensive sites and is more reliable than a number of mobile units. Pipes between the supply and the tools should be calculated to give a minimum pressure reduction and have gradients to prevent the collection of water. Low points in the supply system should be provided with traps for collecting condensate. This type of supply is more convenient for the running of workshops and plant areas and can be used for supplying temporary needs to any area of the site at little additional cost.

2.6.2   Air compressors

There are two main types of compressor, the reciprocating or piston type and the rotary impeller type.

The reciprocating compressor may be either single stage or multi-stage in action. In the single stage type the air is drawn into a cylinder and compressed by one stroke of a piston. With the multi-stage type the air passes through a series of cylinders, each cylinder containing air at increasing pressures. With a two-stage compressor, the air is compressed into a large cylinder at an intermediate pressure then further compressed into a smaller cylinder at the required final pressure. Two-stage compressors give greater efficiency, up to 20 per cent more air being compressed than a single stage compressor of the same power. In addition, the air in the two-stage plant is cooled between the first and second stage, thereby eliminating valve trouble which can be caused by high temperatures in a single stage compressor. The multi-stage compressor is suitable for pressures over 680 kN/m^2, and is capable of producing air pressures up to 6800 kN/m^2 though in most cases the supply will be regulated to between 680 and

850 kN/m². This type of compressor will be used in a centralised plant, where the amount of air required can be as high as 130 m³ per minute.

Rotary compressors consist of a high speed cylindrical rotor mounted essentially in a cylinder. The rotor is slotted to receive a number of blades which are free to move radically in the slots. This compressor, known as the sliding vane compressor, draws air from the intake port by centrifugal force and delivers it through the delivery port when the desired pressure is reached. The sliding vanes create separate chambers on being thrown against the cylinder wall and as the rotor is eccentrically positioned the vanes slide back into the rotor as they rotate, decreasing the volume to each chamber and so compressing the air they contain.

Helical screw compressors are constructed in a similar way to rotary compressors and work on the principle of screwing the air into compression through a cylinder.

The rotary compressor is quieter than the reciprocating unit and maintenance is less because of the smaller number of moving parts.

Air receivers are used to store the compressed air as it leaves the high pressure cylinder and provide a constant source of pressure for the air lines. The main functions of an air receiver are:

To minimise pressure fluctuations, created by the compressor

To minimise frictional losses due to pulsation of air through distributing lines

To store energy for a short period and so enable an unloading device to be used

To reduce the temperature of the air and remove moisture before the air reaches the supply lines.

The last function can also be achieved by the use of an 'after cooler'. If the moisture is not removed it tends to freeze during expansion in air tools; it also washes out lubrication in the tools.

2.6.3   Pneumatic tools and equipment

Pneumatic tools can be divided into four basic types:

Percussion type, in which a piston reciprocates and delivers rapid blows to tools

Percussion type, requiring rotation of the tools

Rotary type, which use the power of air motors

Miscellaneous equipment.

Percussion type tools

The most common tool used is the Concrete-breaker (jack hammer) which is designed for breaking up road surfaces. They vary in weight from 15 to 40 kg and have an air consumption of between 10 and 20 m³/min. These tools can be fitted with a variety of heads including a small pile driving head for driving trench sheeting.

Pneumatic picks are similar to jack hammers but much lighter in construction. They weigh 9 to 14 kg and have a consumption of air of 6 m³/min. Chisels and clay spades are normally fitted for use in hard excavation.

Backfill rammers, used for backfilling trenches and similar work, weigh 23 kg and have a consumption of 10 m³/min.

Chipping, caulking and riveting hammers are all small, lightweight tools, having a low consumption of air (0.5 m³/min or less), and especially suitable for specialised work at low cost.

Pneumatic tools with rotary action

Hammer drills are the most common type, and are used for drilling rock or concrete to depths of up to 6 m. The piston which produces the hammer action also produces a rotary motion of the return stroke. A quick-release retaining device allows rapid changing of drills. This tool can be used for wet or dry drilling, weighs 9 to 32 kg and has an air consumption of from 5 to 10 m³/min.

Rock drills are similar in design to hammer drills but are larger and heavier, weighing 45 to 90 kg. They are used in tunnelling and quarry drilling, with either a dry or wet process. The drills are mounted, owing to their weight, on some form of frame. This frame supports the drill and applies pressure to the bit by automatic feed. In the case of quarry drilling, the drill is mounted in a cradle on a small pneumatic-tyred chassis; the cradle can be pivoted to drill at any angle; air consumption varies from 15 to 24 m^3/min.

Rotary type tools

These include tools which are powered by air motors with rotary sliding vanes. They include chain saws weighing up to 31 kg, with an air consumption of 10 m^3/min, circular saws, drilling, and general forming tools, including woodboring machines.

Miscellaneous tools

These include concrete vibrators and compactors for road construction, external and internal vibrators used with shuttering, pile-driving equipment, sump pumps, paint-spraying equipment, concrete-placing and spraying equipment.

The biggest problem with air tools, especially concrete-breakers and drills, is noise. This can be greatly reduced by using jacket-type silencers, which do not impair the efficiency of the tool.

2.7   BITUMINOUS MIXING AND LAYING PLANT

2.7.1   General considerations

When considering plant for bituminous paving, two stages of work must be considered, namely mixing and laying. In some cases both operations are carried out by the one piece of plant, while in other cases many types of plant carry out specific operations each forming only part of either mixing or laying. The plant used will depend on the type of material to be handled, and this requires careful specification since terminology may get confused if compared with practice in the USA. The binder used in bituminous-bound materials is either bitumen, which is produced by refining crude oil and some natural deposits, or road tar, which is obtained from crude tar produced from coal or coke. Where aggregate is mixed with bitumen an artificial asphalt is produced. Lake asphalt, such as Trinidad Lake Asphalt, consists of bitumen and mineral matter found in large natural deposits, and is normally refined to remove vegetable matter before use. Rock asphalt is another natural deposit, in which a limestone or sandstone contains a high level of bitumen. All the materials mentioned above may be used in the process of producing road surfaces. Other materials, of a low viscosity, may be used for treatments of road surfaces. These include cut-back bitumen, which is bitumen reduced in viscosity by the addition of a suitable thinning agent, and emulsions, which consist of the suspension of one liquid (usually bitumen) dispersed minutely through another liquid in which it is not soluble. The type of plant used will depend on the process selected together with the type and quantity of aggregates and binder specified.

2.7.2   Heaters and boilers

There are many types of bitumen heaters and boilers; these range from small mobile units to large permanent plants. The most common form of boiler is the Mobile boiler; it is mounted on a steel chassis having four wheels and a tow bar. The furnace at the base of the boiler is either gas or oil fired. Mobile boilers have capacities ranging from 350 to 9000 litres.

Static heating and storage tanks are available for high outputs, having a capacity ranging from 9000 to 18 000 litres. These units are heated by oil fired burners and deliver the bitumen at a temperature of 200°C. Some models are strengthened for transportation and are provided with four lifting eyes to allow the whole unit to be transported on a low loader.

Mobile heating and storage units in the form of truck or trailer-mounted tankers can be used for either bulk supply or bulk tank distribution. The bitumen is supplied to the mobile unit in a pre-heated form and oil fired heaters are incorporated in the unit to keep the material at the required temperature.

The choice of boiler will depend on the type of work involved. Repair and re-surfacing work requires constant mobile supplies and central mixing plant requires large static boilers or a battery of heating and storage units. Mobile units have a storage capacity of up to 27 000 litres.

2.7.3   Binder distributors

There are two main methods of distributing binder material, namely Bulk tank sprayers and Trailer-mounted units.

Bulk tank sprayers are heat-insulated and fitted with heating units to maintain the binder at an adequate temperature. The binder is fed into the bulk tanker from a static heating unit or bulk supply unit. In some cases the tank sprayer has sufficient heating equipment to raise the temperatures of cold binder to the desired level in a short period of time. Bulk tank sprayers are truck-mounted, with sealed tanks with a capacity ranging from 2 500 to 11 000 litres. A power driven pump sprays the binder over the surface of the road through a horizontal spray bar mounted transversely at the rear of the unit. The binder is sprayed over the surface in one of three controlled ways:

a constant rate of spread, automatically controlled in relation to the speed of the vehicle

a constant pressure, the delivery of binder being kept constant and the speed of the vehicle controlled to give the desired spread

a constant volume, whereby the volume of binder is controlled in conjunction with the speed of the vehicle.

Trailer-mounted units vary in size from 540 to 4 500 litres capacity, mounted on a trailer chassis with pneumatic road wheels. The spraying unit can either take the form of a transverse mounted bar or power operated lances.

Cold emulsion can, in many cases, be distributed by the same plant as that used for spreading hot binder. The machines are equipped with power units for spraying under pressure. Small units are equipped with hand-lance equipment and very small jobs can be undertaken using a hand-operated pump which feeds directly from standard 180 litre drums, the drum being mounted on hand-towed trolleys.

2.7.4   High speed road-surfacing units

The most common unit in use is one which lays a surface dressing as a low-cost, wearing coat. This form of wearing coat, in which the road is sprayed with hot binder and coated with grit, is used for a majority of re-surfacing projects. The machine, approximately 10 m in length, carries out three operations as it moves forward at a speed of 15 mph. The three operations are

Road cleaning

Spreading of bituminous sealing membrane

Grit spreading.

Road planers and heaters

Road planers are used to shave off the uneven surface of bituminous roads by heating the surface till a softened state is achieved. It then removes the humps with revolving blades. The machine has a long wheel base which prevents too much undulation when planing the surface. The heating burners are positioned below the chassis and protected by hoods. The revolving blades are hydraulically adjusted and on cutting leave a smooth surface ready for further surface treatment.

Road heaters are designed for drying, heating and burning off the road surface ready to receive further treatment. This form of plant is used on road surfaces which have become too smooth, as a result of movement of the binder material in hot weather.

2.7.5   Asphalt and bituminous mixing plant

Asphalt and bituminous mixing plants range from permanent plant installations to small mobile units which are towed from site to site. These units carry out a complete sequence of operations, namely: drying, heating and mixing of aggregates, coating aggregates with binder, and delivery ready for laying. Drying units consist of a long cylindrical steel drum rotating at a slight angle. The unit is heated internally by the passage of hot gases, through which the aggregate passes. The purpose of the drier unit is to ensure that the material is thoroughly dry prior to coating with a binder. The unit may also be used for drying sand for hot rolled asphalt.

Batch-mixing plants have the following individual sections:

Aggregate feeder — normally conveyor

Drier unit

Storage bins for heated aggregate

Binder heater with tank storage

Weighing plant

Mechanical mixer.

The mixing units consist, in the main, of some form of paddle mixer. For batch-mixing the paddle mixer will be the twin-shafted type, the paddles rotating in opposite directions to give a thorough mix in a very short time. A batch weighing 500 kg can be mixed in one minute. Heating pipes or hot air keep the mixer hot during the process.

Outputs from batch-mixing plants depend on the rate at which aggregates can be passed through the drying cylinder. The rate of drying can be regulated by the inclination of the drier but is subject to the amount of moisture contained in the aggregate and the time taken to raise the temperature of the aggregate to the required level. The temperature is subject to weather conditions and varies from 93° to 175°C. Outputs vary from 10 to 100 tonnes per hour for a large batching plant.

Continuous mixing plants have a much higher output than the batching plant. They are capable of producing 100 to 200 tonnes per hour. The plant consists of a series of units mounted on pneumatic-tyred trailers, these trailers being jacked up off the tyres by jacking legs. The units employed include:

Cold aggregate feeders

Cold aggregate elevator

Drier unit

Dust cyclone

Hot elevators

Grading unit

Mixer unit

Bitumen storage tanks

Boiler unit.

Since this type of plant has a very high output, its use is not economical unless certain criteria can be achieved; these are:

Initial quantities of macadam required must be high, in the region of 6000 to 8000 m^3

Transport, spreading and finishing plant must be adequate to handle output

Supplies of raw materials must be adequate to keep the mixing plant in operation.

2.7.6   Spreading and finishing machines

The method of spreading macadam will depend on whether the material is cold-mixed or hot-mixed. Cold-mixed macadam can be either spread by hand, using forks and rakes, or, when the volume of material is large, by a small spreading machine. Hot mixes normally require spreading and finishing by specially designed machines. A suitable machine for this work is the Barber-Greene finisher; this machine, available in two sizes, spreads and finishes the surface coating in a single pass (ie only passing over the area once). The machine is self-powered and self-propelled, consisting of a feeder unit and a screed unit driven by a crawler-mounted tractor. The larger model is capable of laying pavements up to 150 mm thick and 3 to 4.25 m wide. It has a laying speed of 2.4 to 27 m per minute and has a 10-tonne hopper capacity. The screed unit comprises an oscillating tamper, thickness control, screeding heater and screed plate, all of which is carried on a long cranked arm pivoted from the tractor unit. The machine is filled by tipper trucks which back onto the hopper and unload while the paver is in motion. Rollers on the front of the hopper connect with the lorry tyres and push the lorry forward as it is unloading. The thickness of the surface finish is controlled by hydraulic adjustment of the screed plate which is automatically levelled as the machine moves forward. Other types of spreading and levelling machines are available and these are mounted on rubber tyres rather than crawler tracks. Most of the weight of the machine is carried on two or four large tractor wheels; the hopper is supported by small wheels with solid rubber tyres. This machine has the advantage of being more manoeuvrable and having less wear and vibration than crawler-mounted types. It can also move from one job to another without low-loader transport. One such machine, the Blaw Knox PF.90D, can lay pavements from 2.5 to 6 m wide and up to 300 mm deep. The level is determined by a wire guided sensor unit and joint matching is achieved by hydraulic actuating units. Small versions of the rubber-tyred finisher are available for estate roads, car parks, play areas, etc.

Two other machines used in finishing work should be mentioned; they are:

Chipping spreaders

Road rollers.

The chipping spreader is used for depositing bitumen-covered granite chippings onto the road surface or into the surface of hot rolled asphalt. The machine consists basically of a long trough suspended from wheels; the wheel speed is controlled by a chain drive. The chippings are fed through a slot in the trough by means of a revolving drum which controls the rate of spread.

Road rollers range in weight from 2 to 10 tonnes and may be either vibratory or non-vibratory. The road roller normally used on road work weighs 6 to 10 tonnes and is diesel driven. These machines are used mainly in re-surfacing operations, two rollers working approximately 10 m apart when rolling one half of a carriageway.

2.8   PUMPS AND DEWATERING EQUIPMENT

2.8.1   General considerations

One of the most common and yet most important pieces of plant in civil engineering is the pump. It is a piece of equipment that must be reliable in adverse conditions and able to cope with varying factors, such as the total pumping head and various types of water. Since these factors may vary as a contract proceeds it may be good policy to use an all-purpose pump rather than a series of pumps for specialist operations. This choice will depend on the complexity of the project and the amount of liquid to be moved in any particular period of time. Although pumps may be used for moving other liquids and materials such as sewage and concrete, this section deals specifically with the movements of water and sludge.

When selecting equipment for the site the uses of the pumps must be considered. The following operations may be involved:

Keeping foundations, pits etc, free from water

Lowering of water table to below the level of excavation

Pumping out cofferdams or other large quantities of water

Supplying water for jetting and sluicing

Supplying water for general purpose use.

Having decided on the operations there are further factors which will have to be considered before selecting the pump. These include:

The rate at which the water is to be pumped

Height of suction lift (distance from water to pump)

Height of discharge (distance from pump to discharge — vertical)

Altitude of the project

Loss due to friction

Size of pipe to be used

Pressure required at head if pressure is required.

Size of piping is very important since the loss of pumping power due to friction increases rapidly as the pipe diameter decreases. An example of two pipe sizes in wrought iron (or steel) will show the difference. Water to be pumped = 4 500 litres per min. Pipe diameter (internal) 150 mm and 100 mm. Then loss due to friction, shown as extra head, is as follows:

150 mm pipe = 1.88 m per 30 m of pipe)
100 mm pipe = 15.30 m per 30 m of pipe)   obtained from standard tables

This indicates that it may be advantageous to increase the diameter of suction and delivery pipes to reduce friction loss.

2.8.2   Pumps — types

Pumps for general use can be grouped under the following heads:

Centrifugal — normal, self-priming, air-operated

Displacement — reciprocating, diaphragm

Submersible

Air lift.

Centrifugal Pumps

Normal type centrifugal pumps contain a rotating impeller which revolves at such a speed as to cause the water to flow at considerable pressure. The speed of the impeller creates a vortex which sucks air out of the hose and atmospheric pressure causes the water to rise to the pump to commence the pumping action. This pump will require priming every time it runs dry.

Self-priming centrifugal pumps work on the same principle as the normal pump but have a reserve supply of water in the impeller chamber. When the pump is started this supply of water produces a seal against which the pump can draw air from the suction pipe. When the pump is stopped it retains the supply of priming water indefinitely.

Air-operated centrifugal pumps, sometimes named 'sump pumps', are particularly useful in tunnels, foundation pits etc, and will handle sewage, oil or sludge. The pump consists of a small centrifugal pump rigidly fixed to an air motor. The whole unit is enclosed in one tubular casing. They have capacities up to 540 litres per min against a head of 30 m using an air pressure of 680 kN/m².

Sludge pumps are available, using the centrifugal principle, and are classified as:

Unchokeable or fullway pumps

Open impeller pumps

Unchokeable pumps are capable of passing large solid objects through the impeller. This is achieved by having widely spaced vanes on the impeller for the objects to pass through. This design of impeller has an effect on the efficiency of the pump and therefore limits the suction lift. The open impeller pump is similar to the normal centrifugal pump but is capable of moving objects up to 20 mm in diameter before clogging. A strainer is fitted to the suction hose intake to prevent larger objects from entering the pipe.

Displacement pumps

Reciprocating pumps work by the action of a piston or ram moving in a cylinder. When the piston moves in one direction the water is drawn into the cylinder in front of the piston and pushed out at the rear of the piston. This is classified as a double-acting pump; where the water moves in one direction only with the movement of the piston it is classified as single action. Larger pumps may have two or three cylinders and are classified as duplex, single or double acting, and triplex, single or double acting. These pumps have the following advantages:

Ability to pump at a uniform rate against varying heads

Their capacity can be increased by increasing the engine speed

They have a high efficiency regardless of the head and speed.

They have certain disadvantages however, which include:

Being heavy and large for any given capacity

Water is delivered in pulsations

They cannot handle water containing solids.

Diaphragm pumps work on the principle of raising and lowering a flexible diaphragm within a cylinder by means of a pump rod which is connected to an engine crank. When the diaphragm is raised water is drawn through a valve on the suction side of the pump, into the cylinder. The downward movement of the diaphragm closes the suction valve and pushes the water out through the delivery pipe. This pump, sometimes called a 'lift and force pump' can have two diaphragms to increase the efficiency. The pump is very popular since it can handle liquids and mud containing 10 to 15 per cent solids. It is suitable for work where the flow of water varies greatly, because it is self-priming.

Submersible pumps

Submersible pumps are required for ground-water lowering when using the 'deep well system', or for removing water from any form of deep sump. The pump unit, normally powered by electricity, is suspended from the rising main or from a wire cable if flexible hose is being used. The pump consists of a centrifugal unit and motor mounted in a single cylindrical unit having an annular space between pump and casing. The space allows the water to move upwards to the rising main. For civil engineering work these pumps are specially designed for heavy duty work which involves lifting gritty water. Double impeller pumps have a capacity of 4 500 litres per hour against a head of 16 m.

Air lift pumps

Air lift pumps differ from the other air-operated pumps in that no moving parts are used in the lifting operation. This type of pump consists only of a long vertical pipe to the lower end of which is connected a supply of compressed air. The air carries the water up the vertical pipe to the discharge area. This pump is useful for moving silt from the bottom of a cofferdam.

2.8.3   Dewatering equipment

The techniques of dewatering are fully described in Section 3.3 and are not therefore repeated in this section. The main operations which involve the use of pumps are:

Jetting the riser pipes

Dewatering the header pipes.

The first operation is undertaken by using a 'Jetting pump'. This is a pump which is capable of delivering a considerable amount of water at high pressure. The pressure required at the nozzle of the well point depends on the nature of the ground, but will be in the region of 140 to 1 000 kN/m^2. This means an output of between 3 600 and 90 000 litres per hour. The pump normally used for this work will be of the centrifugal type, having an output of 75 000 litres per hour at a pressure of 680 kN/m^2. To achieve this power a pump unit is mounted on a wheeled chassis and driven by a powerful diesel engine. The suction hose is normally 100 mm diameter and the delivery hose 75 mm diameter; both hoses are heavy quality armoured hoses or steel tubing. The delivery hose is connected to the top of the riser pipe with a screwed connection and the pressure is controlled by a gate valve.

The 'dewatering' operation will require a pump of sufficient output to deal with the number of well points being used. This means that the pump for dewatering will vary from job to job based on the amount of dewatering points required as well as the volume of water to be moved. Manufacturers usually state the capacity of their pumps, suitable for dewatering, in number of points or connections to the header pipe. For example, a 100 mm automatic unchokeable pump with an output of 136 000 litres per hour against a head of 11 m will be capable of dewatering 15 to 25 well points. The dewatering pump consists of an air separator valve at the intake, an open impeller type centrifugal pump, a vacuum pump, capable of maintaining a vacuum from 460 mm to 736 mm of mercury (depending on site conditions), and a power unit to drive both pumps. The vacuum pump can be driven by a belt drive from the main pump drive shaft. The water passes through the air separator to the centrifugal pump, then it is pumped through a valve to the discharge point. Water is prevented from entering the vacuum pump by means of float operated containers. The equipment is mounted on a four wheeled chassis and towed by a truck. The most common-sized pump used is a 150 mm diameter suction and delivery unit which has an output of 225 000 litres per hour against a head of 18 m.

It is usual to provide a duplicate pump on standby during pumping operations, to deal with problems of breakdown. The standby pump will be connected to the main header pipe and should be ready for immediate use.

Chapter 3

Earthworks

3.1 GENERAL CONSIDERATIONS AND PLANNING

3.1.1 Site considerations

Having considered the information contained in site investigation reports, the engineer will then consider the following factors which affect the practical planning and costs of earthwork operations —

Nature and extent of excavation

Available work area

Disposal of soil

Existing services and structures.

Nature and extent of excavation

The nature of the excavation, whether for reduced levels, road works*, trenches, basements or pits, will have to be considered in the light of time available for excavation and the sequence of completed earthworks. In the case of large cut and fill operations a detailed plan of the movement of spoil and plant will need to be prepared (see Section 2.2.1). Areas of fill may require some form of retaining wall or drainage, prior to depositing the spoil; this must be taken into account when planning the sequence of operations. Extended work such as trenches for pipelines can be divided into sections and may progress simultaneously. Deep excavations for basements and 'cut-off' walls must be progressed to suit work area and site conditions; in some cases cut-off walls are completed well in advance of other earthworks.

Work Area

Work area can be defined as the total space available for the manipulation of plant and storage of materials. It does not include areas for site administration or accommodation, since such areas are often outside the perimeter of the work area. The total work area should be indicated on a site plan so that movement of plant and materials can be efficiently planned (see Section 1.2.1). On certain sites the work area is sufficient to allow the sides of deep excavations to be battered to a safe angle of repose, thereby giving a work area free from obstructions such as timbering etc. On confined sites the plant may have to work from a position outside the actual work area, eg on a gantry or public highway. Alternatively, plant may have to work its way into the excavation and be lifted out by crane on completion. It is essential therefore that a study be made of the space available and of the effect progress will have on this. The selection of plant for earthworks is discussed in Section 2.2, where further details are considered.

Disposal of soil

The disposal of soil is achieved by one of the following methods —

Immediate use as backfilling elsewhere on the site

Storage in spoil heaps, for use later or removal at a later stage

Immediate removal from site to tip or other destination.

When the material is used for backfilling it must be suitable for the particular operation in hand. This

* For further discussion on earthworks in road construction, see Chapter 7.

should involve separating the cut material into two categories, one suitable for filling and the other for removal or other earthworks. Topsoil will be one such material that is separated into spoil heaps for finishing off embankments and general areas to be grassed.

Consideration should be given to the position of such spoil heaps in order to reduce the amount of handling they receive. They should be so positioned that they do not interfere with access to work areas or become a danger or nuisance because of slumping in bad weather. Consideration must also be given to the stresses induced by spoil heaps on structures or services below ground or adjacent to the spoil heap.

The immediate removal of spoil from the site may involve the control of lorries to allow maximum utilisation of earthmoving plant. The cycle time for removing spoil and returning lorries to site can be calculated to allow for traffic delays and plant 'turn round' time. Some consideration must also be given to spillage of soil when leaving the site: public highways must be kept reasonably clean at all times.

Existing services and structures

Care should be taken to establish the position of all pipes, cables and underground services, which should be clearly marked before earthworks commence. Where excavation involves the disturbance of services, they should be carefully unearthed and supported to prevent damage by movement or vibration; nevertheless, breakages almost invariably occur. Pumping may interrupt the natural flow of underground water, and sheet piling may be required around the excavation to prevent any adverse effect. (See Section 4.1).

Existing structures adjacent to excavation areas will require support during excavations: this may take any of the following forms —

Cut-off walling

Strutting and shoring,using sheet piles

Underpinning.

These techniques are described in subsequent chapters. In very loose or wet conditions the adjacent structures may be subjected to movement by heavy pumping or grabbing.

Whatever the condition of the site, it is expedient to establish a record, both photographic and written, of the state of the existing structures. This will involve a record of levels against a known fixed datum and measurements which delineate the position of the structures. If there are signs of movement in or around the structures, it will be necessary to fix 'tell-tale' markers in strategic positions on the structures to allow rapid checks of horizontal and vertical movement to be made.

3.1.2   Ground conditions

It has been clearly shown in Chapter 1 that it is necessary to establish a clear picture of ground conditions before excavation commences. The information obtained will assist in establishing the following factors —

Ground support during excavation

Best method of keeping the excavation free from water

Type of plant to be used.

The ground support required will depend on the strength and stability of the soil, the depth of excavation and the length of time that the excavation remains open. Consideration must be given to the change in soil stability due to adverse weather conditions. Some clays are particularly susceptible to softening and movement during periods of heavy rain. The movement of clay will also increase the pressure on timbering and this must be taken into consideration when calculating sizes of supports.

In conditions where there are frequent changes in ground strata, attention must be given to the strata at the bottoms of the excavations; these strata may be heavily stressed and subject to slip movement. The best method of keeping the excavation free from water will depend on the type of soil and the source of water. Surface water can be intercepted by some form of ditch, and field drains can be diverted. Sumps or pits can be dug to receive surface water which finds its way into the excavation during heavy rainfall. Ground water can be dealt with in many ways, depending on the permeability of the soil and the methods of control (discussed fully in Section 3.3).

3.1.3   Contract duration and weather prospects

Earthworks are subject to two forms of change due to weather. The first is a superficial change due to immediate weather conditions, eg heavy rainfall; the second is a change due to seasonal conditions, by which soils may be affected for a longer period of time. With this in mind, consideration should be given to the duration of the earthwork programme and the time of year at which the work is to commence. In a rainy period, certain parts of the earthworks may be carried out well in advance of a programme appropriate for a dry period. This would involve excavating cuttings which could be used to channel water away from the site. One carriageway of a motorway could be excavated to within say 600 mm of formation level to drain the other carriageway during inclement weather. Where these methods are not practicable it may be necessary to cut drainage channels during the dry season and to discharge them into ditches or streams.

Embankments should be cambered so that water cannot lie at the centre of the surface and create instability by percolating through the material. Hardcore roads should be formed to facilitate the movement of plant during heavy rainfalls, pneumatic-tyred vehicles being particularly hindered by wet site conditions (see Section 1.2.2).

The compaction of soil

Compaction of soil is affected by changes in moisture content and wet conditions may render satisfactory compaction impossible. Conversely, very dry or hot periods may involve much more wetting and rolling to achieve satisfactory results. It follows that extremes of weather may pose particular problems in the formation of embankments and fill areas. These problems can be eased by leaving fill material in position, i.e. unexcavated, until immediately before it is required for use; this will protect it from excess moisture or from drying out.

Earthworks carried out in winter may be affected by frost and therefore uneconomical to excavate. Frost action causes the moist material to expand and lose density, involving extra problems or work in compaction.

3.1.4   Economic aspects of earthwork design

The economic aspects of earthwork design take into account the following points —

The nature of the work

The availability of suitable plant

The availability of suitable fill material

The time of year.

The nature of the work can be placed in the classification of sites in Chapter 1, namely extended sites or confined sites. The extended site, which would include roads, railways and pipelines, may require flow charts or mass haul diagrams (see Chapter 2 Fig 2.2) to indicate distances and volumes of spoil involved, so that the most economic procedures can be determined. The mass haul diagram will assist in establishing the most economic gradients by comparing the cost of cut and fill areas. The confined site will involve the economic selection of excavation method, ground support and spoil disposal. Both types of site may involve the formation of embankments or cuttings and it will be necessary to determine the nature of the soils and to realise economies of excavation, transportation and compaction. The availability of suitable plant for a project is a problem that often faces contractors who have a large amount of plant tied up on sites. It may involve buying new plant or hiring plant, the latter proving less economical on very large earthmoving contracts. Availability of suitable fill materials may involve import from outside sources or the excavation of 'borrow pits' (ie areas made available by the employer from which suitable soil may be excavated). Borrow pits can be refilled with the excavated material from any other parts of the site. The availability of suitable material will affect the degree of slope on embankment work and the subsequent maintenance of such work. The nature of the fill material will affect the cost of compaction and general soil movement costs.

3.2 EXCAVATIONS

3.2.1 Bulk excavation

Bulk excavation may include the following operations —

Cuttings

Cut and fill areas

Basements and large pits

Hand excavations.

Cuttings

Cuttings include large excavation cuts for roads, canals and similar forms of construction where the excavated material is usually moved to some other part of the site either for bulk fill or for general 'spread and level' operations. With road works the amount of excavation is normally balanced against the fill areas, and normal cut-and-fill operations take place. In other forms of construction where the spoil may be partially waterlogged, such as dock areas, the excavation may require different types of plant or some means of dewatering to allow bulk excavating plant to operate.

The type of plant used will depend on the quantity of soil to be transported and the distance to the disposal point. Bulldozers can be used efficiently if the pushing distance does not exceed 100 m, whereas scrapers would probably be used for distances of over 100 m: the type of scraper would depend on the haul distance (see Section 2.2.3). In some cases the section of the cut will be too narrow for the scraper to turn or too deep for the scraper to ascend the ramps. This will involve the use of drag lines or a combination of plant, e.g. track-mounted excavators, dozers, and loading equipment, e.g. dragline or loading shovels.

Where the excavation is of a restricted length and depth and has suitable road ramps for lorries, the work can be excavated by a face shovel. The angle of repose for the cutting will depend on the type of ground, but can be as low as 20° for some clays and 90° for stable rocks. This angle should be calculated from laboratory tests, or from a site test in which a dry sample of the material is poured in a heap and the slope measured (see Chapter 1 for laboratory tests).

Shallow cut and fill

Shallow cut and fill operations occur mainly in road works and airfield construction. The work is normally carried out by scrapers, skimmers or dozers, which first strip the top soil for re-use and then reduce the level of the site to the required formation level. This type of work can be hindered by wet weather because the limited depth of dig does not allow economic two-stage excavation. Two-stage excavation is suitable for deep cut and fill areas where the first stage is taken out to within 300 - 600 mm of the final formation level and then completed with a second cut when the weather is suitable or when some form of protection to the formation can be placed. In shallow excavation the plant may have to stop work to prevent damage of the formation level, or temporary roads may have to be provided over large areas, either way resulting in extra cost. Areas of cut and fill can be adequately drained by temporary trenches, which could be incorporated into the final sub-grade drainage. The formation level should be protected against water and the drying-out action of wind and sun by some form of waterproof dressing, such as hot tar or bitumen. The compaction of fill areas is covered in Section 3.2.5.

Basements and pits

Basements and pits are defined in the *British Standard Code of Practice* CP 2003 (1959) *Earthworks.**
For all construction purposes the term 'deep pit', which applies to excavations over 4.5 m deep, is synonymous with the term 'basement'.

Shallow pits, which are 1.5 m deep, present little or no problems with excavation or ground support. They are normally excavated with a small backacting machine or by hand. Medium pits, which are classified as 1.5 to 4.5 m deep, require careful selection of plant and ground support. In the case of plant selection, most small machines will dig to a depth of 4 metres but may not be able to dig to the full depth of the pit in question. On the other hand, larger pieces of equipment may have difficulties of manoeuvrability between such pits, and since pits of this nature are usually small in superficial area, the excavation must be completed from ground level. The type

To be superseded by BS 6031.

and amount of ground support will depend on the nature of the soil, the amount of water present and the length of time the excavation will be open; these factors are discussed in detail in 3.2.4 below.

Methods of excavation of basements and deep pits vary. The following are methods commonly used by contractors:

Unshored excavations

Shored excavations

Dumpling method

Cut-off walling method.

All these methods involve some form of support to the ground and as such are dealt with in detail in 3.2.4; but they also have an effect on the choice of plant to be used. With unshored excavations it can be assumed that there is ample working space around the excavation to allow battering of the excavation. This will to a great extent allow more freedom of choice in excavating plant than the other methods. The work may be executed by drag line, backacter or grab, depending on the superficial area of the pit. Other factors to be considered are access to formation level for lorries or dumper if using a face shovel, the amount of water to be encountered, and the permeability of the soil. With shored excavations, the shoring can be made watertight by plugging the joints of sheet piling, thereby eliminating the free flow of water. The method of excavation in this case would depend on the nature of the shoring: the soil could be moved by grab, backacter or small tracked excavator. The dumpling method and cut-off walling method (Figs 3.11 and 3.12) have this in common, that they both involve the construction of a retaining wall, usually concrete, around the excavation area prior to the bulk excavation taking place. In the former case some shoring is necessary during the construction of the retaining wall: in the latter case shoring may be necessary as the excavation proceeds. Both methods lend themselves to the use of tracked excavators, backacters, grabs and draglines.

Hand Excavations

It will be necessary in many cases when excavating deep basements and pits to use pneumatic tools such as clay-spades and picks. This will occur in excavations which are heavily supported, leaving little room for mechanical excavation; it will also be necessary in the vicinity of services which would be subject to damage by machine, or in the case of removing obstacles such as boulders, logs or other projecting objects. Such hand spoil would be put into skips for periodic removal.

3.2.2   Rock excavation

The methods of breaking and excavating rock or other hard material will vary according to the type of material, quantity involved, conditions on site and equipment available. Such methods include:

Use of pneumatic breaker

Breaking by hand with hammer and wedges

Drilling with pneumatic machines and breaking by driving plugs or freezing liquid in the holes

Drilling with pneumatic machines and breaking by blasting.

The first three methods are suitable where any of the following conditions prevail:

The noise of blasting would cause annoyance

Adjacent buildings may be subject to damage

Blasting may cause inconvenience or stoppage of traffic

Landslides or rock falls might result

Accurate cutting is necessary and 'overbrake' would be uneconomical.

However, modern methods of control allow very accurate vibration-controlled blasting in limited spaces. One recent contract involved the excavation of a large basement in very hard rock, some of which was within

30 metres of an important computer. These innovations have made drilling and blasting the most effective and economical method of hard rock excavation. There are two basic methods of drilling and blasting rock in excavations:

Benching

Wellhole blasting.

Benching is used for most foundation and trench excavation in which the face of the rock is taken back in steps or 'benches'. Each bench or step is used as a platform for loading the loosened rock. The height of each bench varies with the type of rock but can be as shallow as 1.5 m or as deep as 6 m (Fig 3.1). Holes are drilled by the use of pneumatic hand tools or rig-mounted drills to a depth of 600 mm below the required excavation level. This allows the blast to clear the rock to or slightly below the required formation. The diameter of the holes is important: increased hole diameters require an increase in the charge required, thus leading to greater vibration. Up to 3.5 m deep the holes should be 38 mm dia; between 3.5 m and 9 m the diameters can be increased to between 50 and 75 mm.

Wellhole blasting involves the drilling of large holes, 150 mm to 250 mm diameter, at large intervals, the spacing of which should be equivalent to the 'burden' or depth of face to be moved. The depth of boring should be at least 9 m and up to 24 m to be economical.

The holes are machine drilled to the required depth and loaded with suitable explosives; this form of blasting produces good fragmentation and thereby reduces the amount of secondary blasting. Since the technique is only economical for deep blasting it has a use restricted to very large foundation excavations.

Explosives

Explosives are discussed fully under Section 1.3 and therefore only those related to excavation are considered here.

Special Gelatine 80%, Opencast Gelignite and the Iregal range of slurries are the main explosives recommended for most types of excavation. They have good water resistance and reliable performance in wet conditions, and give good fragmentation. In the case of very hard rock Special Gelatine 90%, Iregal 455D or Premium Superflex should be used, and in the case of soft rock a lower-powered explosive, e.g. Iregal 385D, will give satisfactory results at lower cost. The explosives are available in cartridges of varying diameters from 22 mm upwards, and weighing between 55 grams and 11 kg. The amount of explosive used varies with the type of rock: as low as 0.25 kg per m^3 for soft rock and up to 0.50 kg per m^3 for hard rock. When the charge has been placed the holes are 'stemmed', this being the term applied to the consolidation of the back filling of the hole prior to blasting. Stemming is best achieved with damp sand or a mixture of clay and sand; large holes can be partly stemmed with rock chippings.

Explosives for secondary blasting: in some cases the main blasting operation may produce stones which are too large for crushing or for loading on to lorries. When this occurs there are two methods of dealing with the problem, namely 'pop shooting' and 'plaster shooting'. With 'pop shooting' a hole is drilled into the centre of the boulder and fitted with a charge of Special Gelatine 80%. The charge is fired by means of a safety fuse and plain detonators or by electric shot firing.

'Plaster shooting' provides a means of breaking large boulders where drilling is difficult or expensive. A charge is primed with a detonator and safety fuse and laid on the surface of the boulder. It is then covered with a shovelful of plastic clay which is pressed into position by hand. A high-strength gelatine type explosive is most suitable, e.g. Plaster Gelatine.

This second method of breaking boulders is limited in use: the *Specification for Road and Bridge Works* suggests that it should not be used within 400 m of a building or structure.

Underwater rock excavation

Underwater rock excavation by blasting is similar to surface operations in that similar techniques are employed in drilling and blasting. Drills are mounted on either platforms or barges and holes are drilled to a pre-determined grid. Factors needing special consideration for underwater work are:

Fragmentation must be sufficient to enable the rock to be dredged easily

Explosive charges need to be heavier

Drilling must be deeper than normally required in 'on-shore' methods, preferably as far below the required blasting depth as the spacing between the holes

Shot holes must be closer together.

The last three considerations arise from the hydrostatic pressure on the face of the rock.

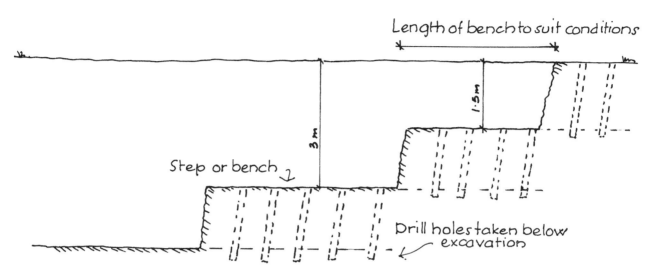

Fig 3.1   *Drilling and blasting by benching method*

There are two main methods of achieving the breakdown of the rock. Drill and blast, which involves normal drilling methods and the use of a suitable explosive such as Submarine Blasting Gelatine — a high density, high powered explosive. Plaster shooting (see 'Explosives for secondary blasting') which involves the placing of charges on the rock bed in a grid pattern. The technique requires sufficient head of water to confine the energy produced in the blast — usually a minimum head of 8 m. It is also suitable for clearing peaks of rock to allow drilling methods to be used.

The method used will depend upon depth of water, depth of rock to be stripped and availability of drilling rigs; the maximum size of charge will be dependent upon the effects of vibrations or shock wave on property in the vicinity. Such work is used for underwater trenching, removing sandbanks, deepening and widening channels, deepening harbours, demolition of wrecks and obstacles, cutting piles, etc.

Methods of removing rock from excavations

The choice of method will depend on the position and size of the rock pieces which may be removed by either of the following methods:

By hand loading on to flat bottomed rock skips

By mechanical excavators, such as draglines, face shovels and loaders (a machine specially designed for rock loading).

In both cases the material will be loaded into trucks, dumpers or railway wagons.

Backfilling

Backfilling with rock must be undertaken with great care to ensure consolidation of the excavation; this will limit the size of the rock fill to that which allows maximum consolidation. In the case of rock fill to embankments the size should be limited so that it can be compacted in layers not exceeding 450 mm. Most rock bulks in volume when excavated, owing to the voids, and is never returned to an excavation without some surplus; but there is one exception to this rule that the surveyor must be aware of, namely the excavation of chalk. When backfilling with chalk the material readily compacts into a volume smaller than that of its natural state, owing to the percentage of voids in the material. This can lead to a situation where extra fill material will have to be imported to complete the backfilling: some allowance must be made for this in the specification or measurement of the work.

3.2.3   Trench excavation

The choice of method of excavating, supporting and backfilling trenches depends on the following factors:

Purpose for which the trench is being excavated

The nature of the ground

The time scale of the work

Ground water conditions

The location of the trench

Number of obstructions.

The first three factors greatly influence the choice of plant; some trenches can be dug and backfilled with a single pass of the machine, a flexible pipe having been laid as an integral operation. Where the trench has to be left open for pipe laying or other work for some hours or days, consideration must be given to ground support. Where possible, the sides of the trenches can be battered to prevent the use of shoring, which would hamper foundation work or pipe laying; this must receive economic consideration, since the extra excavation and fill may not offset the cost of shoring and decreased production caused by supports. Where supports are to be used, the method of support must be decided having regard to the ground-water conditions and method of ground-water control. The location of the trench, whether across open land or along public highways, will affect the selection of plant and in some cases the method of ground support. Location may also involve organisational problems such as diversion and control of traffic, fencing, and lighting during the hours of darkness. The location will also have a bearing on the last factor for consideration, namely obstructions. In built-up areas there is a greater incidence of underground services which may have to be negotiated; this will affect the speed of the operations.

Excavation methods

The methods of excavating trenches are as follows:

Full depth, full length excavation

Full depth, successive stages of excavation

Stage depth, successive stages of excavation.

The first method is suitable for long narrow trenches of shallow depth in which the machine completes the trench non-stop ahead of any other operation. This method is suitable for pipelines and sewers. The second method is suitable for deep trenches where several operations of work can proceed in sequence; this would prevent stretches of trench from being left open too long and thereby being subject to collapse. It also reduces the amount of support and protection employed at any one time. (Specialist work in deep trenches is covered in Section 4.4). The third method of excavation is suitable for very deep trenches in confined areas or adjacent to existing property; it involves the support of the trench as the work proceeds and is most suited for operations such as deep foundations and underpinning.

The first method is also suitable for trenches with battered sides, and would be most suited to works requiring freedom from struts, e.g. cast-in-place foundations, walls and culverts. The plant used for battered trenches ranges from special trenching machines which are capable of producing the required batter in a single pass, to standard dragline equipment or backacting machines. Dewatering and support of trenches are covered in Section 3.3.

Special equipment is available for the formation of narrow trenches; these may be mechanical trenchers with a continuous chain action, or plough type trenches which are hauled through the ground by winches. Mole drainage can be carried out in clay soil by means of a mole plough and small pipes and cables can be laid in a similar manner without the formation of a trench. This work is carried out by a special machine equipped with a self-levelling device; the machine cuts the hole with a mole type blade and feeds the flexible pipe into the holes as it proceeds along a pre-determined line.

3.2.4   Support of excavations

Support of excavations is governed by the following factors: type of soil, ground water conditions, depth and width of excavation. The soil types for discussion are as follows:

Loose sand, gravel and silts

Compact sands and stiff clays

Rocks.

In addition to support to the above soils, special consideration is given to large excavations.

Support for excavation in loose sand, gravel and silts requires some form of continuous support, which may consist of trench sheeting (light-weight pressed steel narrow sheets), steel sheet piling, which is driven ahead of the excavation, or plain timbering which consists of poling boards, walings and struts. Since such soils are likely to slump quickly, the support must be placed immediately after excavation takes place. This means that deep excavations will have to be dug in stages; the first stage by machine, and, after supporting the first stage, any subsequent stages by hand or by grab. Hand excavation is very expensive and therefore the use of driven sheet piles would be more suitable for deep trenching (see Section 4.1). Fig 3.2 and Fig 3.3 show details of support in trenches and basements (Table 3.1 may be used as a reliable guide when establishing the support required). Support to excavation in compact sands and stiff clays can be satisfactorily achieved by the use of open timbering. This involves the use of poling boards or trench sheets at intervals of approximately 1 m; the boards are supported by continuous walings and trench jacks at 2 m centres (Fig 3.4). If the soil is subject to drying out and crumbling the spacing of the poling boards can be reduced accordingly. Dry clays which have become fissured by wind and sun are likely in wet weather to take up rain water and expand: this produces extra stress in the struts and allowance should be made for this at the design stage.

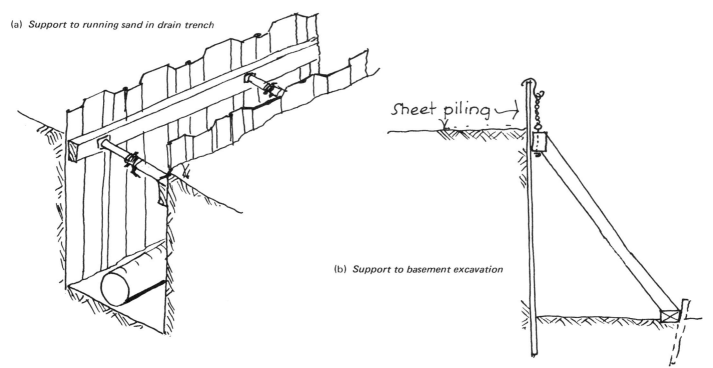

(a) *Support to running sand in drain trench*

(b) *Support to basement excavation*

Fig 3.2   *Showing the use of sheet piling in ground support*

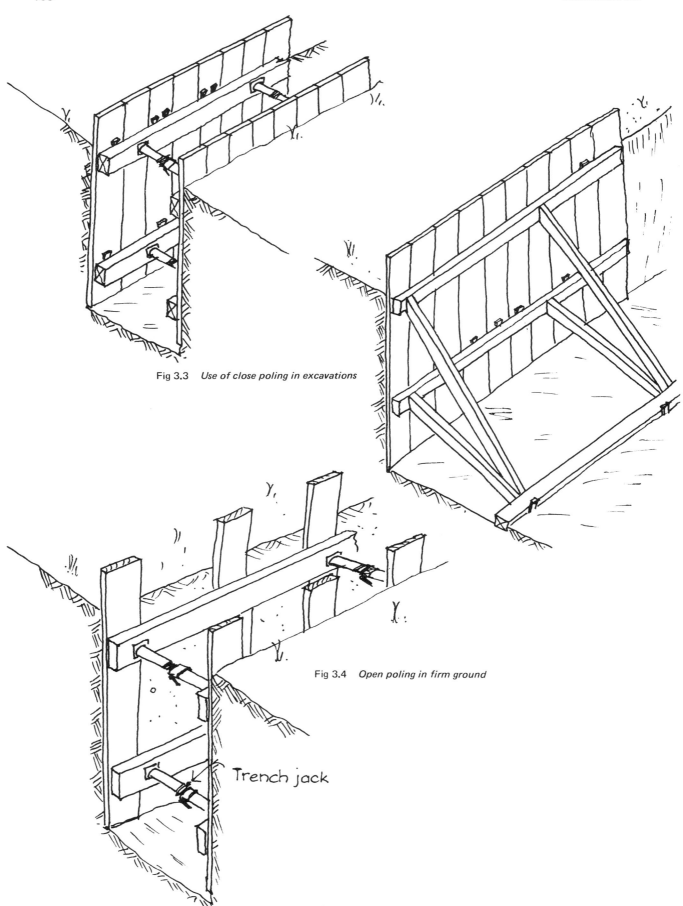

Fig 3.3   *Use of close poling in excavations*

Fig 3.4   *Open poling in firm ground*

Trench jack

TABLE 3.1

SUPPORT REQUIRED FOR EXCAVATIONS WITH VERTICAL SIDES IN UNIFORM GROUND

A   indicates that no support is required
B   indicates that open sheeting should be employed
C   indicates that close sheeting or sheet piling should be employed

TYPE OF SOIL	DEPTH OF EXCAVATION		
	Up to 1.5 m (shallow)	1.5 to 4.5 m (medium)	Over 4.5 m (deep)
Soft peat	C	C	C
Firm peat	A	C	C
Soft clay and silt	C	C	C
Firm and stiff clay	A*	A*	C
Loose gravel and sand	C	C	C
Cemented gravels and sands	A	B	C
Compact gravels and sands	A	B	C
Gravel and sands below water table	C	C	C
Fissured and jointed rock	A*	A*	B
Sound rock	A	A	A

*Open or close sheeting or sheet piling may be required if site conditions are unfavourable.

Note: This table does not apply to complex ground conditions.

Support to rock excavation depends to a large extent on the type of rock and the slope of rock strata: Fig 3.5 shows two different situations likely to be encountered in rock excavation. In the case of unstable rock faces, open timbering should be used to prevent slip. Alternatively, where the depth of excavation is excessive, the rock face may be stabilised by rock bolting (Fig 3.6). Rock bolting techniques are described fully in Section 4.5, but in general terms consits of solid steel rods which are fixed in deep drill holes by means of wedges, sleeves or grouting processes; light steel sections or steel plates are used to support the rock face through which the rods are threaded. Some shales and chalks are subject to movement through weathering, and support of these materials may be expensive; it may be more economical to cut these back to a safe angle of repose if space allows such treatment.

The support of any other type of soil or variable ground can be achieved by modification of the three types given above.

Support of large excavations

Large, deep excavations can be supported by a number of different methods, depending on the type of soil, proximity of structures and depth of excavation.

Unshored excavations involve the battering of the sides of the excavation to a safe angle of respose; for many soils this can be taken to be an angle of 45° (see Section 3.2.5 for embankment slopes). In some cases the site may not be large enough to cope with the extra spoil and may thereby incur extra transporting costs. However, as this method of ground support (Fig 3.7) leaves the area free from cumbersome struts, it allows greater productivity and is the preferred system.

Shoring to deep excavations by traditional methods can be undertaken in two ways, the first by internal support and the second by external support. Internal support (Fig 3.8) consists of poling boards or, more usually, sheet piling, supported by heavy walings and steel or timber struts. External support (Fig 3.9) consists of sheet piling anchored back to the face of the excavation by steel rods or ground anchors. Wide excavations will involve the use of 'H' beam king-piles' at centres across the excavation to carry the main support struts (Fig 3.10).

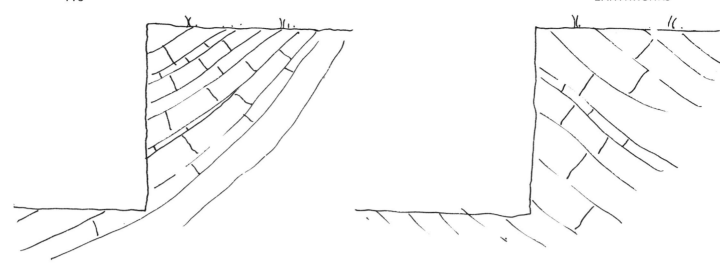

(a) *Unstable conditions in rock excavation*   Fig 3.5   (b) *Stable conditions in rock excavation*

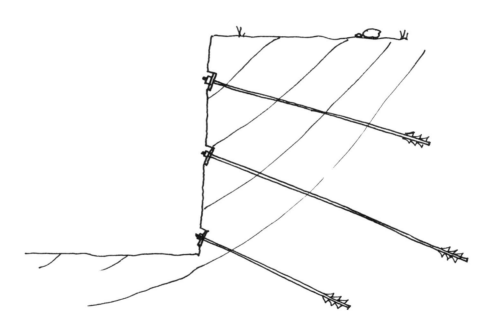

Fig 3.6   *Rock bolting in unstable conditions*

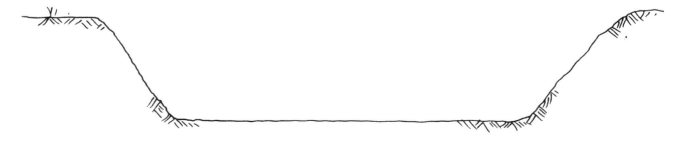

Fig 3.7   *Battered sides to excavation*

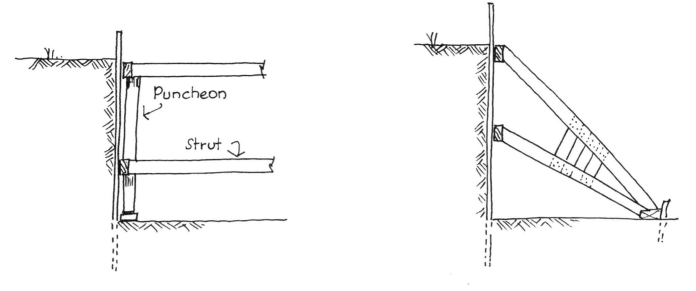

Fig 3.8   *Internal support to excavations*

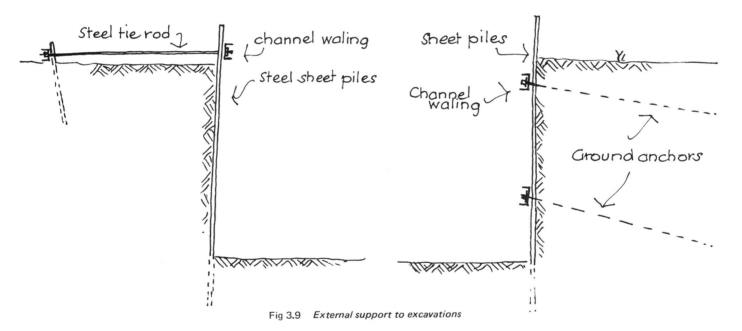

Fig 3.9   *External support to excavations*

Fig 3.10   *Support to wide excavation using 'H' beam piles*

The 'dumpling' method of excavation (Fig 3.11) makes use of permanent retaining walls for the ground support until the bulk of the soil is removed. After reducing the site to a level which requires no support, a perimeter trench is excavated and supported by normal methods until the perimeter retaining wall, including a wide perimeter strip, is constructed. The wall may be supported, from the dumpling of earth left in the centre of the site, until it is complete; the dumpling is then removed by dragline or other suitable excavator.

Cut-off walling methods of support are formed by steel sheet piling or concrete structures: the concrete is cast insitu in the form of deep narrow walls or contiguous bored pile walls (Fig 3.12). They are of particular value when supporting deep excavations which are adjacent to heavily loaded foundations of other structures. They prevent any movement of the existing foundations due to preliminary excavation, and allow greater freedom of movement for mechanical excavation. The latter factor is achieved by one of two methods: either by taking the wall deep enough to support the ground by cantilever action, or by anchoring the walls back into the soil using ground anchors (Fig 3.13).

Steel sheet piling is used as an economical alternative to the concrete cut-off walling methods: it is supported either by ground anchors or by designed shoring. These methods are fully explained in Section 4.

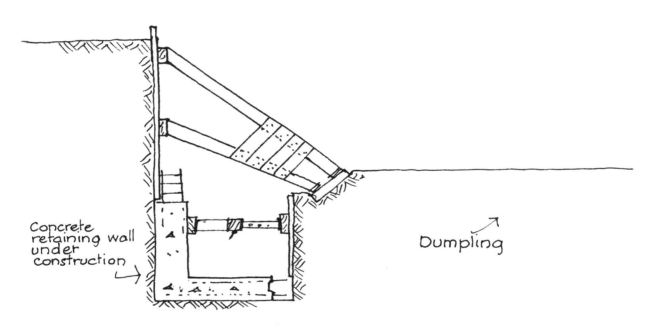

Fig 3.11   *Dumpling method of support*

3.2.5   Embankments

The construction of embankments and the design profile of the sloping sides will depend on a number of factors, such as:

The purpose for which the embankment is constructed, e.g. the loads involved

The consolidation of the fill in the embankment under the proposed loads

The stability of the ground on which the embankment is to be constructed

The extent to which the strength properties of the fill may be affected by the method of construction

The cost of obtaining suitable fill material

The difficulties in construction during adverse weather, when using clays and fine sands.

Fig 3.12   *Contiguous bored piles forming cut-off wall and support to deep excavation* (Soil Mechanics Limited)

Fig 3.13   *Diaphragm cut-off walling tied back with ground anchors* (Cementation Ground Engineering Limited)

Embankment construction — general

The method of constructing an embankment will depend upon the extent of the works, the type of fill material being used and the nature of the site.

The site must be stripped of all vegetable matter which would readily consolidate under the heavy load of fill material. Fill material should be tipped and spread in layers of such a thickness that it can be compacted to the required density — which will be established by laboratory testing. Where large volumes of fill are involved, the density factor obtained in the laboratory may not be achieved on account of practical difficulties in varying the moisture content of large volumes of earth between the two stages of excavating and filling. This discrepancy can be minimised by the correct selection of compaction plant: the plant most suited will depend on the soil type and its working moisture content. Multi-wheeled rubber-tyred vehicles (wobbly-wheel rollers) are very effective for compacting fine fill materials such as PFA and sands; very heavy vibrating rollers, towed by bulldozers, are suitable for compacting PFA and coarser granular materials (Fig 3.14).

Construction in water

Where it is uneconomical to drain the water from the site, attention should be given to the maximum and minimum water levels and to the type of soil beneath these levels. All soft materials, such as mud and peat, should be removed and replaced with coarse granular material, such as rock waste. This material should be placed carefully where the foundation is subject to slip movement through uneven loading; in other conditions the fill can be tipped direct from lorries; or, in the case of deep water, bottom-opening barges may be used. The shape of the embankment below the water line must be monitored to prevent wastage of fill material. In some cases, where appreciable settlement can be tolerated, material which would normally be classified as unsuitable can be used as the centre core of the embankment, provided that it is protected by other suitable material.

Where wave action is likely, the slopes of the embankment must be protected against erosion; and where water pressure affects only one side of the embankment, precautions must be taken to avoid seepage underneath. Further consideration concerning fill materials in water is given in Chapter 6.

Fig 3.14 . *Compaction of PFA by vibrating roller* (Central Electricity Generating Board)

Construction on soft ground

When constructing earthworks on ground containing soft material, the soft material should preferably be removed to a depth which will enable the earthworks to be formed on a firm stratum. This may be achieved by normal methods of excavation or by displacement methods. Displacement methods include:

Bog blasting, in which the soft material is displaced by explosives. This can be achieved in one of three ways:

Underfill blasting — a technique used when the soft strata exceeds 10 m in depth. The embankment is formed on the soft foundation and the soft material is blasted out, thereby allowing the embankment to subside into the cavity.

Trench shooting — a technique used for blasting out the soft material to form an open trench into which the fill material is tipped.

Toe shooting — a technique used in conditions where the sides of the trench would collapse if blasting was undertaken using the trench shooting technique. The site is loaded with fill material and explosives placed under the toe of the bank. As the explosives move the soft material, the fill flows into the toe cavity, thus extending the width of the bank.

Overloading, in which the bank is formed to a considerable height above the finished level, thus overloading the soft ground which flows out from the toe. Surplus material is removed from the embankment when settlement is complete.

Jetting, in which holes are jetted through the bank at 3 m centres each way to a level just above the required formation level. Water is then jetted down through the bank, causing the soft material to flow laterally; the bank moves downwards as the soft material moves out. This technique can be used on soft deposits up to 15 m thick. When peat is to be displaced the embankment should be formed with fine granular materials to prevent impedance of the jetting operation.

Construction on sloping ground

Where the slope is gradual it is necessary only to maintain a good foundation and to provide drainage for the flow of water beneath the embankment. Where the slope is steep it may be necessary to form 'benches' or horizontal steps in the side of the slope, to provide an adequate key for the new earthworks. Drainage must be carefully designed to catch water from the upper side of the embankment and to channel it safely under or through the embankment, thus eliminating any danger of instability due to water pressure.

When the natural slope is 1 in 5.5 or steeper, it will be necessary to investigate the possibility of soil slip: where this is found to be probable, precautions must be taken to prevent such occurence.

Embankment slopes

The safe angle of any embankment slope will depend on the nature of the fill material used and the height of the bank. The safe angle will range from as much as 45° for rock-waste fill down to as little as 20° for some clays. An average range for most rock fills can be taken as 33°–42°, but the behaviour of existing embankments in materials similar to those being used is the best guide to the slope to be adopted. Slopes may also be stated as ratios and percentages: e.g. a slope of 1:3 or 33%; a slope of 1:5 or 20%. Where existing works are not available the safe slope may be determined from the following:

For coarse-grained materials the slope can be taken as the angle of repose for the material, adjusted to give a margin of safety.

For materials such as coarse and medium sands the slope should take account of surface erosion.

Very fine non-cohesive materials may be subject to instability due to pore water-pressure which could cause the slope to flow. The angle would therefore have to be lower than the angle of repose.

Cohesive soils such as silts and clays are subject to factors which do not affect the design of slopes in non-cohesive soils: therefore the angle of repose method cannot be used. The safe angle of these soils can only be determined from laboratory tests which take into consideration such factors as shear strength of soil under adverse conditions, height of bank, development of pore water-pressure during construction, etc.

3.3 CONTROL OF GROUND WATER

There are many ways in which ground water may be controlled during the construction period; some methods deal with water lowering and others with water exclusion. The various methods of ground water control and ground conditions in which these may be best suited are shown in Table 3.2 and described in detail below.

3.3.1 Pumping systems

The control of ground water by pumping is the cheapest and commonest form of control: the various systems of pumping include:

Pumping from sumps

Pumping from wells

Pumping from well-points.

Pumping from sumps

Pumping from sumps is the most widely used method of ground water control, since it can be applied to all types of ground conditions and is economical to install and maintain. The only problem is one of soil movement due to settlement: the ground is likely to move as the water flows towards the sump area. There is also a risk of instability at the formation level in timbered excavations, owing to the upward movement of water. These problems can be partially overcome by positioning the sump at a corner of the excavation at a level below the formation level (Fig 3.15). For excavations which are likely to be open for long periods of time a peripheral drain filled with gravel can be dug to intercept water at formation level and channel it to the sump, thereby giving a drier and more stable work area. When the excavation is taken through permeable soil and continues in impermeable soil, it is preferable to form a drain at the line where the two soils meet. This type of drainage channel, known as a 'Garland' drain, prevents the impermeable soil being softened by the flow of water (Fig 3.16), and carries the ground water to a sump at one corner. The types of pumps used in the construction industry are discussed in Section 2.8.2, but it should be mentioned that the suction lift of most pumps is limited to a depth of 7.5 m: some manufacturers claim a maximum lift of 9 m. This may affect the position of the pumps: for deep excavations where the depth exceeds 9 m the pump will have to be placed in the excavation or on a level suitable for the suction lift. An alternative method of preventing soil movement due to open sump pumping is the use of jetted sumps (Fig 3.17). The sump is formed by jetting a metal tube in the ground by means of water pressure. A disposable well-point, consisting of disposable hose and intake strainer, is lowered into the tube and a sand media placed around it. The metal tube is then withdrawn and the flexible suction pipe is connected to a pump.

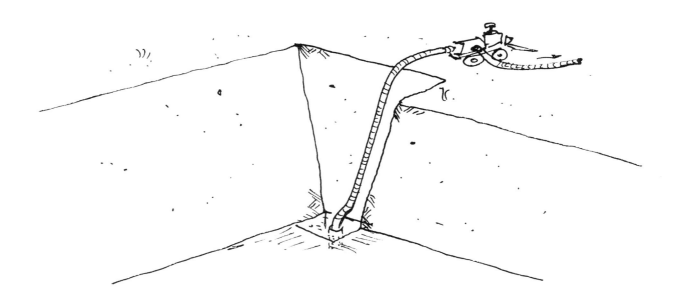

Fig 3.15 *Sump below formation level in corner of excavation*

TABLE 3.2 — Ground water control processes

METHOD	SOILS SUITABLE FOR TREATMENT	USES
Group 1 — Diaphragm, exclusion of ground water		
1. Sheet piling	All types of soil (except boulder beds and rock)	Practically unrestricted
2. Diaphragm walls (structural concrete)	All soil types including those containing boulders (rotary percussion drilling suitable for penetrating rocks and boulders by reverse circulation using bentonite slurry)	Deep basements Underground car parks Underground pumping stations Shafts Dry docks
3. Slurry trench cut-off	Silts, sands, gravels and cobbles	Practically unrestricted Extensive curtain walls round open excavations
4. Thin grouted membrane	Silts and sands	As for 3
5. Contiguous bored pile walls	All soil types but penetration through boulders may be difficult and costly	As for 2
6. Cement grouts	Fissured and jointed rocks	Filling fissures to stop water flow (filler added for major voids)
Grouted cut-offs 7. Clay/cement grouts	Sands and gravels	Filling voids to exclude water To form relatively impermeable barriers — vertical or horizontal Suitable for conditions where long-term flexibility is desirable, eg cores of dams
8. Silicates Joosten, Guttman and other processes	Medium and coarse sand and gravels	As for 7 but non-flexible
9. Resin grouts	Silty fine sands	As for 7 but only some flexibility
Freezing 10. Ammonium/brine refrigeration	All types of saturated soils and rocks	Formation of ice in the voids stops water flow
11. Liquid nitrogen refrigerant	As for 10	As for 10
Group 2 — Water Lowering		
12. Sump pumping	Clean gravels and coarse sands	Open shallow excavations
13. Wellpoint systems with suction pumps (Vertical and horizontal)	Sandy gravels down to fine sands (with proper control can be also used in silty sands)	Open excavations including rolling pipe trench excavations
14. Bored shallow wells with suction pumps	Sandy gravels to silty fine sands and water bearing rocks	Similar to wellpoint pumping More appropriate for installations to be pumped for several months or for use in silty soils where correct filtering is important
15. Deep bored filter wells with electric submersible pumps (long shaft pumps with motor mounted at well head used in some countries)	Gravels to silty fine sands, and water bearing rocks	Deep excavations in, through or above waste bearing formations
16. Electro-osmosis	Silts, silty clays and some peats	Deep excavations in appropriate soils or to speed dissipation of construction pore pressures
17. Drainage galleries	Any water bearing strata underlain by low permeability strata suitable for tunnelling	Removal of large quantities of water for dam abutment cut-offs etc.
18. Jet educator system using high pressure water to create vacuum as well as to lift the water	Sands (with proper control can also be used in silty sands and sandy silts)	Deep excavations in space so confined that multi-stage well-pointing cannot be used. Usually more appropriate to low permeability soils

Courtesy Ground Engineering

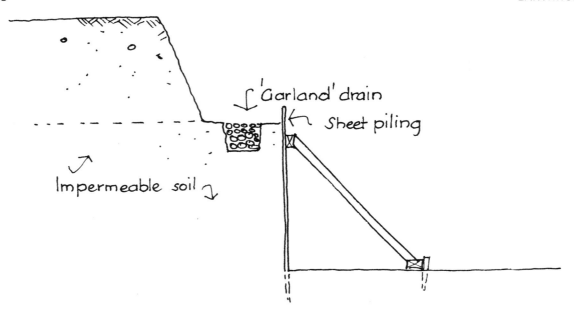

Fig 3.16   *Garland drain intercepting water at the*
            impermeable level

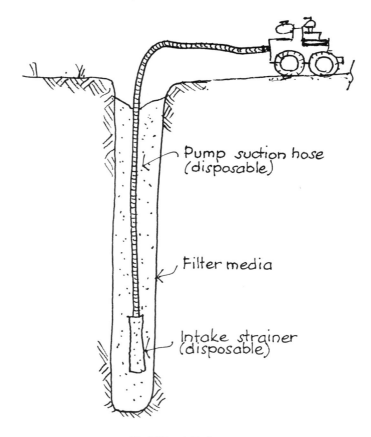

Fig 3.17   *Jetted sump*

Pumping from wells

Since normal pumping methods limit the depth of suction lift to a maximum of 9 m and conditions may not allow the pump to be placed in the excavation, well pumping may be employed. The main use is the lowering of ground water to a considerable depth below 9 m or where the ground may not be suitable for the wellpoint system. The well is formed by sinking a lined borehole, of a diameter between 300 and 600 mm to the required depth. Into this borehole another tube is placed, known as the inner well lining (Fig 3.18), which is provided with a perforated screen for that section over which the dewatering is required. The lower end of the inner lining is unperforated and acts as a sump for the settlement of fine material. The annular space between the two linings is filled with filter material over the length of the perforated section: the remainder of the borehole is backfilled with any suitable material. Depending on the depth of the well, the outer lining is withdrawn as the annular space is filled, or on completion. Before the pump is placed in position, the water in the well is 'surged' by some form of plunger to promote flow through the filter and wash out unwanted 'fines'. The pump used is the submersible type as described in Section 2.8.2. The spacing of the wells is determined by the type of soil being dewatered. The depth of the well depends on the depth of the impermeable stratum: where this stratum is well below the excavation formation level the spacing between the wells can be increased until the draw-down curve is just below the formation level (Fig 3.19).

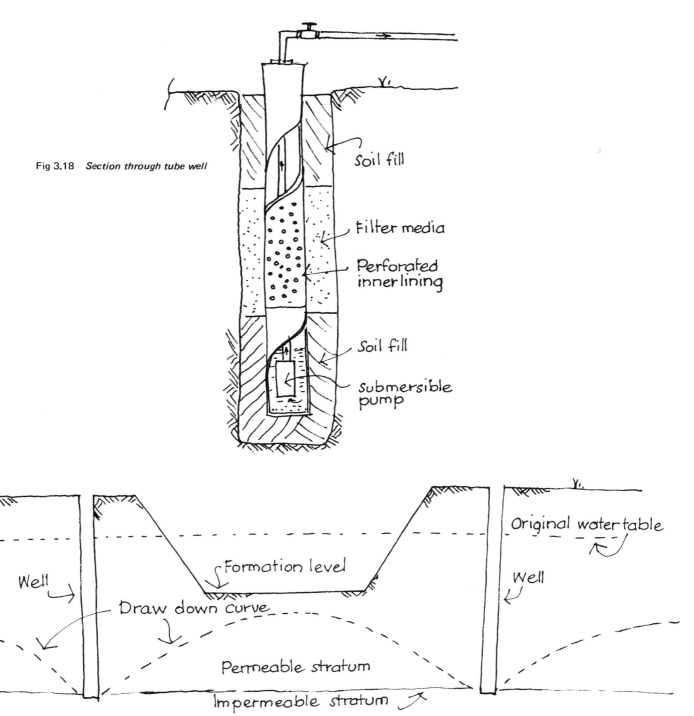

Fig 3.18   *Section through tube well*

Fig 3.19   *Wells used to lower water table to a level below formation of excavation*

Pumping from horizontal wells is suitable when the formation level is at or just slightly within an impermeable stratum in which the draw-down curve in vertical wells would not lower the water to the required level. A well is sunk outside the excavation area to a level below the proposed formation, and horizontal borings are made in a radial pattern from the vertical well. This allows water to drain from the upper surface of the impermeable stratum into the large well and then to be pumped out by submersible pump.

Another horizontal system of ground water control has been introduced by Ground Water Services Ltd. This consists of laying an 80 mm diameter PVC perforated suction pipe at a depth of up to 6 m around the excavation area and connecting it to a pump (Fig 3.20). The suction pipe is covered with a nylon filter sleeve which prevents particles of soil from entering the pipe: it can be laid over sites at a speed of up to 160 metres per hour by a special horizontal well-point placing machine (Fig 3.21) which digs the trench, lays the pipe and backfills the trench in one operation. The length of pipe handled by one pump will depend on the soil conditions and the size and type of pump to be employed. The laying of the pipe automatically breaks up the ground and forms a drainage channel to the pipe. For continuous drainage of pipelines an overlap between the ends of the pipe is required to effect a continuous draw-down.

Pumping from well points

The well-point system of dewatering is perhaps one of the most well known on civil engineering projects since it is used very frequently for ground water control in non-cohesive soils (Fig 3.22). The system consists of a number of small diameter vertical wells connected to a header pipe which is under vacuum from a pump. The ground water is forced out of the soil by atmospheric pressure into the header pipe, via the well-points, and discharged by the pump. The well-point itself is only a small part of the equipment, consisting of a perforated or slotted tube covered with a strainer or fine mesh, approximately 1300 mm long (Fig 3.23). A cast iron or steel jetting shoe is fixed to the well-point, containing a rubber ball which allows the 'jetting' of the well-point and prevents solids from rising up the tube when under vacuum. The well-point is connected to 38 mm internal diameter mild steel riser pipe which in turn is connected by swing connection to the header pipe. A recent development is the fully disposable well-point (Fig 3.24), which consists of a 65 mm diameter perforated plastic inner strainer with a nylon filter sleeve: the strainer is capped top and bottom, the former to receive a 40 mm diameter flexible riser pipe. The riser pipe is also made of plastic and is disposable: since the riser pipe is flexible it eliminates the swing connection normally used in conventional systems.

Jetting the well-points prior to connecting them to the header pipe is achieved by a powerful pump (see Section 2.8.2). The well-point is screwed on to the riser pipe and connected to the pump by means of a high-pressure flexible hose (Fig 3.25): the water pressure from the jetting pump washes out the soil below the well-point, which is lowered into the ground as the process continues. The holes that result from jetting may be 150 mm to 200 mm in diameter and these are backfilled with coarse-grained sand to form a supplementary filter. This process is knows as 'sanding-in' the well-points.

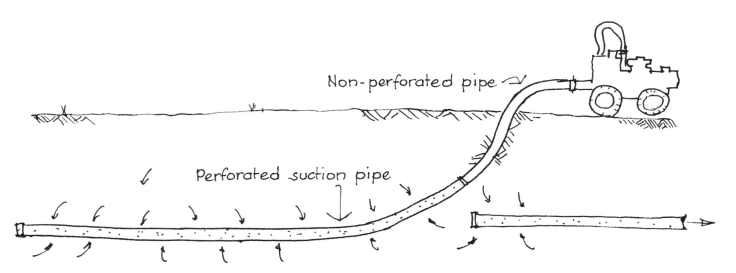

Fig 3.20   *Horizontal system of ground water control*

Fig 3.21 *B.600 trenching machine laying perforated pipe for horizontal dewatering*
(Ground Water Services Limited)

Partial collapse caused by sump pumping

Excavation after installation of well-point system

Fig 3.22 *Typical conditions in which the well-point system should be used* *(Ground Water Services Limited)*

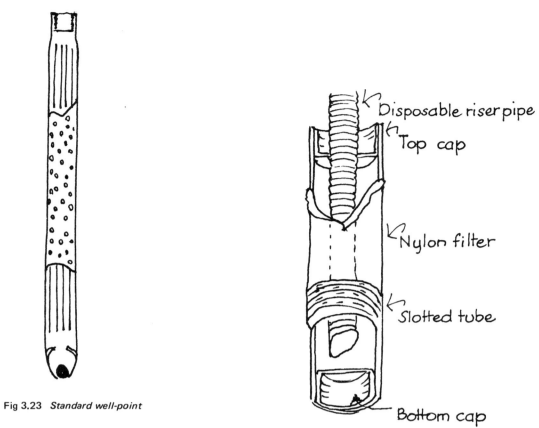

Fig 3.23 *Standard well-point*

Fig 3.24 *Disposable well-point*

Fig 3.25 *Jetting the well-point* (Ground Water Services Limited)

There are two methods of installing the well-point system, 'Ring-main' or 'Progressive Line'. With the former method the header pipe is placed around the excavation to be dewatered (Fig 3.26) and connected to the two pumps: two pumps are connected to the header pipe, one for the pumping operation and one as a standby should the first pump break down, since a delay in connecting a second pump could result in collapse of the excavation.

In the case of the Progressive Line method, sometimes called the rolling method (Fig 3.27), the header pipe is laid along the side of a continuous excavation, e.g. a trench; pumping is confined to a length of header pipe which allows work to progress without hazard. Further well-points are jetted ahead of the excavation to receive the progressive header pipe and when backfill has been completed the rear section of well-points is withdrawn. For narrow excavations it is sufficient to have a header pipe on one side only of the excavation; wide trenches or trenches in soils containing impervious materials will require header pipes on each side of the trench.

The well-point system is limited in its suction lift to a practical height of 6 m maximum: any attempt to lift water by well-points above this height results in loss of pumping efficiency, owing to air being drawn into the system through the joints in the pipes. Where dewatering is necessary in depths over 5 m it is common practice to introduce multi-stage well-points (Fig 3.28). These allow dewatering to any depth, providing the pump can work against the head involved; but practical aspects of excavation limit the number of stages employed. The use of multi-stage well-points involves the formation around the excavation of platforms on which the header pipe is situated; it may also involve battering the sides of the excavation to a safe angle of repose. While the safe angle of repose for dewatered sands is much steeper than that for normal soil, it still produces a large area of excavation for the first stage. The number of stages to be employed can be reduced if the excavation is taken down to the original ground water level before installing the first header pipe: in many instances this operation will eliminate one stage (Fig 3.29).

Fig 3.26 *Two-stage ring main well-point installation* (Ground Water Services Limited)

Fig 3.27   *Progressive line or rolling well-point installation*   (Ground Water Services Limited)

Fig 3.28   *Multi-stage well-point installation*   (Ground Water Services Limited)

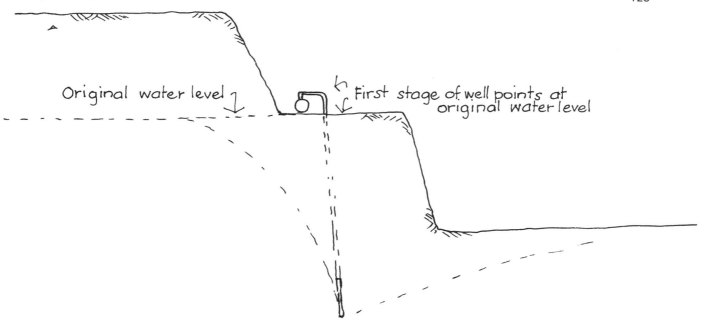

Fig 3.29 *Excavation of basement to natural water level before positioning well-point*

Regardless of the number of stages involved in dewatering a deep excavation, the depth of the inclined layer of soil being dewatered is limited to approximately 5 m and is therefore subject to seepage pressure from the mass of soil surrounding the excavation, which could cause instability. This pressure can be reduced by the use of deep wells positioned at the edge of the upper slope (Fig 3.30).

The well-point system of drainage is suitable only for dewatering non-cohesive soils with a minimum grain size of 0.1 mm: below this grain size the normal well-point system fails to produce the desired results. Where the grain size is below 0.5 mm, another method of well-point pumping may be employed, i.e. the 'vacuum' method.

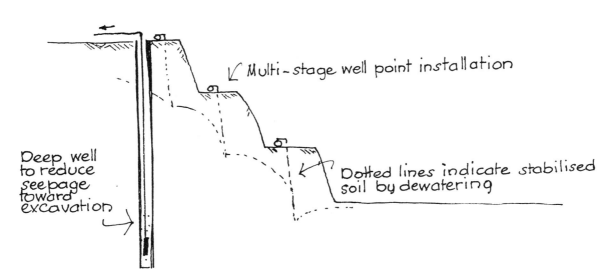

Fig 3.30 *Combination of deep wells and well-point system*

The vacuum method is similar to the normal method in that well-points are jetted into the ground and sanded in, but it differs in that the top metre of the hole is sealed with clay. The clay seals the well-point hole and when pumping commences creates a vacuum in the sand filter around the well-point. The ground water, which is being held in the very fine-grained material by capillarity, moves towards the vacuum as the force of atmospheric pressure attempts to equalise the pressure in the soil surrounding the well-point. After soil has been drained by the vacuum method, the particles of soil are held together by a pressure equal to the unbalanced atmospheric pressure. Since only the free water has been removed, the voids, although minute, are full of water and therefore likely to collapse if subjected to sudden shock, such as that of pile driving.

On large contracts the type of pumping and the number of well-points required can be determined from a pumping test (Fig 3.31), used to assess the permeability and storage co-efficient of the soil. The test consists of sinking observation wells in the area to be drained and dewatering the area by a small diameter ring main system. The level of water in the observation wells is recorded at given times.

Sand drains or sandwicks may also be used to lower the level of natural ground water and can be used to prevent hydrostatic pressure causing heave or 'boiling' in open excavations. They are also used to accelerate the settlement of clays and silts which may be subjected to applied loads, and they have particular value in the design and formation of embankments and roads over waterlogged ground.

The principle involved is the reduction of the drainage path in the layers of clay or silt, thereby allowing faster movement of water as the load is applied: this results in reducing the settlement time of the soils under load. The work is carried out by specialists who bore holes, 150 mm to 300 mm in diameter (Fig 3.32), at 2 to 5 m centres depending on ground conditions, and fill them with sand: in some cases a long nylon sleeve (sandwick) is filled with sand and lowered into the holes. Where fill material is placed directly above the drains, a horizontal blanket of granular fill must be provided over the sand drains to allow movement of the rising water.

Fig 3.31 *Pumping test in action* (Soil Mechanics Limited)

CIA rigs engaged in 6,500 No. 300mm sand drains 20 metres deep

Fig 3.32   **Construction of sand drains** *(Soil Mechanics Limited)*

3.3.2   Electro-osmosis

This technique of dewatering is used in soils which are cohesive in nature, eg silts and clays, and where the vacuum method of pumping does not produce satisfactory results. The unsatisfactory movement of water in cohesive soils is caused by the natural balance of electric charges in the particles of soil and molecules of water. Every particle of soil carries a negative charge of varying intensity, which attracts the positive (hydrogen) ends of the water molecules and thereby creates a balanced state. The fundamental principles in the complicated balance between soil and water are covered fully by Terzahgi and Peck*. The balance described above has to be disturbed to cause the water to flow: this is done by inserting two electrodes into the saturated soil and passing a direct electrical charge between them. The positive electrode (anode) can be sheet piling or steel rods driven into the ground; the negative electrode (cathode) is normally a well-point. When the current passes through the ground between the electrodes (Fig 3.33) it disturbes the balance of the water in the capillaries causing the outer film of water (which is positive), together with any free water, to flow towards the negative point: the water is then pumped off from the well-point.

This method of dewatering was developed during the Second World War for the stabilisation of soils in deep cuttings for railway works and in the construction of U-boat pens at Trondhjem. The cost of using such a system of dewatering in the UK has proved prohibitive when compared with other methods. The power requirements are in the region of 0.5 to 1.3 kw per m^3 of soil dewatered in large excavations, and up to 12 kw per m^3 of soil on small excavations.

3.3.3   Freezing methods

Freezing as a method of stabilising waterlogged sands and gravel has been known for over a hundred years: it was first used in 1862 in Wales to prevent the ingress of waterlogged soils into mine shafts. The basic principle of the process is that it changes the waterlogged soil into a solid wall of ice which is completely impervious, thus allowing men and machines to work inside the wall without danger. To produce the low temperatures required to freeze the water content of the soil, steel freeze pipes are installed at approximately 1 metre centres around the site to be excavated: these pipes consist of an inner and outer tube. The outer tube, 100 to 150 mm in diameter, is sealed at the bottom and connected by a gland to a return pipe at the top. The inner tube, 38 mm to 75 mm in diameter, is open at the bottom and connected to the flow pipe at the top (Fig 3.34). The flow and

* *Soil Mechanics in Engineering Practice: Articles 4 and 21, by Terzahgi & Peck Published by John Wiley & Sons*

return pipes around the site carry chilled brine which is pumped down the inner tubes and back up through the annular space between the tubes to the return pipe. The temperature of the brine circulating in the freeze pipes ranges from -15 to $-25°$ C, and therefore all pipes above ground level are insulated with polyurethene. The freezing medium must have a freezing point well below this temperature range and to achieve this a solution of calcium chloride or magnesium chloride is normally used. The liquid is cooled by a refrigeration plant, shown diagrammatically in Fig 3.35, and constantly re-circulated through the pipes: this causes the surrounding soil to freeze. Trailer-mounted refrigeration equipment (Fig 3.36) that requires little installation work makes this technique an economical proposition for many a problematic situation. In other cases where rapid freezing is required the medium is liquid nitrogen.

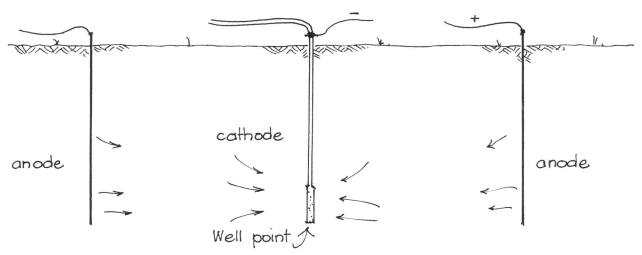

Fig 3.33 *Electrodes used in dewatering*

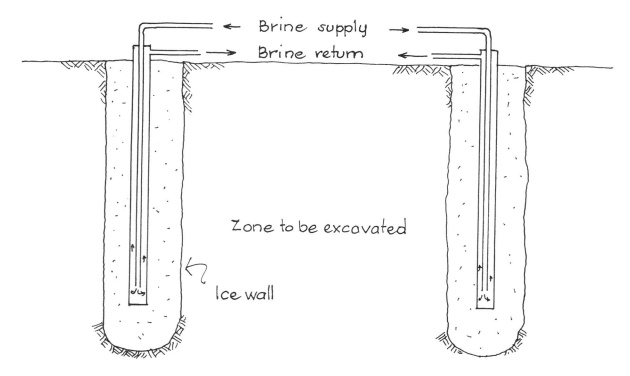

Fig 3.34 *Freeze pipes in position — ice wall formed,*
ground ready for excavation

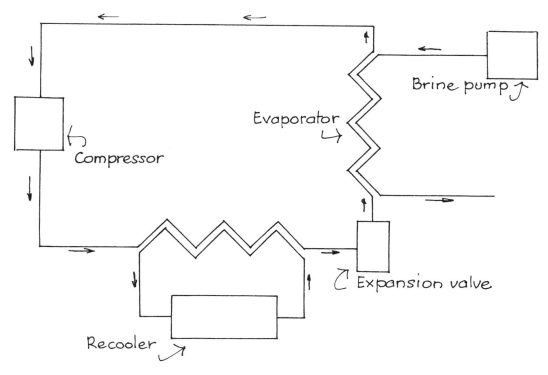

Fig 3.35   *Diagrammatic presentation of the freezing cycle*

Fig 3.36   *Freeze unit*   (Foraky Limited)

The system is competitive with other forms of ground support-and-dewatering systems for excavations over 7 m deep: unlike other systems, it is cheaper as the depth increases. The system does not require a high moisture content in the soil before it can be employed: a moisture content of 8 per cent of the voids is all that is required. Another misconception is that the length of time taken to freeze the ground makes the system prohibitive: this is totally misconceived, since the use of liquid nitrogen as a circulating medium allows work to commence within days. Even using a brine medium, the time to obtain a wall of ice is reasonably short and depends on the spacing of the freeze pipes, the quantity of refrigeration used and the type of soil being frozen.

At a spacing of 1 metre, a frozen wall 1 metre thick in sand and gravel can be achieved in 10 to 12 days; the same wall in clay would take 15 to 17 days. A completely continuous frozen wall is essential before excavation commences: this is determined by sinking an observation borehole in the centre of the treated area. The borehole is lined with a perforated lining which allows the ingress of water. As the wall freezes it forces the water inside the enclosure into the borehole: the water rises up the borehole and sometimes overflows on the ground. The rise in the level of water will indicate the closure of the wall.

This method is particularly suitable for the sinking of deep shafts (Fig 3.37). Shafts have been sunk to a depth of 600 m using this method, driving tunnels (Fig 3.38) and freezing large excavations (Fig 3.39 and Fig 3.40). The problem of volumetric increases in the soil due to freezing occurs only in clays and silts: other materials such as sands and gravel do not suffer measureable volumetric increase when frozen artificially. Silts can exhibit a volumetric increase of up to 2 per cent and precautions have to be taken when adjacent structures could be otherwise affected by soil movement.

The need for insulation of exposed ice-walls will be determined by the conditions. The completed walls may be covered with white reflective polyethylene film to prevent thawing out by radiant heat, (Fig 3.39) or insulated with fibreglass blankets sandwiched between twin polythene sheets.

Fig 3.37   *Freezing tubes in position for shaft sinking* (Delmann-Haniel)

Fig 3.38   *Freezing method employed in tunnel driving*   (Delmann-Haniel)

Fig 3.39   *Aerial view of large excavation (17m deep) employing freezing method — note reflective polyethylene sheeting*
(Delmann-Haniel)

Fig 3.40   *Freezing installation for large excavation inside existing factory at Blackpool* (Foraky Limited)

3.3.4   Compressed air

Compressed air systems of ground water control are used in conjunction with caisson sinking (see Section 6.2) and tunnel driving (see Section 5.1) in waterlogged ground. The safe working in such conditions is of paramount importance; the problems involved are covered in Section 1.2.8. In the UK the air supply to caissons is governed by the Factory Acts and the *Work in Compressed Air Special Regulations*, which requires a delivery of 300 litres of fresh air per minute per person in the working chamber. The plant normally used for supplying the compressed air is a reciprocating compressor twin cylinder with single-stage piston (see Section 2.6.2). The capacity of air supply must be at least 50% above the normal requirements to allow for emergencies, and standby compressors with an alternative supply of power should be included in the plant set-up.

The air pressure required to keep water out of the excavation must equal the value of the hydrostatic pressure in the pore water at the level of the cutting edge of the caisson. For all practical purposes the air pressure in which men can work is 340 kN/m^2 (3.4 bar): this will normally allow working at depths of up to 35 m below the water table. Further details of this system of ground water control are given in Section 5.1.5.

3.3.5 Grouting methods

Grouting methods can be used in situations where the permeability of the soil would create a heavy demand on pumping or where the ground conditions would make the boring of wells and sinking of well-points very costly. The basic method is to inject the soil or rock with fluids which, on setting, seal or reduce the permeability of the material. The grout used will depend upon the particle sizes of the soil or the size of fissures in the rock formation. Since this process is costly it must be carefully controlled to prevent wastage of material: this is achieved by additives in the grout which control the gelling properties, thus limiting their spread in the ground. Attention must be given to the position and vulnerability of existing underground structures such as sewers, basements etc., because pressure grouting can penetrate the fine cracks that may be present and so create problems. The choice of grouting materials used in this method include:

Cement grout

Bentonite grout

Chemical grout

Resin grout

Bituminous grout.

Cement grouting

Cement grouting is suitable for injecting into coarse materials which have a high permeability. A 'grout-curtain' is formed by boring holes into the ground around the excavation area and injecting cement grout of varying consistencies. It is usual to commence grouting with a batch of thin grout and then to increase the viscosity of the grout as the process continues, by reducing the water-cement ratio. Secondary holes are bored between the lines of the primary boreholes to ensure complete grouting of the curtain.

The grout used may be composed of neat cement and water or a mixture of sand and cement in the ratio of up to 4 parts sand to 1 part cement, the latter giving better economies in the consumption of materials. A system of grout curtains constructed at the nuclear power station beside the Severn estuary at Oldbury, North Avon, is a good example of controlled water flow: the ingress of water was reduced from 4500 litres per min. to 16 litres per min.

PFA can be used in conjunction with cement grouting, or it may be used in lieu of sand or as a partial cement replacement. The spherical particle shape of this material improves the flow quality of the grout. On one contract, grit-stone, which was adjacent to an earth dam, was grouted satisfactorily with a solution of 1 part PFA; 1 part cement; 2 parts water, by weight: the grout was pumped through a 38 mm diameter pipe for a distance of 400 m without blockage or appreciable drop in pressure. Cementitious grouts are often referred to as 'filler grouts'.

Bentonite grouting

Bentonite or clay grouting is used in ground conditions where the particles of the soil are too small for cement grouting. While clay adds little if any strength to the soil, it has a high resistance to water flow and therefore produces an excellent barrier. Bentonite is produced from montmorillionite clay, which has thixotropic properties: when it coagulates it forms a gel which is highly resistant to water, and if mixed with certain additives, such as Portland cement or soluble silicates, the barrier formed will be permanent. It is particularly useful for grouting alluvial soils beneath dam foundations to prevent the seepage of water under the finished structure.

Chemical grouting

The chemical grouting or consolidation process is used in sandy soils of medium to coarse grading. The materials are liquid when mixed prior to injection and form into gels or solids by chemical reaction which takes place between the base substance and the hardener. The time taken for solidification depends on the particular system being used. There are two main processes, namely 'two-shot' and 'one-shot'. In the 'two-shot' process (known widely as the Joosten and Guttman process, after the engineers who developed the process), pipes are driven into the ground at 600 mm centres, and the first chemical, normally sodium silicate, is injected: this is followed immediately by the injection of the second chemical, calcium chloride. The reaction between the two chemicals is immediate, resulting in a tough, insoluble 'silica-gel'. The process gives considerable strength to the soil and greatly reduces its permeability.

The 'two-shot' process has been largely superseded by the 'one-shot' process, which consists of mixing together prior to injection two chemicals whose gel time can be sufficiently delayed to allow full penetration of the soil before gel occurs. The extent of the delay can be accurately controlled by varying the proportions of the two chemicals. The extra time available for placing this grout allows wider spacing of the boreholes.

A typical 'one-shot' chemical grout consists of a liquid base which is further diluted with water before use, and a liquid catalyst added at a rate to give a pre-determined gel time. The mixed solution has a viscosity less than 10cp and will penetrate fine sands. The resultant gel is permanent and is not washed out by running water; it gives a relatively high strength in sand, having a crushing strength ranging from 1 to 4 N/mm^2.

Chemical grouting has several advantages over other methods of grouting, some of which include:

Stricter control of gel time, which can range from a few seconds to many hours

Economies in the boring of grout holes, since fewer holes are required

Greater penetration of the grout

Greater flexibility in grouting time.

Resin grouting

The term resin grout is used for grouts which are formed by interaction of soluble materials. They are of low viscosity and are formed by adding a catalyst to a base solution. The difference between resin grouts and chemical grouts is one of viscosity; the former have a very low viscosity capable of penetrating fine sands in which silicote solutions are of little value. Resin grouts include tannin-based grouts, phenol-formaldehyde and resorcinol-formaldehyde. The type to be used depends to a certain extent on the chemical content of the ground-water. The chemical content of the ground-water may affect the setting of the particular grout.

Bituminous grouting

Bituminous solutions such as cut-back bitumen emulsion can be used as a suitable grouting medium: they can be injected into fine sands to form an impermeable barrier to water. Such solutions are suitable for forming cut-off walls beneath dams and similar structures but add no strength to the soil: for this reason they have no value in underpinning work.

Methods of injection

Almost all grouting work is executed by driving pipes or boring holes in the ground and pumping the grout solution through tubes at high pressure. The spacing of the holes will vary according to the type of grout used and the ground conditions encountered, but as a general guide the spacing ranges from 600 mm centres for the 'two-shot' process in sand to 10 m centres for cement grouting in rock. The area to be grouted is first investigated to determine the required extent of grouting and this is followed by the calculation of a drilling pattern, which takes into account the size, spacing and depth of holes required. Holes or pipes are then sunk to the required depth by means of pneumatic tools, diamond drills or wash-boring, depending on site conditions; holes formed in alluvial soils are cased to prevent collapse.

The pressure at which the grout is pumped into the ground varies according to soil conditions and the reasons for grouting, but can range from 1 N/mm^2 for sands to 7 N/mm^2 for grouting fissures in rock. The most suitable pressure for grouting is difficult to determine in advance and tests may be necessary in-situ before the final choice is made.

3.3.6   Comparison of methods and costs

The choice of a method of ground water control will depend in the main on the type of soil involved and the depth to which the ground is to be excavated. For most shallow excavations where the sides of the excavation are battered or supported by timbering, normal pumping from sumps will suffice: where the soil is non-cohesive and the flow of water to a sump could create problems with soil movement, a well-point system can be employed. However, where the soil consists of coarse gravel and the flow of water is very heavy, some form of cut-off walling may be necessary before the well-point system can produce satisfactory results.

   Where adjacent structures could be endangered by the excavation of soil or movement of water, special treatment will be required: this may be achieved by a permanent cut-off wall, such as a diaphragm wall, or by freezing the soil. The use of chemicals in the formation of cut-off walls will normally prove uneconomical because chemical grouting is 6 to 8 times more expensive than cement grout per cubic metre of soil treated. Since the soil particle size greatly influences the choice of method, reference should be made to a chart which identifies the various processes in conjunction with soil grading. Suitable charts have been produced by Glossop and Skempton which indicate the type of process or method of control to be used (Fig 3.41: see also Table 3.2).

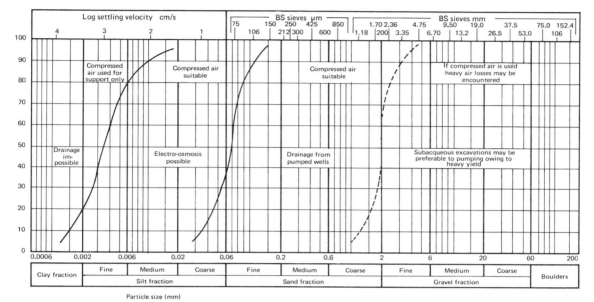

Tentative limits of application of various geotechnical processes. Groundwater lowering and compressed air. From 'Particle-size in silts and sands', by R. Glossop and A.W. Skempton. Extract from CP 2004: 1972

Fig 3.41(a)   *Groundwater lowering and compressed air*

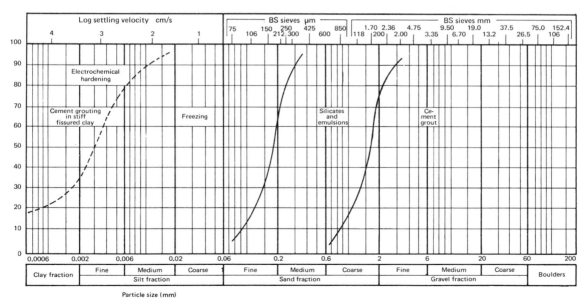

Tentative limits of application of various geotechnical processes. Artificial cementing. From 'Particle-size in silts and sands', by R. Glossop and A.W. Skempton. Extract from CP 2004: 1972

Fig 3.41(b)   *Artificial cementing*

Chapter 4

Piling, Diaphragm and Retaining Wall Systems

4.1 SHEET PILING

4.1.1 Types of piles

Sheet piles are normally formed of steel or reinforced concrete; they can, however, be formed of timber in countries where there is an ample supply. Fig 4.1(a) shows a typical diagram of sheet piling available, and Fig 4.1(b) shows the various sections manufactured in the UK.

Timber sheeting, where it is used, is suitable for temporary work such as cofferdams and ground support where the head of water or ground pressure is within the capabilities of the material strength. The piles may be formed in various ways to provide interlocking joints for waterproofing or strengthening. Fig 4.2 shows a method of interlocking and a typical treatment of the head and toe of the pile. Their value is limited since they are subject to damage before reaching suitable cut-off depths for anything but shallow excavations.

Reinforced concrete sheet piles are similar in design to timber sheeting, but are of much greater value in the construction of permanent embankments to rivers, canals and other forms of water-orientated structures. The piles are suitably interlocked and the toes of the piles are shaped to facilitate easy driving and interlocking (Fig 4.3). The heads of the piles are cut down to the required level before finishing off by casting a capping beam (Fig 4.4). The concrete and reinforcement for the piles should comply with the current Code of Practice.

Steel sheet piling is the most common form of sheet piling used in temporary and permanent works. It is used in such structures as cofferdams, retaining walls, river frontages, quays, wharves, dock and harbour works, land reclamation and sea defence works. It has an advantage over other forms of sheeting in that it has high structural strength combined with watertightness and can be easily driven into most types of ground. The sections (Fig 4.1(b)) are interlocking and can be driven to depths which provide adequate cut-off to prevent piping (sub-surface boiling of soil due to water pressure) in waterlogged soils.

Steel sheet piles are available in three basic forms in the UK:

Normal sections

Straight web sections

Composite sections.

Normal section sheet piles include the well-known Larssen and Frodingham sheet piles. Larssen piles were named after an engineer who worked in Bremen at the turn of the century. He developed the principle of inter-locking sheeting for temporary work. The sections were first rolled in one operation in the UK in 1929. The Frodingham sheet pile is the English name given to a section which was designed by Hoesch (a German company) as an alternative to the Larssen pile; it appeared in the UK in 1937. The sections are designed to provide the maxi-mum strength at the lowest possible weight, consistent with good driving qualities.

Section interlock (Fig 4.1(b)) facilitates ease of pitching (positioning the pile ready for driving) and driving; it also results in a close-fitting joint which forms an effective water seal. In some cases, however, the joints may be caulked to prevent ingress of water under pressure (see Section 4.1.4). A wide range of sections is pro-duced, as shown in Tables 4.2 and 4.3. These sections are available in various grades of steel, including copper-

TABLE 4.1

| | Ultimate Stress | | Minimum Yield Stress | | | | Minimum Elongation on 200 mm | |
			Up to and including 16 mm thick		Over 16 mm up to and including 25 mm thick		Up to and including 9 mm thick	Over 9 mm thick
	kg/mm²	N/mm²	kg/mm²	N/mm²	kg/mm²	N/mm²	%	%
BS 4360:1979 (Mild Steel) Grade 43A	43.8/52.0	430/510	26.0	255	25.0	245*	16	20
Medium Tensile Steel	52.0/60.2	510/590	31.5	309	29.9	293	16	20
BS 4360:1979 (High Yield Steel) Grade 50B & 50C	51.0/63.2	490/620	36.2	355	35.2	345	15	18
Similar to ASTM—A328 or CSA G 40.7	49.2 min	482.6 min	27.0	265	27.0	265	—	17

Notes: COPPER BEARING STEEL — all the grades of steel are available with 0.20% up to 0.35% or over 0.35% up to 0.50% Copper content.
*Section Larssen No. 6 (28.6 mm) Yield Stress = 240 N/mm²

1 N/mm² = 0.101972 kg/mm²

(British Steel Corporation)

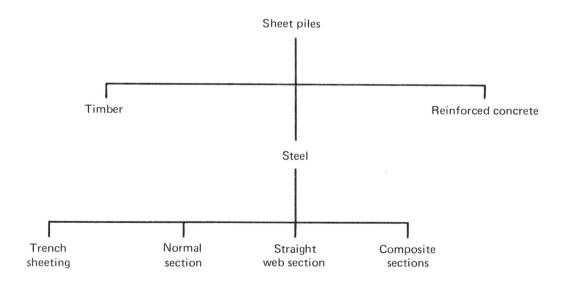

Fig 4.1 (a)   *Types of sheet piles*

bearing steel for increased corrosion resistance. Table 4.1 shows the steel grades and their corresponding strengths. It will be seen from Tables 4.2 and 4.3 that the Larssen steel sheet pile is the strongest available section, having a section modulus of 5 000 cm^3/m for section No 6, compared with a section modulus of 3 168 cm^3/m for the Frodingham section No 5. A series of corners, junction and closure piles is also available to facilitate piling to various plan shapes.

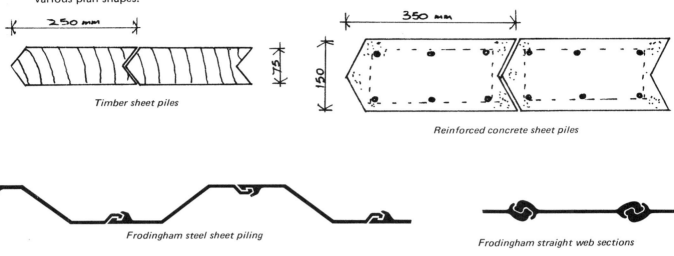

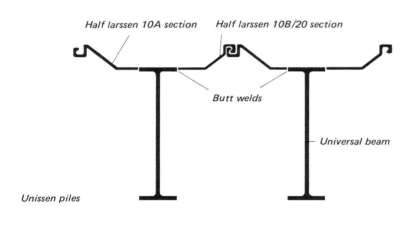

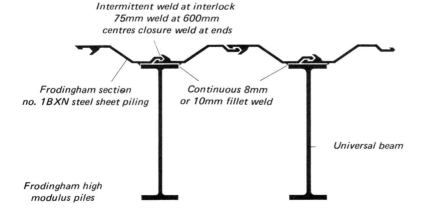

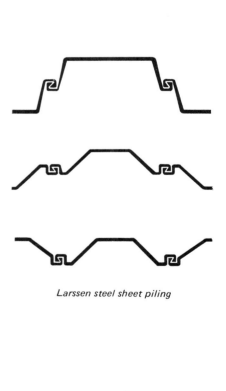

Fig 4.1 (b)   *Various sections of sheet piling*

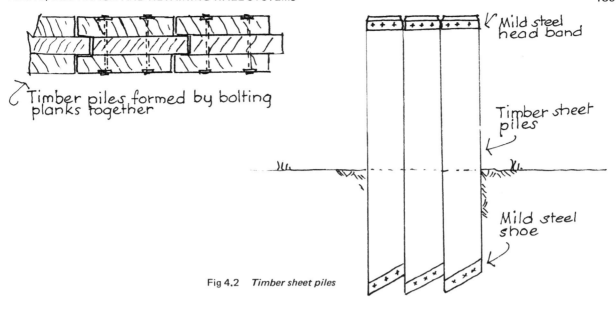

Timber piles formed by bolting planks together

Mild steel head band

Timber sheet piles

Mild steel shoe

Fig 4.2   *Timber sheet piles*

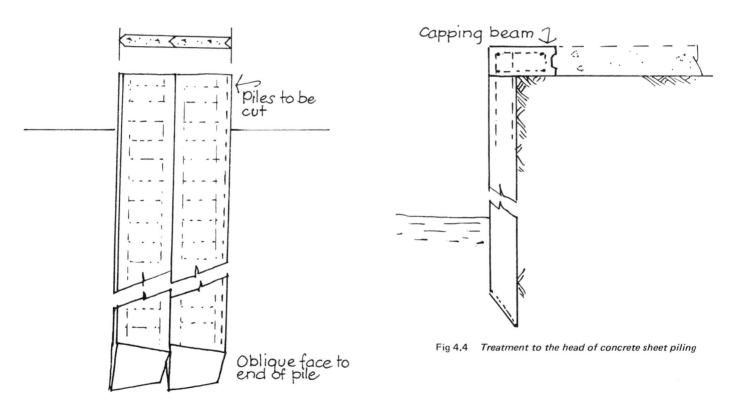

Piles to be cut

Oblique face to end of pile

Fig 4.3   *Reinforced concrete sheet piles*

Capping beam

Fig 4.4   *Treatment to the head of concrete sheet piling*

Slinging holes are provided in both types of sheet pile; the Frodingham piles have a 32 mm diameter hole located 75 mm from the top of the pile, whereas the Larssen pile has the same-sized hole located 150 mm from the top of the pile. Frodingham sheet piles are normally supplied interlocked in pairs, which saves time in handling and pitching; Larssen piles are normally supplied as single piles.

Straight web piling is used to construct cellular cofferdams (see Section 6.1). It is interlocked and driven to form cells which are then filled with gravel or broken rock. The outward pressure of the fill material develops high circumferential tensile forces in the piling. The Frodingham straight web pile is designed to resist these forces by virtue of the shape of the interlock. This 'crane-hook' shape gives a high tensile strength in the plane of the

TABLE 4.2

Section	b mm (nominal)	h mm (nominal)	d mm	t mm (nominal)	f Flat of pan mm	Sectional area cm² per metre of wall	MASS		Combined moment of inertia cm⁴ per metre	Section modulus cm² per metre
							kg per linear metre	kg per sq. metre of wall		
1U	400	130	9.4	9.4	302	135	42.2	106.0	3184	489
2	400	200	10.2	7.8	270	156	48.8	122.0	8494	850
2B	400	270	8.6	7.1	248	149	46.7	116.8	13663	1013
2N	400	270	9.4	7.1	248	156	48.8	122.0	14855	1101
3	400	247	14.0	8.9	248	198	62.0	155.0	16839	1360
3B	400	298	13.5	8.9	235	198	62.1	155.2	23910	1602
3/20	508	343	11.7	8.4	330	175	69.9	137.0	28554	1665
4A	400	381	15.7	9.4	219	236	74.0	185.1	45160	2371
4B	420	343	15.5	10.9	257	256	84.5	200.8	39165	2285
4/20	508	381	14.3	9.4	321	207	82.5	162.4	43167	2266
	508	381	15.7	9.4	321	218	86.8	170.9	45924	2414
5	420	343	22.1	11.9	257	303	100.0	237.7	50777	2962
	420	440	22.0	14.0	248	370	122.0	290.0	92298	4200
6	420	440	25.4	14.0	251	398	131.0	312.2	101689	4618
	420	440	28.6	14.0	251	421	138.7	330.3	109968	5000
10A	450	171	12.7	12.7	130	176	62.2	138.0	4166	486
10B/20	508	171	12.7	12.7	273	167	66.4	130.7	6054	706
10A−10B/20	450/ 508	108	12.7/ 12.7	12.7/ 12.7	130/ 273	171	62.2/ 66.4	134.1	2250	356

Rolling margin is within 4% over and 2.5% under theoretical mass; 75 mm over and 50 mm under on length.

(British Steel Corporation)

piling while at the same time permitting angular deviation between one pile and the next. The normal trough-shaped sections are not suitable for cofferdam work because the interlocks are not designed for tensile strength and therefore would deform and open out when subjected to tensile stress. Junction piles are provided to facilitate the jointing of the cells (Fig 4.5).

Composite sheet piling or high modulus section piling has been developed to support bending moments which are in excess of the capacity of normal sheet pile sections. This is of particular importance in waterfront protection where larger ships have needed increased wharf height beyond the limit provided by Larssen and Frodingham sections. Its ability to support large bending moments and heavy axial loads simultaneously makes it suitable for quays carrying heavy cranes and for permanent load-bearing abutment walls. Two composite piles were developed, the first being the Frodingham high modulus section (Fig 4.1(b)), which consists of a double Frodingham IBXN section welded to one flange of a Universal Beam; this was found to give the highest section modulus to weight ratio whilst retaining a minimum sheet pile thickness of 12.7 mm. The second type of composite pile is the Unissen Section (Fig 4.1 (b)) which comprises half a Larssen 10A section and half a Larssen 10B/20 section butt welded longitudinally to one flange of a Universal beam.

Any of the larger Universal beams can be used together with any length of sheet pile to meet driving requirements and designed loading. The system produces a wall of identical units which can be produced in a range of sizes giving optimum economy.

Lightweight trench sheeting is used for supporting the sides of trenches and excavations, cofferdams in shallow depths of water and small retaining walls. The sheeting is available in lap-jointed and interlocking sections (Fig 4.6) and is obtainable in standard lengths from 2 to 6 metres. The lap-jointed sections are rolled in mild steel and High Yield Stress Steel; interlocking sections are rolled in mild steel. A distinguishing feature of the interlocking section is that it can be interlocked from the side, if desired, by entering one sheet into the joint of the adjoining sheet and then turned into position through an angle of 60° to form the lock.

TABLE 4.3

SECTION		b mm (nom.)	h mm (nom.)	d mm	t mm (nom.)	$f1$ mm (nom.)	$f2$ mm (nom.)	Sectional area sq. cm per metre of wall	MASS		Moment of inertia cm⁴ per metre	Section modulus cm³ per metre
									kg per linear metre	kg per sq. metre of wall		
IBXN	Normal	476	143	12.7	12.7	78	123	168.0	62.1	130.4	4919	688
1N	Normal	483	170	9.0	9.0	105	137	126.0	47.8	99.1	6048	713
2N	Normal	483	235	9.7	8.4	97	149	143.0	54.2	112.3	13513	1150
3N	Normal	483	283	11.7	8.9	89	145	175.0	66.2	137.1	23885	1688
	Modified	483	283	11.2	9.5	86	140	175.0	66.3	137.3	22951	1622
4N	Normal	483	330	14.0	10.4	77	127	218.0	82.4	170.8	39831	2414
5	Normal	425	311	17.0	11.9	89	118	302.0	100.8	236.9	49262	3168

Rolling margin is within 4% over and 2.5% under theoretical mass; 75 mm over and 50 mm under on length.

(British Steel Corporation)

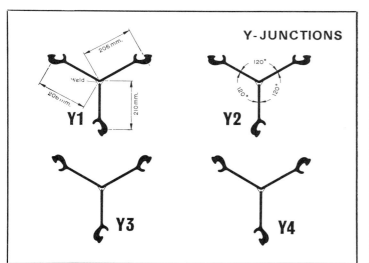

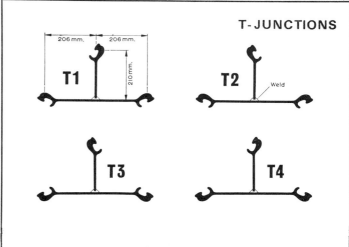

Fig 4.5   *Junction piles*

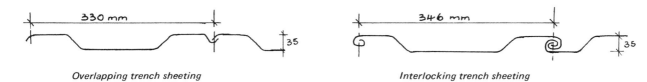

Overlapping trench sheeting   Interlocking trench sheeting

Fig 4.6   *Trench sheeting* (Foraky Limited)

4.1.2 Methods of driving

When piles are being driven they have a tendency to lean in the direction of driving; this tendency must therefore be restricted by some form of guide control. There are various ways in which piles may be guided during driving but the two principal methods in popular use are:

Driving in panels

Use of trestles and walings.

Driving in panels is a very satisfactory method of positioning sheet piles and ensuring that the piles do not creep out of verticality. Work is commenced by pitching and driving a pair of piles to part-penetration, care being taken to maintain correct position and verticality. A panel of piles, from six to twelve pairs, are then pitched and interlocked in position. The last pair of piles in the panel are driven and then guide walings are bolted between the first and last pair of piles (Fig 4.7) to support the panel during driving. The remaining pairs of piles are then driven to their final penetration. The last pair of piles are left in a partly driven state to form the support of the next panel of piles. When driving long piles it is preferable to use a light hammer for the first stage, following up with a heavy hammer for final driving. This is best achieved by using two cranes, one handling the smaller hammer, the other following behind with the heavy hammer.

Trestles and walings are the common alternative method of supporting sheet piles during driving. The method involves the use of very heavy trestles which have to be moved and positioned by craneage, which in turn support long heavy walings (Fig 4.8). The trestle may be constructed in timber or steel, the timber sections being of the order of 300 mm x 300 mm. Where steel piles are to be driven through water the guide walings may be supported on temporary timber piles (Fig 4.9) which form a heavy duty or light duty guide. With this second method of support the piles are often driven in pairs directly after pitching and there is a greater possibility of vertical creep than in panel driving. A slope of more than 1 in 300 may be difficult to close, although special tapered piles may be used. This method of support is therefore suitable for soft or loose ground conditions where control of verticality is satisfactory.

In addition to providing support for the driving of sheet piles, further support will be required in the form of spacer blocks (Fig 4.10) to obtain a good line of piling and to control the width of each pair of piles.

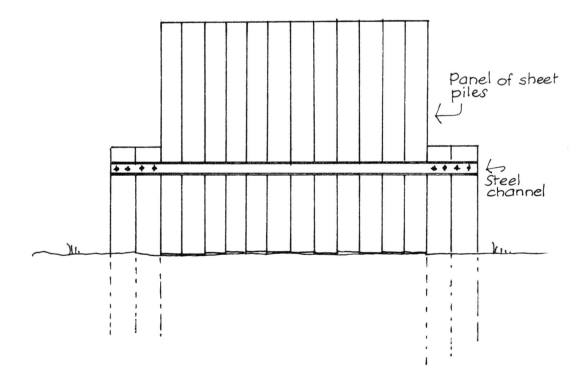

Fig 4.7 *Driving sheet piles in panels*

Fig 4.8   *Trestle guide*

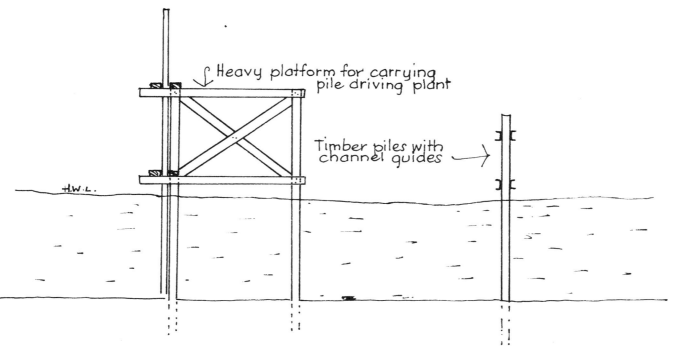

Fig 4.9   *Guides for pile driving in water*

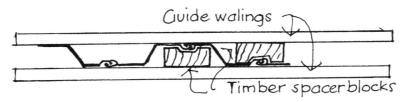

Fig 4.10   *Guide blocks to prevent pile spread*

Driving in restricted headroom

Steel sheet piling can still be installed even when overhead clearance is limited; the procedure however is slow and costly, and consideration should be given to the possibility of removing the obstacle. However, two methods should be considered: the first being to drive the piles in two or more lengths, and the second to jack the piles into the ground. In the first case the piles may be plated or welded together as the sections are driven. The second method employs the obstruction, say a bridge, as a resistance for hydraulically jacking the piles into the ground. When sufficient headroom has been achieved by jacking, a normal hammer may then be employed. The pitching of piles in a restricted area can be facilitated by using travelling chain blocks suspended from steel beams.

Pile driving equipment

Pile drivers for sheet piling fall into three basic categories:

Percussion drivers

Hydraulic drivers

Vibratory drivers.

Percussion drivers can be used in any suitable ground including soft rock, which would require high frequency blows. These include drop hammers and drivers for use with steam, compressed air or diesel, the last being the most popular.

Hydraulic drivers work on the principle of pushing sheet piles into the ground by means of a hydraulic ram acting against a firm reaction. The reaction is provided by the skin friction of piles already partially driven. The classic example of this plant is the Taywood 'Pilemaster' (Fig 4.11) which has been developed by Taylor Woodrow Construction Limited to overcome the problem of noise normally associated with sheet piling in built-up areas. The Pilemaster is vibrationless and almost silent, and as there is no ground vibration, steel sheet piles can be safely driven close to occupied buildings without damage to the fabric or disturbance to the occupants. The Pilemaster is an oil hydraulic piledriver which generates its driving force from the frictional restraint of other piles in the panel contained by the machine. Piles are pushed into or pulled out of the ground almost silently and without vibration.

It consists of a power pack, a steel crosshead, eight hydraulic rams with pile connectors, a guide system and an electrical control system. The rams have a stroke of 750 mm, operate at constant speed and are capable of a downward thrust of 229 tonnes or an upward pull of 168 tonnes. The noise of the Pilemaster has been recorded as 69 dBA at a distance of 1.5 metres from the piles. A pile connector mechanism allows the maximum available thrust of 229 tonnes to be transferred from the rams to the piles. Pairs of steel plates are bolted to the piles at ground level prior to pitching. The driving or extraction load is transferred from the rams to these plates and then, by frictional engagement, from the plates to the piles. Panels of seven or eight piles are pitched between timber or steel guides as is customary with other piling methods; the Pilemaster is then mounted on top of the sheet piles by means of a crane and the rams are connected to the plated piles via the connector mechanism. Two rams are operated to force the attached piles downwards; when these have been driven to the full 750 mm stroke of the rams, the next pair is driven, and so on until all eight piles have been driven 750 mm. All the rams are then retracted, allowing the Pilemaster to lower itself to a new level, and the cycle is then repeated sequentially. The Pilemaster is effective in driving sheet piles in clays, silts and most fine granular soils such as fine sand, but is not generally successful in driving through dense gravel or sand. A system of pre-trenching through unsuitable soils and backfilling with cohesive material has been developed to enable the machine to overcome the high toe resistance and low skin friction experienced in these conditions.

Vibratory drivers such as the 'Tomen Vibro' (Fig 4.12), are very suitable for the initial driving of sheet piles but must be avoided in heavy clays since the clay tends to dampen the vibrations. Another problem is that of noise: the vibratory hammer uses the steel sheet pile like a sounding board, producing a noise well in excess of any acceptable level. Some hammers have been enclosed in a sound-proofed box in the attempt to overcome this problem.

The head of the pile must be protected during driving by an anvil block, which, may be double or single-sided to suit the hammer being used. The anvils used for double-acting hammers are wide flat blocks of steel without packing, those used with drop hammers and single-acting hammers requiring a hardwood or plastic dolly. If the hammer is suspended by ropes it should be provided with long leg-guides or leg-grips which position the hammer on the piles and ensure that the hammer remains vertical. The leg-grips incorporate rubber-mounted insert plates which grip the pile but which are sufficiently resilient to allow the pile to enter the grips easily and permit the hammer to be removed when driving is completed. Leg-grips contain inserts shaped to suit any pile section; they are also adjustable to accommodate more than one section of pile.

Extraction of piles

Piles that have to be extracted should have greased joints during driving. The speed and method of extraction will depend upon many related factors, such as:

The section and length of pile

The length of time the piles have been in the ground

Soil and water conditions

The method of driving and weight of hammer used.

The types of extractor available are:

Inverted double-acting hammer

Heavy duty extractor

Vibrators.

Further reference should be made to section 2.4.4. The driving and extraction of trench sheeting is similar, in principle, to other forms of sheeting, but a light weight hammer is employed and the sheeting is protected by a special alloy cast steel cap which fits all sections of trench sheeting. If the special driving cap is not used, the sheet piles are very quickly damaged by driving.

4.1.3   Corrosion and protection

Any exposed steel structure may deteriorate as a result of the formation of rust, and sheet steel is no exception. Corrosion is of particular importance in the case of permanent steel sheeting because some parts are embedded in the ground and become therefore inaccessible for painting and maintenance. Research over a period of years has indicated that the useful life of a steel-pile retaining wall can be based on an average reduction in thickness of about 0.076 mm per year in sea water and 0.051 mm per year in fresh water. Where the back face of the piling is in contact with the ground or other suitable fill material, corrosion on that side can be neglected. In some industrial atmospheres or polluted water the corrosion may be as high as 3 mm per year.

Protection of the sheeting is normal practice where corrosion is likely to affect the strength of the material. However, it should be realised that with an average corrosion factor of 0.05 mm per year, many sheet piles with a heavy web section would have a life of 20 years before 50% of the pile was corroded away. It may be economically viable to replace the piles at that stage rather than to apply an initial protection which may be damaged during driving. Where protection is required it may take the following forms:

Paint treatment

Cathodic protection.

Paint treatments are applied to steel sheet piles after they have been effectively cleaned by shot blasting. The pile should be primed and finished with either bituminous paint to a thickness of 1 mm to 2 mm or with tar manufactured to BS 1070: 1973. Where corrosion is likely to be minimal, a black varnish may be used in lieu of bituminous paint. Conversely, in very severe conditions such as soils containing acids, the coating should be an epoxy resin-based paint. The disadvantage of surface treatments is that they are subject to damage by stone-scouring during driving. The advantage is that they can be readily renewed in marine works where the water level can be lowered for maintenance purposes.

Cathodic protection is based on the principle that all metals have electro-chemical potential and that material in the electro-chemical series can be protected by materials that are higher in the series (i.e. towards the anode end of the scale). The material used for protecting steel sheeting, known as the anode, must be high in the

Fig 4.11   *Taywood Pilemaster*
(Taylor Woodrow Construction Limited)

Fig 4.12   *'Tomen Vibo' driver/extractor*
(C. Evans & Sons Limited)

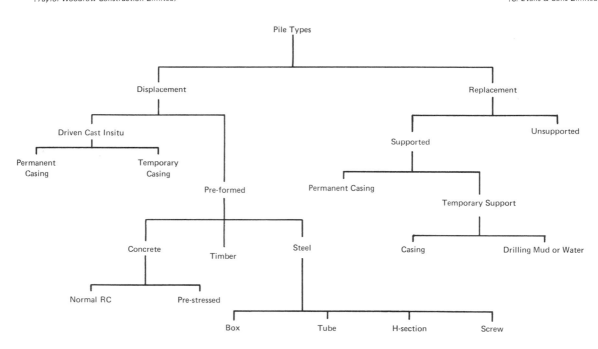

Fig 4.13   *Various types of bearing pile*

electro-chemical series; magnesium is often used. The material is connected electrically to the piling, which acts as a cathode, and the current escapes via the anode into the soil. This makes the whole structure cathodic and steel is preserved while the magnesium is sacrificially corroded away; the anode must be replaced from time to time. Alternatively, a power-supplied system may be used, in which the anode takes the form of lumps of carbon or scrap iron. A DC current is passed through the anode to the cathode by means of a generator, or AC transformer-rectifier, causing the sacrificial wastage of the anode. The cathodic system is suitable for protecting steel sheet piling below water level but it does not prevent atmospheric corrosion. Therefore piling above low water level must be protected by the painting method.

Copper-bearing steel is more resistant to atmospheric corrosion than is ordinary mild steel, but proportions of copper higher than the standard proportion of 0.25% to 0.35% do not give any improved resistance.

For further information, reference on corrosion may be made to CP 1021:1973 and BS 5493:1977.

4.1.4 Selection and use of sheet piling

This will depend upon factors such as:

Whether for permanent or for temporary work

Site conditions (e.g. headroom, type of soil)

The depth to which piles must be driven

The bending moments involved

Nature of the structure (e.g. circular cofferdams or straight piling)

The type of protection required, where necessary.

Most of these factors can be solved by simple reference to standard tables which include the properties of sheet piling, but in the case of reinforced concrete sheet piling the size of the pile will have to be calculated from first principles. Where steel sheet piling is used in permanent structures, such as pump houses, the interlocks may require 'caulking' (i.e. making the joint watertight by driving a dry material into it). This can be achieved by using lead wool or a special caulking rope made of asbestos and quick-setting cement.

4.2 BEARING PILES

4.2.1 General considerations

With the exception of sheet piles it can be said that piles are relatively long, slender members which support or restrain loads. Those piles which wholly support vertical loads are termed 'bearing' piles, while those that restrain loads may be termed 'anchor' piles. The term 'bearing' pile is used for driven piles as well as bored piles and serves to distinguish all such piles from sheet piling. This section deals only with bearing piles since the principles of piling used for other functions can be easily determined from the data given. Piling is used in many different circumstances, some of which are:

The support of a structure which would otherwise overstress the allowable bearing capacity of the soil at normal foundation depths

The unpredictable settlement of underlying strata where rock is to be found at a depth which can be reached economically

Differential settlement likely to be caused by strata changes across a site or by the close proximity of other structures

The seasonal shrinkage and swelling of the upper layers of soil

Building over water or waterlogged ground

The resistance of forces, such as uplift or overturning, which may be created by wind pressure or cantilever structure

The resistance of lateral forces, such as strata slip or other soil movement, which may cause instability of the structure

The underpinning of existing structures.

Piles must be driven, bored or screwed to the desired depth without damage to the pile shaft; this applies particularly to driven piles where the driving stresses may exceed the permissible working stress. The stresses during pitching and handling should not exceed the safe bending stress.

Loads should be applied concentrically with the axis of the pile on the centre of gravity of a pile group. Some difficulties may arise from the inaccuracy of pile positions, particularly in the case of isolated piles, and allowances must be made in the design since such conditions may result in eccentric loading of the pile. The usual tolerance, on plan, for all types of piles is 75 mm. (See specification for piling). Where the eccentric loading is of a significant nature, the pile cap should be restrained from lateral or rotational movement; the restraint should also be sufficient to resist the eccentric loadings.

Where vertical piles are subjected to substantial horizontal forces, the top stratum of ground should be able to resist the stress without permitting excessive lateral movement. Where the top stratum is incapable of providing such resistance, the piles must be connected by horizontal beams; if this measure is insufficient, raking piles should be used.

Preliminary work

Investigation of the substrata should be carried out as outlined in Chapter 1 and in accordance with the recommendations of BS 5930:1981. The borings, supplemented by penetration tests where appropriate, should reach depths which allow the exploration or testing of soil both around and beneath the toe of the pile. Samples of the soil at these lower levels should be tested for strength, compressibility and other characteristics which will assist in determining the length and spacing of the piles. Certain soil conditions do not permit adequate point bearing at an economic depth; this will involve the determination of skin friction at various levels in the ground before an economical design can be achieved. With the pressure of ground water it will be necessary to establish the source and the water table gradients between boreholes to determine its effect, if any, on soil stability.

Where other structures are in the proximity of the proposed pile foundations it will be necessary to survey the structures in question, since the choice of pile may be influenced by the effects which its installation may have on the adjacent structure.

Preliminary piles

Preliminary piles for determining the ultimate bearing capacity should be installed near the bore holes; the piling data can then be studied and compared with the site investigation data. The preliminary piles should be of the same materials and dimensions as the working piles, to ensure comparable behaviour under load. The testing for load bearing capacity and other characteristics are covered in Section 4.2.5. Where driven piles are to be used, a special preliminary pile, designed to withstand hard driving, is employed. A record is kept showing the number of blows per unit of linear measurement of penetration into the ground: this record will show the variations of soil resistance at various depths. Driving will continue until an acceptable 'set' has been reached (the 'set' is the desired final penetration of the pile, normally not more than 5 mm per blow of the driving hammer). The soil is then allowed to recover from the compression stresses. The time for recovery will depend on the nature of the soil and will vary from a few hours in non-cohesive soils to two days for clays. Re-driving is then started and continued until the resistance is similar to that previously achieved. This information, together with the specialised knowledge of ground conditions, will provide the engineer with data to complete the design and specification of the piling installation.

4.2.2 Types of bearing piles

The main classification of bearing piles is related to their effect on the soil. There are two main types: 'displacement piles' and 'replacement piles' (sometimes referred to as 'non-displacement' — CP 2004 : 1972). A displacement pile is either driven, jacked, vibrated or screwed into the ground; this action displaces the soil outwards and downwards but material is not actually removed. In the case of the screwed pile it may be argued that very little soil is displaced; this is true, but nevertheless some soil is displaced and in principle it should be found in this category: the screw pile can be classified as a 'small displacement pile' (CP 2004 : 1972). The replacement pile consists of forming a hole in the ground, by any of the various methods, and replacing the spoil with concrete. Classification of pile types is shown in Fig 4.13 in the form of a family tree.

Displacement piles (Fig 4.13) may be sub-divided into two groups:

Driven cast-in-place

Pre-formed.

Driven cast-in-place piles are of two types, the first having a permanent concrete or steel casing and the second without any form of permanent casing. In both cases a tube, closed at the bottom with a plug or shoe, is driven into the ground to the required set or depth; a cast-in-place pile is then formed inside the tube. Where the tube is permanent, it may be formed of a series of concrete shells about 1 metre long, adjusted for length by simply adding or subtracting shells; alternatively, steel tubes may be used which can be extended by welding or shortened by cutting tools. Temporary casings are formed in steel tube which is withdrawn either during or after the casting of the pile, depending on the particular system employed.

Pre-formed piles are prepared from timber, concrete or steel to the design requirements before driving. Care must be taken during driving to prevent damage to the pile by stresses, exerted by the hammer, which may be in excess of the working stresses of the pile. A further problem with this form of pile is the calculation of length. The operation of lengthening piles is very costly, while the alternative of shortening of over-length piles may prove laborious and costly in both time and materials. The handling of long concrete piles must be carefully supervised, since incorrect handling may result in exceeding the bending stresses, causing damage to the pile. The Code of Practice (CP 110: 1972) covers the requirements for the provision of steel reinforcement used to resist stresses due to lifting.

Replacement piles may be classified as:

Supported or

Unsupported.

In both cases a hole is formed in the ground by some form of cutting or boring and then filled with reinforced concrete. The unsupported hole will normally require a short tube at the top to prevent debris from falling into the concrete during placing. Support to holes may be provided by means of a medium or heavy sectional casing, screwed together as boring proceeds, or by a head of water or drilling mud (usually bentonite suspension). The concrete is placed in the hole by means of a tremie pipe to prevent segregation of material and pollution or weakening due to mixing with the water or drilling mud. In all circumstances the lower end of the tremie pipe should penetrate well into the freshly placed concrete. Where dry holes are obtained, the tremie pipe need not be used.

Piles 600 mm or more in diameter are commonly known as large diameter piles, because their construction always requires the use of large heavy plant. Large diameter piles may have their bearing capacity increased substantially by under-reaming the shaft at the base. This is achieved by an expanding cutting tool which expands and cuts a conical shaped base up to three times the diameter of the main shaft.

The various pile types shown in Fig 4.13 are now discussed in detail and various proprietary types are shown by means of sketches or photographs.

Displacement piles

Driven cast-in-place piles

As stated above, this type of pile is formed by driving a casing into the ground and filling the casing with concrete. Fig 4.14(a), (b) and (c) shows the principle employed in achieving both forms, i.e. permanent casing and temporary casing. In the first diagram a heavy steel casing is closed at the end with a plug of dry concrete. The plug of concrete, driven with a drop hammer, expands, grips the sides of the casing and takes the casing into the ground. On reaching the required depth the casing is restrained by cables and the plug of concrete is driven out into the ground to form a bulb at the end of the pipe: this bulb is often increased in size by a further batch of dry concrete. The cage or reinforcement is placed and the casing is filled with concrete as the casing is withdrawn. In some systems the casing is partially withdrawn and then re-driven; this consolidates the concrete and forms a keyed surface at the soil face. Most cast-in-place piles are constructed with high slump self-compacting concrete. The permanent casing is usually formed with reinforced concrete shells (the reinforcement can be of glass fibres rather than of steel); the shells are stacked over a steel mandrel, which has a special driving head, and a concrete shoe is placed at the foot of the bottom shell. Alignment of shells is maintained by steel bands at each joint, the bands being coated internally with sealing compound to provide waterproof joints. The pile is driven by a heavy drop hammer weighing up to 8 tonnes) which transmits the stress through the driving head to the mandrel, which drives the shoe. The stress on the actual shells is just sufficient to push them into the hole made by the shoe. The mandrel can be extended and further concrete shells added until the desired depth has been reached. On completion of driving, the mandrel and spare shells are removed and the reinforcement cage and concrete are then placed. The plant used consists of an excavator fitted with a special crane head and special leaders (see Chapter 2.4 and Fig 4.14(c)). The main advantages of this type of pile are:

Easily modified in length

Continuous cross-section can be maintained

Cast-in-place core is not subject to driving stresses.

Disadvantages include:

Vibration and noise during driving

Heavy equipment and plant for driving makes the method unsuitable for small sites

High skin friction on concrete shells can result in crushed shells, owing to increase in driving stress.

The cast-in-place core may be reinforced over the whole length of the pile, over part of the length, or simply provided with short splice bars at the top for bonding into beams or pile caps. The amount of reinforcement will depend on whether the pile is used to resist tensile or bending forces, the possibility of ground movement and the type and form of foundation.

When the core is cast in a tube that is to be withdrawn, care must be taken not to damage freshly poured piles, now unsupported by casings, by driving new piles in the vicinity.

Pre-formed piles

These may be constructed using:

Concrete

Timber or

Steel.

Concrete pre-formed piles

These are further sub-divided into:

Normal reinforced concrete and

Pre-stressed concrete.

In both cases the normal method of driving is achieved by heavy hammer blows while the pile is guided by a leader or pile frame — see section 2.4. The piles may be driven by any type of hammer, provided that penetration to the prescribed depth is achieved without damage to the pile. The hammer blow generates a stress wave down the length of the pile, which, if excessive, may cause failure by compression or tension. Failure due to excessive compression occurs mainly at the head of the pile and this can be eliminated by the correct head cushion and weight of hammer used. Plastic head packings have proved to be more successful than traditional packings of sand. Longitudinal tension, caused by reflection of the compression waves along the pile, may cause the pile to fracture. This may be avoided by restraining the pile laterally during driving and reducing hammer rebound by increasing the hammer weight or reducing the stiffness of the head packing.

The weight or power of the hammer should be sufficient to ensure the required 'set', which will be a final penetration of between 5 mm and 25 mm per blow, depending on the soil. The size of the hammer will depend on whether the pile is to be driven to a given resistance or depth, but it should not be less than half the weight of the pile. The fall or stroke of the hammer should be limited to 1 metre for a single-acting or drop hammer; greater heights may damage the pile. Protection of the head of the pile is essential: this is normally achieved by means of a resilient packing, sand, or a plastic disc, which is held in position by a helmet (Fig 2.27 (Chapter 2)). The helmet is provided with a dolly of hardwood or other suitable material to dissipate the blow from the hammer.

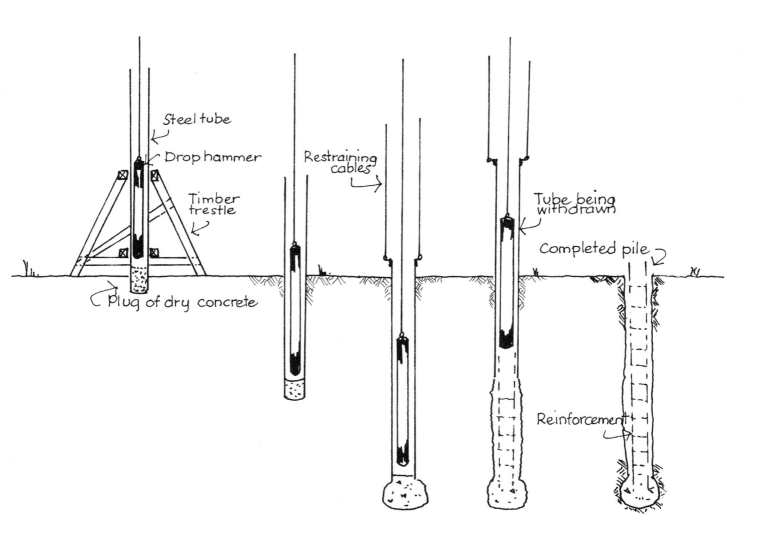

Fig 4.14(a)   *Driven cast-in-place pile (temporary casing)* *(West's Piling and Construction Limited)*

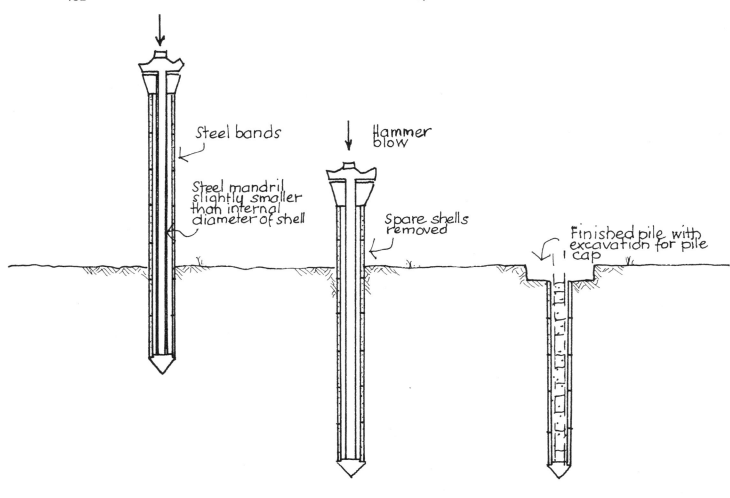

Steel bands

Steel mandril slightly smaller than internal diameter of shell

Hammer blow

Spare shells removed

Finished pile with excavation for pile cap

Fig 4.14(b)   *Driven cast-in-place pile (permanent casing)*

Fig 4.14(c)   *Driving equipment for West shell piles*   (West's Piling and Construction Limited)

Jetting of pre-formed piles: jetting may be employed in the placing of pre-formed piles when the frictional resistance at the sides of the pile or at the toe creates very hard driving conditions. Such conditions can be overcome by increasing the weight of the hammer, but this will result in increased vibration which may be very undesirable. Jetting is achieved through single or twin tubes which may be fixed on the sides of the pile or cast into the lower part of the pile (Fig 4.15). Central jet pipes have proved to be more efficient than the exterior fixed pipes. The quantity of water required for effective jetting is directly related to the cross-sectional area of the pile (including pipes and fittings), and the type of soil. For dense fine sands up to 2 litres per cm^2 of pile section will be required, ranging up to 5 litres per cm^2 for sandy gravels. The pressure should be from 0.5 N/mm^2 to 1.00 N/mm^2, though pressures may exceed 1.00 N/mm^2 in some cases. Jetting however is effective only in non-cohesive soils, where the water can readily displace the material and dissipate without creating problems to adjacent structures or piling plant; provision for leading away any water that rises to the surface may be necessary.

The pile is suspended from the pile leaders and lowered gently into the ground by means of the pile winch, the pipe leaders controlling its vertical accuracy. Jetting should be stopped when the pile toe is within 1 metre of the estimated final position and it is then driven to the required depth or set. Jetting may also be used to aid penetration of occasional piles which refuse to be driven: in these cases an independent jet pipe is used. All pre-formed piles should be driven to an accuracy of not more than 1 in 75 when vertical, or 1.25 in the case of a specified batter. Where this is not achieved the pile cap may have to be redesigned to cope with the eccentricity: at the discretion of the engineer some piles may have to be replaced or supplemented by additional piles.

Stripping and lengthening pre-formed concrete piles: when pre-formed piles have been driven to the required depth, the concrete at the head of the piles is stripped to a level that allows a 50 mm to 75 mm projection into the pile cap. The reinforcement is bent down into position within the pile cap and bonded with the cap reinforcement. Before stripping commences a check should be made on the level of the pile to ensure that it has not risen; piles are subject to rising as a result of ground heave or the driving of adjacent piles. Risen piles must be re-driven to the original depth or resistance. Piles may be lengthened by welding extra reinforcing bars on to the newly stripped reinforcement; the pile head should be stripped to expose the original reinforcement for a length of 200 mm to prevent spalling of the concrete during welding operations. If the extension of the reinforcement cannot be achieved by butt welding because of site conditions, it may be extended by overlapping the steel; for this the reinforcement at the head of the pile should be exposed and lapped for a distance of at least 40 times the bar diameter to make a satisfactory joint.

Lengthening of pre-stressed piles may be achieved by one of the following methods:

Incorporating mild steel bars in the head of the pile to allow normal stripping and welding

Using a mild steel splicing sleeve which fits over the pile and receives another precast pile for extension; the sleeve should be of a length equal to four times the pile width, with a central diaphragm

Drilling the head of the pile and connecting the extension pile by means of dowels and epoxy resin.

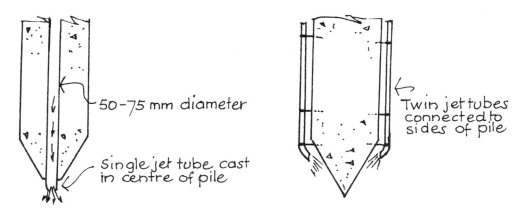

Fig 4.15 *Jetting tubes*

Modular concrete piles: the problem of lengthening pre-formed concrete piles has led to the development of precast modular piling. This system of piling consists of standard interchangeable precast piles which have a unique jointing system. The piles, which vary in length from 2.5 m to 10 m, incorporate steel connections at each end of the pile for simple assembly. One such system is the West's Hardrive precast modular pile (Fig 4.16), which employs a central aligning sleeve and four locking pins providing a flexural strength equal to that of the pile (Fig 4.17). Any two sections can be quickly locked together to allow driving to continue with a minimum of delay (Fig 4.18). This particular pile is capable of supporting loads up to 800 kN but it can also be supplied with a central longitudinal hole through which wires can be passed for post-tensioning.

Another system in this category is the Herkules pile, which originated in Scandanavia in the 1950s and is now produced in Scotland by A. Johnson Construction Company Limited. The piles, which are available in standard lengths of 6, 9 and 12 metres, are connected together with a bayonet-type joint (Fig 4.19) capable of resisting the same compression, tension and bending stresses as the body of the pile. The joint comprises male and female steel fittings machined to give a close fit when coupled together. Steel reinforcement bars, identical to those in the main body of the pile, are screwed into the structural end plates to ensure continuity of pile strength through the joint when coupled together. The joint assembly is cast integrally with and at each end of the pile unit (Fig 4.20). Piles have been successfully driven 100 metres in length, using this particular mode of connection.

Fig 4.16   *West's 'Hardrive' pile being driven*

Fig 4.17   *The Hardrive standard steel joint. Four H-section pins are used in the West's Swea joint to lock the pile sections together*   (West's Piling and Construction Limited)

Fig 4.19   *Bayonet connection for Herkules modular piles*   (A. Johnson Construction Company Limited)

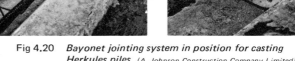

g 4.1.8   *Two sections of West's 'Hardrive' being locked together*   (West's Piling and Construction Limited)

Fig 4.20   *Bayonet jointing system in position for casting Herkules piles*   (A. Johnson Construction Company Limited)

Timber pre-formed piles

Timber piles are not often used for permanent structural support in the UK but they are frequently used for supported temporary platforms, such as gantries for river and maritime works, and for the support of falsework for in-situ bridges over rivers. The most common timber used is Douglas Fir, which is available in sections up to 400 mm square and 15 metres long. Pitch pine is also used; this is available in sections up to 500 mm square and also 15 metres long. Where timber piles are required for permanent works, the timber must be highly resistant to rot, and in the case of marine works, resistant to marine borers. The most suitable timber is greenheart, a hardwood from Central Africa, which can be obtained in sections of up to 475 mm square and up to 18 metres long: lengths of up to 24 metres can be obtained by special order.

All softwood used for permanent works should be treated in accordance with BS 913 or BS 4072; hardwoods such as Greenheart, Jarrah and Opepe may not require treatment, but where sapwood is present it may be advisable to apply standard treatment.

Before driving, a timber pile should be fitted with a steel or iron ring at the head (Fig 4.21(a)) to prevent 'brooming' (i.e. crushing and spreading of the timber) and splitting. The toe of the pile should also be protected by an iron shoe (Fig 4.21(b)) unless the driving is wholly in soft ground. The pile is guided by a pile frame and driven by standard equipment such as a drop hammer, which should be equal in weight to the pile being driven, for hard conditions, or half the pile weight in soft conditions. Permanent piles should be cut off at or below the lowest anticipated ground water level and capped with a reinforced concrete pile cap. The splicing of timber piles can be achieved by using steel channels, plates or purpose-made box sleeve sections, the butt ends of the piles being accurately squared off.

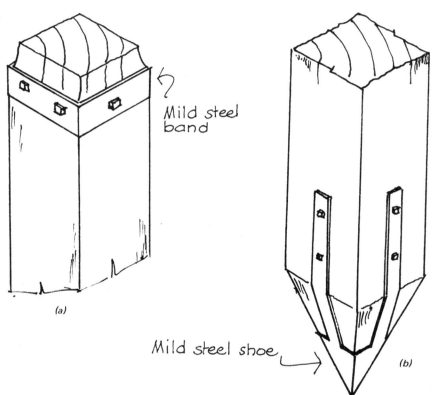

Fig 4.21   *Treatment at the head and toe of timber piles*

Steel pre-formed piles

Steel pre-formed piles can be formed in a wide variety of sections and can be adapted to suit almost any ground condition. The most common types of steel pile are:

Box piles

Tube piles

H-section piles

Screw piles.

Box piles can be formed by welding or riveting sheet piles together or by producing purpose-made sections. Three basic types are available in the UK, namely:

Larssen box piles

Frodingham box piles

Rendhex box piles.

Larssen box piles are formed by welding together two sheet pile sections (Fig 4.22(a)) with either continuous or intermittent welds. The sections used are normally those from No 2 upwards (see Table 4.3); increased web thickness is available in sections 4/20; 5 and 6 to accommodate greater stresses (Table 4.2).

Frodingham box piles are available in three different sections; standard box piles, plated box piles and double box piles. The standard box piles (Fig 4.22(b)) are symmetrical in section and of constant wall thickness. They are formed by welding together semi-octagonal units, two, three or four units to form box pile sections Nos 4, 6 and 8 respectively. Frodingham plated box piles (Fig 4.22(c)) are formed by continuously welding a plate to a pair of interlocked and intermittently welded sheet piles. The plate may vary in thickness to suit any particular application. Double box piles (Fig 4.22(d)) are formed by riveting together two pairs of interlocked sheet piles. They are also welded together at the head and toe to prevent movement during handling and driving. If double box piles are used as individual units they should be intermittently welded over their length, as well as being riveted.

Rendhex box piles (Fig 4.22(e)) consist of two semi-hexagonal rolled steel sections continously welded together along a specially prepared joint to form the complete hexagonal unit. They can be supplied in lengths up to 33 metres in various grades of steel with or without a copper content.

Box piles in general are driven open-ended. Soil displacement is small in the upper strata but the open end usually gets plugged with soil, resulting in high displacement. Shoes or plates can be provided for all box piles; and may be used to advantage when maximum resistance from a soft stratum is required or where ground heave is acceptable. The head of the pile is protected by a helmet, without a cushion packing between pile and helmet but including a dolly or packing between helmet and hammer. Any type of hammer may be used for driving.

Steel tube piles are very similar to box piles in principle but are formed by the Driam process. This process consists of welding a plate which has been formed into a continuous helix. Automatic welding is used with two passes, one inside the tube, the other outside, which ensures full penetration of the weld through the thickness of the plate. Since the process is continuous the length of the tube is limited only by transportation. Diameters vary from 250 mm to 600 mm and require driving equipment of appropriate diameters and weights. Tubes also vary from box piles in that they are normally base-driven; top driving is unlikely to be employed except in exceptional circumstances. Some forms of tubular pile are fitted with a welded flat plate shoe and are driven by means of a drop hammer striking on a plug of earth dry concrete: the concrete plug should have a compacted height of 2½ times the diameter of pile. Others are driven by the same method but without the flat base plate. In the latter method the concrete plug, expanded by the drop hammer, grips the sides of the tube, taking the pile into the ground. When the desired depth has been reached the tube is restrained at the top by cables and the plug of concrete is driven out to form a bulb at the end of the pile. Alternatively tube piles and steel casings may be vibrated into the ground (Fig 4.23). Reinforcement is not normally required for this type of piling, since the tube remains in the ground as a permanent casing. Protection and temporary driving guides to box piles are the same in principle as those shown in section 4.1 on sheet piling (Fig 4.24).

H-piles or universal steel beams are being increasingly used as bearing piles. They offer several important advantages such as:

Guaranteed integrity of the pile after driving

Ease of stacking and handling on site

Ideally suited to the support of heavy axial loads and bending moments

Suitable for very hard driving, and have small displacement.

The universal section used has approximately equal depth and width in addition to having flanges and web of equal thicknesses; it can be delivered to site in lengths of up to 26 metres (Fig 4.25).

These piles derive their support mainly from end-bearing conditions and should be spaced to suit bearing resistance. The recommended minimum spacing for piles driven in groups is 1070 mm or three times the diagonal measurement of the pile, whichever is the greater. The piles may be driven by any type of hammer or vibrator, the only limitation being that the type of hammer must suit the angle of driving when driven on the rake.

Piles may be supplied coated with various forms of protective paint.

Fig 4.22   *Types of box piles*

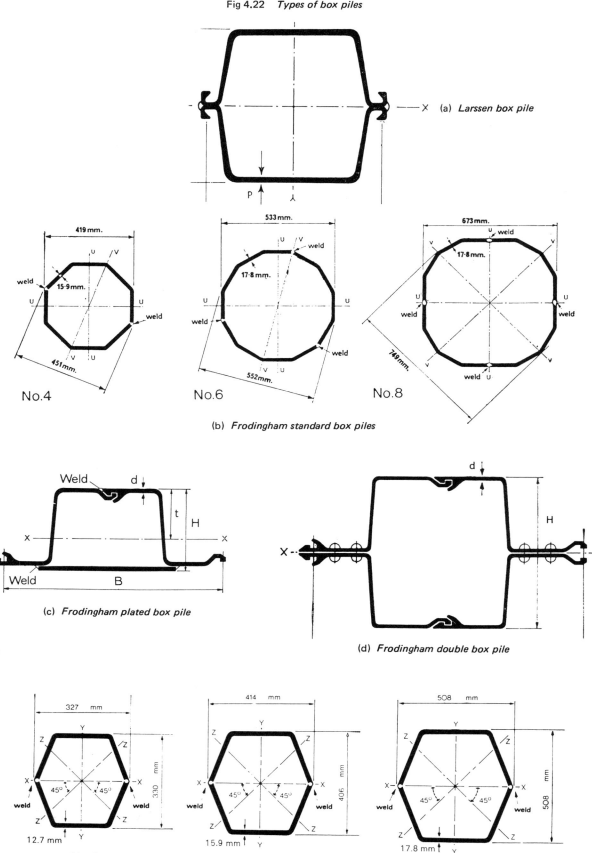

(a) *Larssen box pile*

No.4   No.6   No.8

(b) *Frodingham standard box piles*

(c) *Frodingham plated box pile*

(d) *Frodingham double box pile*

No.3   No.4   No.6

(e) *Rendhex box piles*

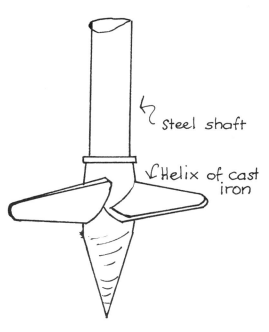

Fig 4.26   *Screw pile*

.23   *Cementation vibrosinker vibrating casing through unstable ground*
(Cementation Piling and Foundations Limited)

Fig 4.24   *Support for steel tube pile*
(BSP International Foundations Limited)

Fig 4.25   *H-section piles being pitched and driven for the Hamilton Yard Development Lower Clyde*
(Edmund Nuttall Limited — Consulting Engineer: Crouch & Hogg, Glasgow)

Screw piles are a form of displacement pile in which the shaft or cylinder is fitted at its lower end with a large diameter helical blade (Fig 4.26). The piles are screwed into the ground by applying torque at the upper end of the pile shaft, which may be hollow or solid: hollow shaft piles are fitted with a square section head. Torque is applied to the pile head or mandrel by means of a cable and a powerful winch; alternatively, electric screwing capstans, which operate in pairs within a specially designed head frame, may be employed.

Screw piles have the advantage over other piles in their uplift resistance in very soft ground and they also provide good resistance to lateral forces. This type of pile is suitable for marine work and for other forms of construction where the sub-strata are very soft. Difficulty in sinking is likely to be encountered if they are used in dense sands, owing to the resistance of the blades, which vary in diameter from 600 mm to 3 metres to suit the bearing capacity required. Jetting may be used to assist penetration of dense sand layers and screwing can be stopped when the pile reaches a suitably dense stratum. Screw piles with wide diameter blades are suitable for foundations on very soft clays and silts. The blades or helices may be cast iron, welded mild steel or cast steel; alternatively, screw piles may be constructed entirely of reinforced concrete.

Replacement piles

These are particularly valuable on sites where vibrators and ground heave may be a nuisance or cause damage to surrounding structures or services. The ground is drilled or bored by one of several methods, and the hole, after reinforcement has been inserted, is filled with concrete. The method of drilling or boring the hole has in the past given rise to an inaccurate classification of replacement piles. They are often referred to as 'percussion bored piles' or 'rotary bored piles', where in fact the percussion and rotary element of the title refers only to the formation of the hole and not to the type of pile. A more recent and perhaps better description would be 'supported and unsupported' piles (Fig 4.13), since the form of support to the pile or borehole affects the formation of the pile. Variations on the formation of the pile toe, such as bulbing and under-reaming, can be carried out on both types of pile.

Unsupported piles

In soils which are stable it will often be possible to bore an unlined hole with a mechanical auger or percussion tool and to place the concrete without lining the hole. The only precaution to be taken is to line the first metre of the hole to prevent surface spoil falling into the hole. Alternatively, a special hopper with lead-in tube may be used (Fig 4.27).

Supported piles

These can be divided into two categories:

Those having a permanent casing or lining

Those having a temporary lining or some other form of temporary support, such as drilling mud

Where a casing is used, the hole is formed by means of percussion or rotary drilling (Fig 4.28), depending on the accessibility and head room.

The first is achieved by mounting a heavy cutting tool on a small tripod and dropping it from its raised position so as to cut out a cylinder of earth. The heavy cutter is raised by a diesel-operated winch and the operation is repeated until the hole has been sunk to the required depth. As the cutting proceeds a thin sectional lining is introduced into the hole to prevent its collapse. The lining is formed with screwed joints to facilitate alignment and to prevent ingress of water.

Permanent linings may be welded together in long lengths and lowered into an overdrilled or temporarily cased hole. The latter technique is used by Franki Piling Company to offset excessive 'downdrag' (downward movement of a pile due to heavy settlement of fill) and to provide constant shaft dimensions in ground strata which are known to have voids (Fig 4.29).

Temporarily supported piles are very popular and offer a wide variety of choice in the finished pile. In many cases, the hole is supported by a screw-jointed steel lining which is retrieved either when the concrete has been placed or during the placing of the concrete: the tube may be winched or jacked out of the ground. The

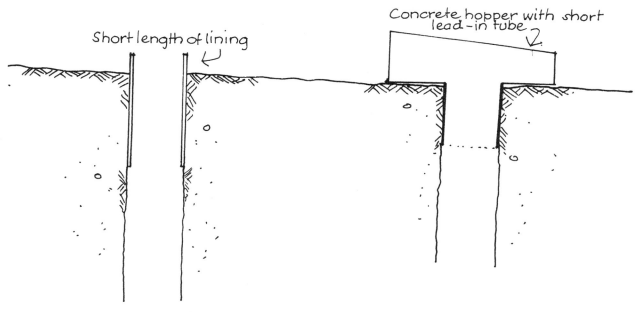

Fig 4.27 *Protection of unlined holes during concreting operations*

Commencement of boring and sinking tube

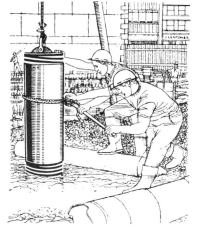

Use of tube lifter for placing or removal of sections of tube

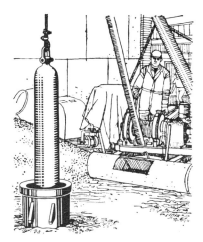

Hammer compacting concrete base

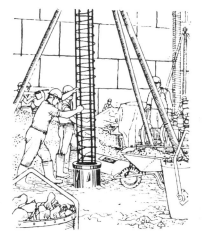

Placing cage of reinforcement after completion of base

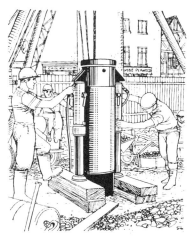

Jacking out tubes whilst concreting pile

Fig 4.28(a) *Percussion drilling*
(Frankipile Limited)

Fig 4.28(b)   *Rotary boring equipment*
(Soil Mechanics Limited)

Fig 4.29   *Permanent lining being lowered into oversize hole*
(Frankipile Limited)

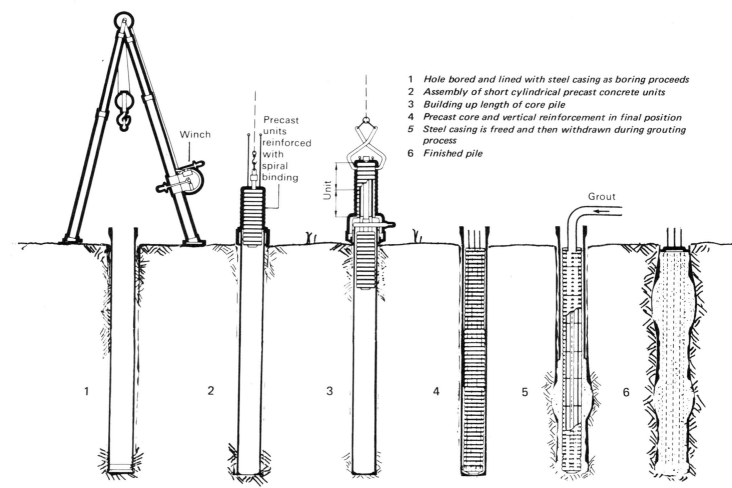

1 *Hole bored and lined with steel casing as boring proceeds*
2 *Assembly of short cylindrical precast concrete units*
3 *Building up length of core pile*
4 *Precast core and vertical reinforcement in final position*
5 *Steel casing is freed and then withdrawn during grouting process*
6 *Finished pile*

Fig 4.30   *Prestcore piling*

inner core of the pile is usually in-situ concrete, but it may consist of precast concrete units which are pressed into the ground as the casing is withdrawn (Fig 4.30). Such units are pressure-grouted on completion. Alternatively, the casing may be vibrated as it is withdrawn, producing a ribbed finish to the pile and giving greater skin friction.

Where large diameter piles are sunk through unstable ground to a suitable bearing stratum the ground may be supported by the use of drilling mud. This mud consists of bentonite suspension with thixotropic properties which restrains the particles of soil and forms a membrane over the sides of the borehole. The membrane is kept in place by the hydrostatic pressure created by filling the hole with the liquid. The first stage of the borehole is bored by mechanical auger Fig 4.28(b)) and lined with a temporary steel casing. This short length of casing prevents the collapse of loose surface soil, the accidental kicking of materials into the hole, and the loss of the drilling mud in made-up ground which may overlay a site. On completion of the first stage boring the hole is filled with bentonite suspension from storage tanks. The boring continues through the bentonite, which is continuously fed into the hole as boring proceeds. On reaching the required depth, reinforcement is lowered through the bentonite suspension and concrete is placed through a tremie tube. The concrete displaces the mud, which is pumped back into the storage vessels as it rises up the borehole; it is then strained to remove soil particles before re-use. The short temporary casing is withdrawn as the concrete reaches the upper level of the hole. The most commonly used cutting tool in this type of work is the open flight auger (Fig 4.28(b)). When the flights are full of spoil the auger is raised above ground and rotated to throw the spoil clear of the hole. Alternatively, a bucket auger may be used: a hollow tube with a bottom sealing slap. The flap contains one or more openings accommodating cutting teeth. As the bucket is rotated, spoil is cut by the teeth and fed up into the bucket. Emptying the bucket is achieved by opening the complete bottom flap. In both cases there is a small loss of drilling mud owing to the thixotropic properties of the fluid, but since the borehole is constantly topped up from storage tanks there is no danger of its collapse. One disadvantage of this technique is the disposal of drilling mud. Local authorities have reservations about allowing the mud to flow into the public sewers, and it has created problems on public tips in wet weather by becoming fluid. Some contractors have dumped the liquid in the sea, thereby achieving a natural breakdown. The alternative solution is to add chemicals to the mud to break down its thixotropic properties and render the slurry suitable for tipping.

Support by water

This method of support is integral with the method of spoil removal. It is sometimes referred to as 'flush boring', because the water constantly flows into the borehole and is sucked out to remove the cuttings of soil. As the hole is bored, water is pumped into it. The water flows through a hole in the cutting tool up through a special hollow kelly (drilling rod), the top of which is connected by a swivel connection to a suction pipe. This technique allows the cutting tool to remain in the borehole while the spoil flows out via the kelly tube into settlement tanks or ditches. The finer particles of spoil are kept in the fluid to act as a sealing material for the sides of the hole. When the required depth has been reached, drilling is stopped, but the water flow is maintained until all spoil cuttings have been removed. Concreting is then carried out by means of a tremie tube, as described above. This technique has been largely superseded by the bentonite suspension method, owing to the problem of providing settlement tanks or ditches near each borehole.

Under-reaming

Replacement piles can if necessary be enlarged at the base to carry an increased load. This method of enlarging the base is known as 'under-reaming' or 'belling' and is achieved by a belling bucket rotated by the drilling rod (Fig 4.31). The bucket can have arms hinged at the top or bottom to allow the sides of the bucket to be jacked out to the desired position. The bucket with top-hinged arms is the most popular tool since it cuts a conical shape which is suitable for maintaining stability in fissured soils. Most buckets can under-ream a base diameter of up to 3.5 metres, but it is possible to obtain buckets which will form a 'bell' of up to 5.4 metres in diameter. Larger bells can be formed by hand, but some form of temporary support would be necessary before hand excavation is commenced. The inspection of larger diameter boreholes and other aspects related to their construction should strictly comply with BS 5573:1978, which covers all safety aspects for this type of work.

4.2.3 Methods of driving

Details of support for piles and pile-driving plant are discussed in Chapter 2, section 4, to which reference should be made. The overall picture of equipment used may be seen in Fig 4.32(a) and (b) in which driving equipment and boring equipment are each shown separately.

Driving hammers

There is an increasing use of diesel hammers because they are completely self-contained and require no ancillary equipment such as boilers or compressors. Single-acting diesel hammers vary in size and weight from 360 kg to 12000 kg; (energy 1085J to 178970J); these hammers have superseded most other types of hammer, with the exception of double-acting hammers which have a higher rate of operation. The hammers can be used in conjunction with piling frames, hanging leaders and short rope-suspended leaders. In the latter case the hammer is suspended from a crane jib on a single rope and a trestle frame is provided for guiding the pile. With hanging leaders, hydraulic rams are sometimes incorporated for control of the slewing and raking angles; this gives a greater control in movement, (Fig 4.33 to 4.35 show diesel drivers in action).

Bored piles

The drilling of bored piles can be divided into two clear categories: rotary and non-rotary drilling. The various methods are shown in the table in Fig 4.32(b). Large diameter piles, better known as caissons, can be sunk by rotary drilling. Modern drilling rigs are capable of sinking shafts up to 60 metres deep by means of telescopic kellies, and diameters of up to 2 metres are common. Depending on the required depth and diameter, this type of drill is either crane-mounted or truck-mounted. Where soil conditions pose problems in drilling, owing, for example, to collapse or water seepage, some form of support must be employed. This could include support from bentonite suspension, water circulation or some form of temporary casing which would require sinking by vibrator. Non-rotary drilling includes the normal tripod-mounted percussion rigs and special grabs which work within a semi-rotary moving casing. The latter method includes the use of either the Beneto machine (France) the Bade machine (West Germany) or the Hochstrasser-Weiss machine (West Germany), to name three well-known grabs. These machines are best suited to soils which are difficult to bore with rotary machines, such as soils containing coarse gravel and cobbles, or boulder clays. The casing is given a continuous semi-rotary motion to keep it sinking as the grab is advanced in depth. Holes up to 1.5 metres in diameter and 30 metres deep can normally be achieved, using this form of plant.

Fig 4.31 *Under-reaming tool* *(Cementation Piling and Foundations Limited)*

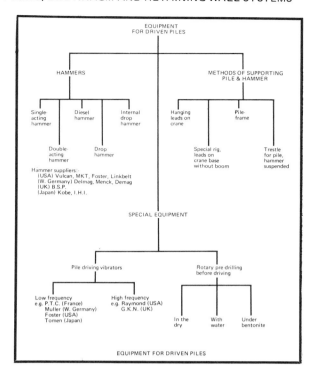

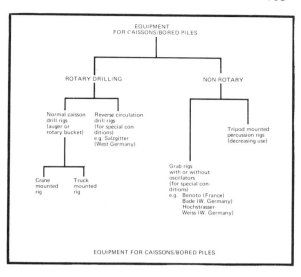

Fig 4.32(a)   *Equipment for driven piles*
(C.E.T. Plant Limited)

Fig 4.32(b)   *Equipment for bored piles*
(C.E.T. Plant Limited)

Fig 4.33   *Delmag D 55 diesel pile driver driving a 3330 mm casing 42 m long* (C.E.T. Plant Limited)

Fig 4.34   *Delmag D12 on turn-table piling frame, fitted with noise-reduction mantle* (C.E.T. Plant Limited)

Fig 4.35   *Delmag D 36 diesel pile driver used for batter piling* (C.E.T. Plant Limited)

4.2.4   Caps and capping beams

Pile caps are usually constructed of concrete to such a depth as will ensure full transfer of load to the piles and, at the same time, resist punching shear. Since it is almost an impossibility to bore or drive piles exactly vertical or to an exact rake, the pile cap should be large enough in plan to accommodate any deviation in the final position of the pile heads. The piles should project into the pile cap and, in the case of concrete piles, have the pile reinforcement bonded to the cap reinforcement. Steel piles may be fitted with cleats to ensure full transmission of load from cap to pile; alternatively, the pile may be bedded deeply in the pile cap. Timber piles should be squared off at the top, suitably treated with preservative, and embedded in the pile cap. Steel box piles and H-section piles may be 'capped off' with steel plates and angle stiffeners or drilled to receive mild steel reinforcing bars (Fig 4.36).

Capping beams should be used to connect a series of caps together, when the number of piles being capped is less than a group of three. Three is the least number that will ensure stability against lateral forces, with the exception that caisson piles provide their own stability and very rarely require even a pile cap. Capping beams are also suitable for distributing the weight of a load-bearing wall, or of close-centred columns to a line of piles. The piles in this case may be staggered (Fig 4.37) to allow for any eccentricities that may occur under loaded conditions. Where eccentricity is likely to be only slight, owing to light loading, the piles can be driven in a line beneath the centre of the capping beam. If the purpose of using piles is to overcome the problem of swelling and shrinkage of the subsoil, the capping beam must be kept clear of the ground. This can be achieved by casting the capping beam on 50 mm of polystyrene or ashes covered with polythene: this will allow an upward movement of the ground without consequent damage being caused to the beam.

The size of the pile cap will be determined by the spacing of the piles which form the pile group; this will depend a great deal upon structural considerations. The general rule for spacing piles in clay is a minimum spacing of three times the diagonal measurement of the pile; in most cases this would not be less than 1 metre centres. The pile cap should overhang the outer piles by a distance of 150 mm. Economies can be achieved in the construction of caps and beams by constructing concrete block walls to the exact sizes of the cap and filling the space with concrete, having first backfilled the wall with soil (Fig 4.38). This method achieves a saving over methods which require formwork and extra dig for positioning the formwork.

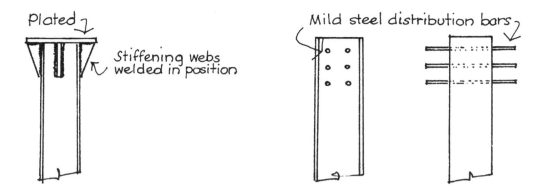

Fig 4.36   *Capping to steel H-piles*

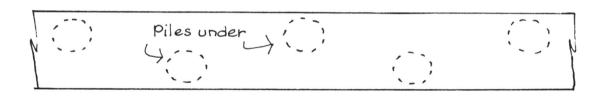

Fig 4.37   *Plan of capping beam showing staggered piles*

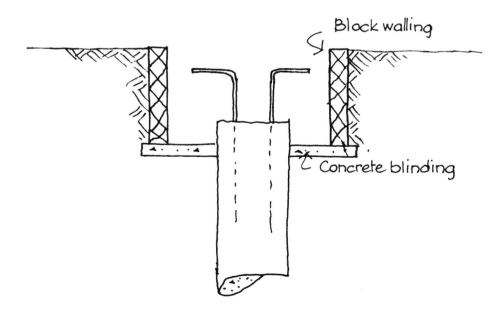

Fig 4.38   *Method of forming pile cap using blockwork as permanent formwork*

4.2.5   Testing for load-bearing capacity

The bearing capacity of a pile will depend upon several factors, such as the size, shape and type of pile, and the particular properties of the soil in which the pile is embedded. The ultimate bearing capacity is that which equals the resistance of the soil; further loading than this will cause the pile to penetrate still further into the ground. The Code of Practice CP 2004 (1972) states: 'For practical purposes, the ultimate bearing capacity may be taken to be that load, applied to the head of the pile, which causes the head of the pile to settle 10% of the pile diameter, unless the value of the ultimate bearing capacity is otherwise defined by some clearly recognisable feature of the load/settlement curve.' This statement has been qualified by experts as being a settlement of 10% of the diameter for end bearing piles in clay but as little as 1% of the pile diameter for a friction pile.

The method of calculating ultimate bearing capacity of a pile will depend upon the magnitude of the work involved, the type of soil and the specification laid down by the client. The following alternative methods of calculation may be used:

Dynamic pile formulae

Static formula

Test loading.

Dynamic formulae are used for calculating the bearing capacity of piles in non-cohesive soils and are based on certain assumptions, namely that the resistance to driving is determined from the energy delivered by the driving hammer together with the movement of the pile under a blow; and that the resistance to driving is equal to the ultimate bearing capacity for static loads.

There are several ways in which these formulae can be derived, but the basis of each is the same, namely, that the energy delivered by the hammer on impact is equated with the work done in overcoming the resistance of the ground to penetration. The most popular formula for driven piles is the Hiley formula, which can be found in most comprehensive text books on piling. This formula is intended only for the calculation of the bearing capacity in non-cohesive soils, and though it may be used in hard clay it must not be used for calculations in other cohesive soils. On achieving the ultimate bearing capacity a factor of safety must be applied before calculating the safe working load. The safety factor can vary according to rate of settlement of the pile permitted at working load, this being subject to variation according to the size of pile and the compressibility of the soil. It has been suggested by some engineers that a factor of 2 will be adequate for most circumstances. Since dynamic formulae are based on the mechanics of a falling weight, it is unsuitable for certain other types of driving equipment such as vibrators and diesel hammers.

The static formula or soil-mechanics method of calculating the ultimate bearing capacity of a pile has been criticised by many engineers as being too approximate compared with test loading and dynamic formulae. Since such an outcome is to be expected when comparing theoretical and practical results, allowances can be made for this in design. The advantage of the soil mechanics method of calculation is that allowable loads can be assessed from the properties of the soil before piling work commences. The normal tests for non-cohesive soil include the standard penetration test and the Dutch or cone penetration test. In the latter test a cone 36 mm in diameter is fixed on the end of a rod enclosed in a tube having the same diameter as the base of the cone; the assembly is pushed into the soil and the forces required to advance the cone and the tube independently are measured. The ultimate bearing capacity is taken as being equal to the resistance of the cone. If the soil is cohesive, laboratory tests are more applicable, and such additional factors as frictional resistance and pore pressure must be calculated. With soft clays and silts the friction or adhesion to the pile may increase over a period of time, but the amount of increase will vary with the type of soil and pile material (eg concrete, timber or steel); a loading test should be applied to verify the specified working load.

Test loading of piles serves a two-fold function: firstly to check the ultimate bearing capacity of the pile, and second to check the workmanship involved in forming the pile. The test is carried out on a trial pile in close proximity to the borehole used for the other tests, so as to obtain an accurate correlation of the various tests. The pile head should be cut off or built up to the necessary elevation and suitably capped to produce a horizontal bearing surface. The pile is then tested by one of two tests:

The maintained load test, or

The constant rate of penetration (CRP) test.

In the maintained load test the load may be applied either by means of a jack, which obtains its reaction from kentledge heavier than the test load (Fig 4.39), or by means of a jack which obtains its reaction from a suitable anchor. When using the anchor method, the anchor pile should be at least 3 test-pile diameters away from the test pile (centre to centre). The load is applied in increments of about 25% of the working load, up to the full normal working load. Smaller increments are then added until the specified limit has been reached. Settlement is measured until it has ceased, or is as little as 0.1 mm in 20 minutes. When this state has been reached a further increment should be applied and the final settlement noted. At each stage of loading the settlement and time scale is plotted. Loading may be stopped at working load, at one-and-a half times working load, or at ultimate bearing capacity.

Fig 4.39(a)   *Test loading using kentledge*
(BSP International Foundations Limited)

In the constant rate of penetration test the pile is made to penetrate the soil at a constant speed by continually increasing the load. The pile movement creates stresses in the soil until it fails in shear, thus having reached the ultimate bearing capacity of the pile. Since the purpose of this test is the determination of the ultimate bearing capacity, it is difficult to establish the exact settlement under any given load. The equipment used in this test can be the same as that used in the maintained load test. The reaction achieved by kentledge or anchor method should be greater than the estimated ultimate bearing capacity of the pile. The force from zero to ultimate bearing capacity is applied through a hydraulic jack which has sufficient travel to accommodate the total movement of the pile. The jack is operated to give a uniform rate of penetration, ranging from 0.75 mm/min. in clay to 1.5 mm/min. in sand or gravel. By plotting load against penetration the ultimate bearing value can be established.

4.2.6 Economics and selection

The economic selection of any particular piling system is not based solely on the cost per unit length of pile. Other factors which have to be considered are:

The possibility of having to sink one or more piles to a greater depth than is anticipated

The contractor's experience of very difficult sites

The contractor's ability to complete the piling work within a phased construction programme

The cost of extensive test loading if required

The cost of maintaining the contractor's site organisation and overheads, whilst waiting for the piling work to be completed.

Fig 4.39(b)   *Test loading using anchorage piles* (Frankipile Limited)

These and other factors, which may vary from site to site, will influence the final economic choice of the piling system. However, in addition to the economic factors, there are certain physical aspects that affect the choice of the piling system:

The type of soil

The surface gradients — water-bearing ground, obstructions, adjacent structures

The type of superstructure

The location of site.

The soil type will have some influence on the choice of pile; rock sub-strata may, if sloping, require a pile that can be bored or driven into the upper layer to anchor the pile toe. Soft rocks can easily be bored for replacement piles. Cohesive soils are suitable for all forms of displacement pile, but where boulder clays and clays with shale occur it may be necessary to use replacement piles, in some cases using the grab method of excavation. For very soft clays the screw pile may be used. Non-cohesive soils, such as sand and gravel, are suitable for displacement piles since the displacement of soil will be negligible in most cases. Some care will be necessary when driving in very dense sands if in close proximity to other structures.

The surface gradient of the site to be piled may have a great influence on the selection of system. Unless the site is at a gradient less than 1 in 20, it may have to be levelled before piling work·can commence. The exception to this is the use of small diameter percussion piles which can be installed on gradients up to 1 in 5 without difficulty. Rotary bored piles can also be installed on gently sloping sites without too much difficulty in setting up the plant.

Water-bearing ground does not affect the progress of piling, but it does affect the cost. Where bored piles are used, the borehole must be lined as the work proceeds, increasing in cost with the depth of the bore. In some cases the lining will need to be of a permanent nature to prevent damage by water flow to the newly-formed pile.

In such cases displacement or partially pre-formed piles should be used. If the casing is removed, compressed air methods may have to be used in placing concrete.

Obstructions create the biggest problem in piling work. In some cases the obstruction will be reduced headroom, which may require a system such as small-diameter percussion boring to be used. Where the headroom extends to 10 metres it will be possible to employ rotary boring equipment, providing that the diameter is not too large. An alternative method is to jack the piles into the ground (see section 5.2). Underground services and existing foundations are the main forms of obstruction and accurate location is necessary before piling commences. Where the service or structure is subject to damage through vibration or ground heave, it will be necessary to use some form of bored pile. If the soil is waterlogged silt or sand, its shear strength may be greatly reduced by vibration, inducing failure of existing services. Piling should be kept clear of existing foundations, but since most plant is limited if used within 2 metres of a structure, any boring nearer than that would have to be carried out by percussion rig.

Adjacent structures can be seriously affected by the vibration and ground heave caused by piling operations. The amount of damage however will depend on the type of construction and the state of repair of the building in question. If the structure or contents are highly susceptible to vibration, then displacement piles, using a high frequency vibrator, may be used. Alternatively, some form of replacement pile may be used. Where the existing structure is founded on displacement piles, care must be taken not to bore in the proximity of those piles, since boring may release ground stresses, thus reducing the bearing capacity of the existing pile foundation.

The type of superstructure has less influence on the type of piling system than might be imagined. This is because larger diameter piles can be used, either singly or linked together by caps or beams, to carry any form of structure and load involved. Light structures can be founded on short-bored piles, whilst heavy high-rise structures may require large-diameter piles or groups. Where loads are high and adequate bearing capacity can be found only at great depth, it may be most economical to form piles by boring or by driving sectional piles; this will overcome the problem of transport and handling of very long precast piles. If the number of piles required on a site is less than fifty, some form of mobile boring rig or percussion boring method may be more economical than other proprietary methods of piling which require heavy plant and result in correspondingly higher transport costs.

The location of the site may influence the choice of method of piling. For example noise and vibration can cause nuisance, particularly in urban areas, and thus give rise to claims and complaints. The inaccessibility of the site may inhibit the use of large driving rigs, even though displacement piles may be otherwise best suited. Remote sites may also preclude the use of heavy driving plant, owing to the cost of transporting the equipment to and from the site.

Timber piles are suitable for temporary works or light loads, but they are not suitable for marine works where water fluctuations may cause decay or marine borers cause collapse.

Concrete piles are suitable for all types of soil and loading conditions, but if precast they require additional reinforcement against the handling and driving stresses. Their greatest disadvantage is that they are difficult to extend or cut down. Steel piles are suitable for all types of work and can be extended and cut back easily. They are, however, subject to corrosion and therefore require expensive treatment when used in marine conditions.

For final selection consider Tables 4.4 to 4.8.

Specification of piling

A specification for cast-in-place piling, together with notes for guidance, has been published by the Federation of Piling Specialists and is reprinted here by their kind permission (see page 175).

TABLE 4.4

Displacement Piles

Pile type			Ref. No	Normal range of size available		Normal load range
				Cross-section	Length	
Preformed	Timber		1	Up to 400 mm x 400 mm	Up to 20 m	Up to 600 Kn
	Concrete	Normal RC	2	Up to 450 mm x 400 mm	Up to 27 m	Up to 1000 Kn
		Prestressed	3	Up to 400 mm square Up to 750 mm dia. hollow	Up to 27 m	Up to 1000 Kn
	Steel	Box	4	Rendhex standard Frodingham octagonal Sheet pile fabrication	Up to 36 m	Up to 1500 Kn
		Tube	5	Heavy gauge up to 900 mm dia.	Up to 36 m	Up to 1500 Kn
		'H' beam	6	200 mm x 200 mm to 300 mm x 300 mm	Up to 36 m	Up to 1700 Kn
		Screw	7	600 mm to 2400 mm Dia. helices	Up to 24 m	Up to 2500 Kn
Driven cast insitu	Precast & in situ concrete		8	450 mm to 600 mm dia.	Up to 50 m	Up to 2000 Kn
Permanent casing	Steel & in situ concrete		9	250 mm to 500 mm dia.	Up to 18 m	Up to 800 Kn
Temporary casing	Concrete		10	250 mm to 600 mm dia.	Up to 24 m	Up to 1500 Kn

(Ground Engineering)

TABLE 4.5

Replacement Piles

Pile type (NB. Classification by method of boring			Ref. No	Normal range of size available		Normal load range
				Cross-section	Length	
Percussion bored	Small diameter		11	450 mm to 600 mm dia.	Up to 24 m	Up to 1200 Kn
Flush bored	Large diameter		12	600 mm dia. and over	Up to 45 m	Up to 10000 Kn
Rotary bored	Large diameter	Straight shaft	13	600 mm to 1 800 mm dia.	Up to 45 m	Up to 10000 Kn
		Under reamed	14	As above with bell up to 3 times shaft diameter	Up to 45 m	Very high loads possible
	Small diameter		15	225 mm to 550 mm dia.	Up to 36 m	Up to 1000 Kn

(Ground Engineering)

TABLE 4.6

Types of subsoil in which pile is to be founded	Suitable pile types	Notes
I ROCK Hard (Granite (Limestones (Marbles (Slate	1,2,3,4,5,6,8 9,13,14	Consider implications of bedding planes Caverns Fault movements Dip of strata Pile selection may depend upon overburden
Soft (Chalk (Shales (Soft sandstone	4,5,6,10,11 13,15	Continuous core sampling important. Test piling essential.
II NON-COHESIVE SOILS Compact well graded sands and gravel/sand mixtures	1,2,3,4,5,6, 8,9,10,11,12	Replacement piles may need to be sleeved full length during boring
Loose well graded sands and gravel/sand mixtures	1,2,3,7,8,9, 10	Screw piles most appropriate in off-shore position suitable to use off floating craft
Compact uniform sand	1,2,3,4,5,6,7,8,9,10	
Loose uniform sand	1,2,3,7,8,9,10	Running sands may not permit the use of driven insitu piles.
III COHESIVE SOILS Very stiff boulder clays and hard clays with a shaly structure	2,3,4,5,6,8, 9,11,13,14,15	If large boulders are numerous or large then 11,13,14 may be most appropriate combined with use of hammer grab or chisel
Stiff and firm clays and sandy clays	4,5,6,9,11, 12,13,14,15	In stiff clays large number of driven piles may result in considerable ground heave.
Soft clays and silts	7,10,11,12, 13,14,15	Piles may need sleeving for full length. (If soil very soft it is usually penetrated by displacement preformed piles driven to firmer stratum)
IV COMPOUND SOILS Coal measures (Alternating sandstones, clays soft rocks)	2,3,4,5,6,8, 9,13,14	Detailed borehole information essential to at least 6 m beyond toe of piles. Large diameter rotary bored piles permit inspection of bearing strata.
Made ground		Usually penetrated to sound natural ground. Detailed investigation may indicate conditions similar to natural soils, but boreholes should be at frequent intervals, and beneath all important loading points. Check corrosive nature of fill.

(Ground Engineering)

TABLE 4.7

Feature	Suitable pile types	Notes
I SURFACE CONDITION		
Level (gradient < 1 in 20)	All piles	
Sloping (gradient > 1 in 20)	11,12 (All pile types possible if preliminary earthwork undertaken). 13,14,15 — using track mounted equipment.	Other piles may require ground to be levelled
Multilevel	All piles	Requires benching to be done before piling
II DRAINAGE CONDITIONS		
Waterlogged	11	Movement of heavy equipment may be difficult
High water table (depth < 1.5m)	All piles	Replacement piles may need sleeving
Well drained	All piles	
Horizontal ground water movements	1,2,3,4,5,6,7,8,9	
III OBSTRUCTIONS		
Low headroom (< 6 m)	8,11	
Medium headroom (6 m to 18 m)	8,11,12,15	
Limited side clearance (< 4.5 m to pile centre)	1,2,3,4,5,6, 7,8,9,10,11,12,15	
Existing foundations	4,5,6,9,11,13,14,15	Chiselling in sleeved piles may be necessary
Existing main services	11,12,13,14,15	Replacement piles reduce vibrations
IV ADJACENT STRUCTURES		
Structure sensitive to vibrations	8,12,13,14, 15	'Jacked in' piles may be appropriate (8)
Contents (Equipment) sensitive to vibrations	8,12,13,14,15	
Structure intolerant of settlements	13,14,15	Sleeved to avoid over digging
Shallow foundations	13,14,15	
V MARINE STRUCTURES (Piled through water)		
Off shore (Dolphins, piers, etc)	1,2,3,4,5,6,7,9	
Access possible from shore (jetties, quays, bridge piers)	1,2,3,4,5,6, 7,8,9,11,12,13,14,15	Replacement piles may be bored in cofferdam

(Ground Engineering)

TABLE 4.8

Grading	Examples	Suitable pile types	
I GROSS LOADING INTENSITY			
Light	1 - 2 storey schools and residences	1,8,10,11,12,15	
Medium	Residences to 8 stories, hospitals, offices to 7 stores	All types	
Heavy	High buildings over 8 stories, heavy warehouses, workshops, etc.	2,3,4,5,6, 8,9,10,13,14	
II PROBABLE NUMBER OF LOADING POINTS			
Few $<$ 20	Small buildings, large span sheds	2,3,11,12, 15	Using standard precast piles
Average 20 – 200	Normal schools, hospitals, offices, etc.	All types	
Many $>$ 200	Large developments, factories jetties	All types	
III SENSITIVITY TO SETTLEMENT			
Highly sensitive	Rigid frames, multi-storey buildings, cross wall construction, many partitions	2,3,4,5,6, 8,9,10,11, 13,14,15	
Average buildings	Framed buildings, bridges	All types	
Flexible structures	Light factory and warehouse frames 1 - 2 storey framed structures	All types	

Specification for Cast-in-place Piling
by Courtesy of the Federation of Piling Specialists

Design

1   The general design of piles shall be in accordance with the British Standard Code of Practice for Foundations CP 2004.

2   The average compressive stress in concrete piles under working load shall not exceed 25% of the specified works cube strength at 28 days calculated on the total cross-sectioned area of the pile shaft. Where the casing of the pile is permanent, the allowable compressive stress may be increased.

3   Piles shall normally be designed to carry all compression loads in the concrete on the cross-sectional area of the nominal diameter.

4   In the case of piles required to act in tension or bending, the stresses in the reinforcement shall be in accordance with CP 114 (See also CP 110).

5   The ultimate bearing capacity of a pile shall be taken as defined in CP 2004.

6   The factor of safety shall be taken as defined in CP 2004 as the ratio of the ultimate bearing capacity to the working load. Piles shall be designed to provide a factor of safety of not less than 2 (see notes for guidance).

7   The cover on all reinforcement, where used, including binding wires, shall not be less than 40 mm.

8   The piles shall be designed to carry the working loads shown on the drawings and, in addition, allowance shall be made for stated negative skin friction loads (see notes for guidance).

Materials

9   Cement shall be ordinary or rapid hardening Portland cement complying with BS 12 or sulphate resisting cement complying with BS 4027.

10   Aggregates shall comply with BS 882.

11   Clean water free from acids and other impurities and in accordance with BS 3148 shall be used in the works.

12   All steel shall be in accordance with the appropriate British Standard unless otherwise agreed.

13   The slump of the concrete shall normally be in accordance with the following standards.

Piling mix	Slump Minimum mm	Range mm	Typical conditions of use
A	75	75-125	Poured into water-free unlined bore. Widely spaced reinforcement leaving ample room for free movement between bars.
B	100	100-175	Where reinforcement is not spaced widely enough to give free movement between bars. Where cut-off level of concrete is within casing. Where pile diameter is less than 600 mm.
C	150	150 or greater	Where concrete is to be placed by tremie under water or drilling mud.

14   Any additive used in the concrete must be stated.

15   Ready-mixed concrete may be used and shall comply with BS 1926.

16   Test cubes shall be prepared and tested in accordance with BS 1881 (see note for guidance).

Driven piles

17   Piles shall be installed in such sequence that their construction does not damage any piles already constructed.

18   Adequate measures shall be taken to overcome any detrimental effect of ground heave on the piles. When required by the Engineer, levels shall be taken to determine the amount of any pile movement resulting from the driving process (see notes for guidance).

19   When a significant change of driving characteristic is noted, a record shall be taken of the driving resistance over the full length of the next adjacent pile (measured as blows per 250 mm penetration).

20   In the case of end bearing piles, the final set of each pile shall be recorded either as the penetration in millimetres per 10 blows or as the number of blows required to produce a penetration of 25 mm.

21   The temporary casing shall be dry after driving and before concreting commences.

22   Where cut-off level is less than 1.5 metres below working level, concrete shall be cast to a minimum of 150 mm above cut-off level with a tolerance from 150 mm to 450 mm above cut-off level. For each additional 0.3 metres below working level of the cut-off level an additional tolerance of 100 mm will be allowed. Cut-off shall be a maximum of 3.00 metres below working level.

          (See also Clause 35 and notes for guidance).

23   A minimum length of 1.0 metres of temporary casing shall be inserted in every borehole unless otherwise agreed.

24   When boring through non-cohesive or very soft cohesive strata liable to collapse, temporary casing or other suitable technique shall be used to stabilise the hole. Temporary casing when used shall extend a sufficient depth below such strata adequately to seal off the unstable materials.

25   In dry non-cohesive strata water may be used to assist the advancement of the boring.

26   When subsoil water which cannot be sealed off is encountered the water in the bore shall be maintained above the standing level of the subsoil water.

27   When it is proposed to use a prepared drilling mud suspension the Engineer must be advised.

28   When under-reaming of the bore is carried out the slope of the under-ream must be a minimum of 55° to the horizontal.

29   When it is not practicable to exclude ground water from the finished bore the concrete shall be placed by tremie tube.

30   Where cut-off level is less than 1.5 metres below working level, concrete shall be cast to a minimum of 150 mm above cut-off level with a tolerance from 150 mm to 450 mm above cut-off level. For each additional 0.3 metres below working level of the cut-off level an additional tolerance of 50 mm will be allowed. (See also Clause 35 and notes for guidance).

31   When concrete is placed by tremie tube the concrete shall be cast to piling platform level or to a minimum of 1.0 metres above cut-off level with a tolerance from 1.0 metres to 2.0 metres.

General

32   Piles shall be constructed within the following normal tolerances.

In plan	75 mm in any direction at piling platform level
Verticality	1 in 75
Raking up to 1:6	1 in 25

33   Each batch of concrete in a pile shall be placed before the previous batch has lost its workability. Removal of temporary casings must be completed before the concrete within the casing loses its workability.

34   In cold weather, ice and show shall be excluded from the material used in the manufacture of concrete for piles.

          Aggregate must not be heated to more than 38°C, and the concrete when placed must have a minimum temperature of 5°C. The tops of the piles must be protected immediately casting is completed.

35   When concreting dry pile holes through water-bearing strata the concrete must always be cast to a minimum of 0.3 metres above the standing level of the subsoil water, unless all water-bearing strata are effectively sealed off by permanent

casing, and this level of 0.3 metres above standing water level shall be regarded as cut-off level for the purpose of calculating tolerances as defined in Clause 30 or Clause 22.

36   Where concrete is not brought to piling platform level the empty pile holes shall be backfilled.

37   Safety procedures during piling operatons shall comply with the recommendations of CP 2011, where applicable.*

38   The following records shall be kept of every pile.

Pile number
Piling platform level related to OD
Nominal shaft/base diameter
Date driven or bored
Date concreted
Depth from piling platform level to toe
Depth from piling platform level to cut-off level
Depth from piling platform level to top of concrete
Final set (for driven piles) weight and drop of hammer
Length of permanent casing
Details of any obstructions encountered and obstruction time.

Notes for guidance

1   Preliminary test piles — Whenever possible a preliminary test pile or test piles should be installed to check the pile design. These should be constructed under the closest supervision in an area where the soil conditions are known and tested to a specified load of not less than twice the working load.

2   Tests on working piles — Working piles for testing are selected at random by the Engineer and should be tested to one and a half times the working load.

3   Factor of safety — pile design should ensure (a) an adequate Factor of Safety is provided against reaching the Ultimate load of the pile or pile group; (b) the required load settlement characteristics are achieved at and near to the design working load.

4   Negative skin friction — The usual method of providing for this is to calculate the working load from the Ultimate Bearing Capacity using the Factor of Safety and then add a nett allowance for negative skin friction.

5   Concrete — Concrete for piles placed in the dry should contain not less than 300 kg/m^3 of cement, and when placed under water by tremie tube a minimum cement content of 400 kg/m^3 should be employed.

6   Concrete test cubes — Opinions vary as to the number of test cubes which should be required on a piling contract, but it is suggested that 4 cubes be taken for every 50 cubic metres of concrete used.

          The anticipated number of test cubes should always be included as a measured item in the Bill of Quantities.

7   Heave — The acceptable amount of heave depends upon whether the piles are designed to carry the majority of their load by shaft friction or by end bearing. Heave has generally a minor effect on a pile which carries its load mainly by shaft friction. In cases where the pile carries the majority of its load in end bearing heave may be reduced by pre-boring or, alternatively, the contractor may elect to re-drive piles where this is a practicable solution. The particular measures required will vary with each site and those adopted should be a matter for discussion and agreement with the piling specialist concerned.

8   Tolerances and cut-offs — When deep cut-offs are involved or long temporary casings have to be used in the construction of piles, it is not possible to estimate the amount of concrete to form the finished level within the normal tolerances. In such cases the tolerance should be a matter for discussion and agreement with the piling specialist concerned.

9   Data sheet — A piling enquiry data sheet should be enclosed with all piling enquiries.

          When piles are designed by the client, the enquiry data sheet will give all details including pile diameters, length or penetrations required, reinforcement and concrete specification.

          When piles are to be designed by the piling specialist or when alternatives are permitted, the enquiry data sheet will state the required Factor of Safety (if different from that given in the Specification), the acceptable settlement of individual piles under test at working load and any other basic requirements which must be fulfilled by alternative pile designs.

          The enquiry data sheet will detail any variations from the standard specification which are required by the client.

Currently being revised.

4.3   VIBRO-FLOTATION AND VIBRO-REPLACEMENT

4.3.1   Introduction

Where structures cannot be safely founded on loose soils or fill material, piling may be considered as a means of transferring the loads to suitable levels. However, piled foundations are not the only means of achieving satisfactory foundations in such situations — the engineer may wish to consider geotechnical processes or vibratory processes. Geotechnical processes are discussed in section 3.3.5 as a means of ground water control, but they can also be used to increase the bearing capacity of the ground. Of the processes discussed, the most economical is likely to be cement injection. However, vibratory processes can be used to consolidate and strengthen ground conditions at a comparatively low cost; this is achieved by stabilising the soil so that greater loads can be carried without risk of settlement. It also allows simple, shallow foundations to be used on otherwise poor sites. Vibratory processes can also be used on recently filled sites which contain brick rubble, soil, concrete or other miscellaneous material. This means that sites which were considered totally unsuitable for construction operations can now be economically considered without pile foundations.

4.3.2   Methods and materials

Two principal methods are employed for the compaction of the ground, namely vibro-flotation and vibro-replacement. In the vibro-flotation method, a heavy vibratory unit is jetted into the soil. The unit consists of eccentric weights driven by an electric motor on a vertical axis, the whole unit being enclosed in a heavy metal tube. The total weight of the unit is of the order of 2 tonnes. The vibratory unit is suspended from a crane over the area for compaction, and it penetrates the ground by means of jetting. The jetting of the vibroflot is achieved by passing water down the main hollow tubes (Fig 4.40) and out through jets at the tip of the vibroflot. By this means the unit can be jetted to a depth of 12 metres in sands and gravels. After reaching the required depth the jetting pressure is reduced and the hole is filled with graded granular backfill. The consolidation of the granular backfill can be achieved by vibration alone or it can be assisted by water through upper jets in the vibroflot (Fig 4.41). The unit is withdrawn in stages of 300 mm until full compaction is achieved; the unit effectively compacts the soil for a radius of 1 metre to 1.5 metres. The radius of compaction will affect the centres at which the unit should be jetted because the process is repeated until the whole area is covered by overlapping cylinders of soil.

The vibro-replacement process uses the same principle, ie a large vibrating tube, but in this process the jetting technique is not employed. The vibrator penetrates the ground under its own weight assisted by vibration. When the vibrator has reached the required depth, which can be up to 12 metres, it is withdrawn to allow backfilling with a small quantity of coarse-graded granular material. The vibrator is then re-introduced to compact the material or to displace the material within the surrounding weak soil. This process is repeated until a column of granular material is built up to ground level. Whilst vibro-replacement consists of forming a pattern of stone columns, it should not be considered that the columns carry the load. The effect of forming the columns is to compact the soil between and around them. If correctly designed they will produce a whole area with fairly uniform consolidation and little chance of differential settlement. The disadvantage of the vibro-replacement technique is the uncertainty of excessive settlement under concentrated load. With this in mind the technique may be best applied to wide foundation areas where some differential settlement is not detrimental to the structure.

4.3.3   Economic considerations

These processes may be an economic alternative to piling and grouting methods used to improve bearing capacity. However, the site must be large enough to justify the use of the special equipment involved in the process. Since the depth compaction using these methods is approximately 12 metres, it can be used satisfactorily only on sites which will provide suitable resistance at these depths. The vibro-flotation method is capable of achieving safe bearing pressures of up to 430 kN/m^2 in natural granular soils and vibro-replacement will give safe bearing pressures of up to 220 kN/m^2. While these pressures are suitable for most spread foundations, they may prove unsuitable for concentrated loads such as those found in framed buildings, and the formation of extensive capping beams may be uneconomic. In both cases large quantities of fill material have to be used. Where stone is used for forming columns in very soft soil, the quantity of material used may produce cost figures which are only marginally cheaper than conventional piles, and the latter will give much higher safe bearing capacities. The vibro-flotation method is particularly valuable for consolidating loose sands prior to the formation of raft foundations and may accordingly be used in conjunction with raft construction more economically than piling. Where, however, these processes are employed, their effectiveness should be calculated by measurement of in-situ density by Dutch cone penetration tests before and after tests with the vibrator.

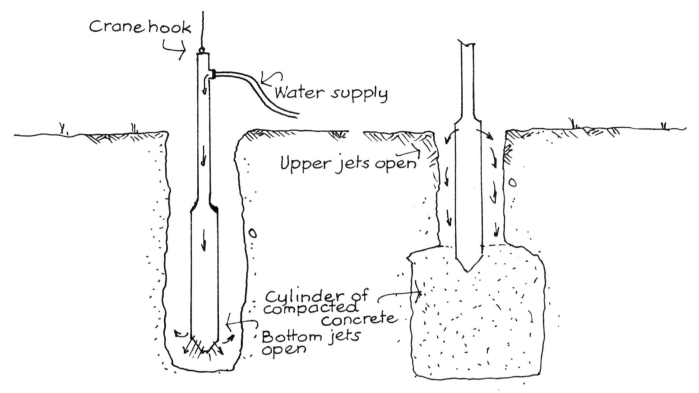

Fig 4.40   *Jetting the vibroflot*

Fig 4.41   *Consolidation of granular backfill*

4.4   DIAPHRAGM WALLING

4.4.1   Introduction

Diaphragm walling is a term that was first used for the construction of continuous in-situ concrete walling. The process, sometimes called the slurry trench method, involves the excavation of a narrow trench to the required depth and filling the trench with reinforced concrete. The most interesting factor is the method of trench support during excavation, which is achieved by means of a thixotropic mud called bentonite. Bentonite, or fullers earth, is composed of the clay mineral montmorillonite and consists principally of silica, alumina and traces of sodium which act as exchangeable cations on the surface of the bentonite. The bentonite powder, trade name 'Fulbent', is mixed with clean water to form a creamy slurry. The slurry has a specific gravity of about 1.2 and is therefore suitable for maintaining a head of pressure which will prevent ingress of water and soil. A shallow perimeter trench provides storage for the slurry while at the same time providing a guide for the grab or drilling equipment to excavate the trench. The trench is excavated in sections and the slurry follows the trenching equipment as it digs, thus supplying a constant head of pressure. The process was originally used for sinking oil wells in desert areas and was first used as a means of wall construction in the UK in 1961. The process is a tremendous advantage in the construction of basement walls in built-up areas, since it can be carried out without first underpinning adjacent property. Walls can be taken out alongside existing buildings and anchored back as the excavation takes place to provide support for existing structures and clear working space for the construction of the new basement. Where this slurry method of support is used, precautions have to be taken against loss of mud which could lead to a collapse of the trench. Such a precaution may include a supply of bentonite, stored in a separate storage tank, mixed with some lightweight material such as polystyrene, which would act as a sealing material. Alternatively, the trench may have to be quickly backfilled.

This form of construction may also be used as retaining and cut-off walls in civil engineering work. Diaphragm walling, as a term, has been developed in recent years to include other forms of construction which perform similar functions to those mentioned. These forms include mix-in-place walls, precast diaphragm and flexible diaphragms.

4.4.2 Methods of construction

Thick cast in-situ diaphragms

The use of bentonite or slurry wall diaphragms is suitable for the formation of deep basement walls or retaining walls where there is water in the soil and heavy loads in the vicinity of the excavation. The first step is to construct a perimeter slurry trench, between 1 metre and 1.5 metres deep, and the width of the proposed wall 450 mm to 1 metre. When the perimeter trench has been excavated formwork is fixed and the trench lined both sides with 150 mm concrete (Fig 4.42). In some cases a concrete apron may be provided (Fig 4.43). The trench is then filled with bentonite slurry from large storage tanks, and excavation is carried out by suitable equipment in predetermined sections. Each section is approximately 5 metres wide and the excavation is taken to the full required depth (Fig 4.44). This may be up to 50 metres deep. As the excavation proceeds the slurry flows from the perimeter trench into the deep section under construction, thus giving the necessary support. Reinforcement, made up into cages on site, is then lowered through the bentonite, spacers on the reinforcement cage ensuring correct positioning to allow the specified cover of concrete. When the reinforcement is in position (Fig 4.44) steel stop-end pipes are positioned at the ends of the panel to act as a shutter; this produces a semi-circular joint between the panels. In some cases the joints may be specified as waterproofed or double keyed; this can be achieved by various systems which involve forming a cavity or a cavity with a water stop (Fig 4.45) and pressure grouting the cavity on completion. The concreting of the trench takes place through tremie pipes (Fig 4.44) which displace the bentonite up into the perimeter trench or storage vessel. Care must be taken to keep the density of the slurry below the density of the concrete so that the slurry will be readily displaced. This process is carried out in alternating sections along the line of the perimeter trench until the wall is complete.

The above method of construction normally uses grab type equipment (see section 4.4.3) to remove the soil, but there is another method of excavating the trenches which removes the excavated soil in the form of cuttings. The process uses the reverse circulation of mud, which is a principle well-known in oil and water well drilling. The excavation is carried out by a rotary or percussion tool which is connected to a mud pipe by means of a hollow drill pipe and flexible connection. The machine moves to and fro at ground level over the length of the panel being constructed (Fig 4.46), while the mud and soil cutting are pumped to the surface. At the surface the slurry is screened to separate the soil and the mud returns to the trench. Such machines are capable of sinking trenches 1.2 metres to 1.5 metres wide up to a depth of 67 metres.

Thin cast in-situ diaphragm (non-structural)

Not all diaphragms need to fulfil a structural role as well as being a screen against water. Where space on a site permits, it is usually more economic to place the screen far enough out from the excavation to allow space for a berm (a horizontal ledge at the top or bottom of an earthbank to ensure stability), and for ground at an appropriate slope to give the necessary structural support to the screen on the inside.

Under these conditions, the diaphragm can be an unreinforced concrete slurry trench, or better still a grouted diaphragm. The latter system is particularly well suited to work in made ground or in very permeable gravel strata where bentonite processes are not satisfactory.

There are several methods of forming a thin slot in the ground and filling it with suitable material to form the diaphragm. The most common method used for forming thin diaphragms employs the use of steel H-beam or box sections. The steel section is driven into the ground to the required depth and the space is cement grouted as the section is withdrawn (Fig 4.47). The grout injection pipe is fixed to the web of the H-section and connected by flexible hose to a grout pump.

Fig 4.42 *Trench lined with concrete and temporarily supported with timber struts*

(Port of Bristol Authority
Contractor: Nuttal-Bachy & Company Limited
Engineer: W.J. Sivewright MA CEng FICE
(Consulting Engineers: Rendel Palmer and Tritton)

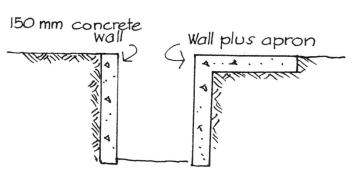

150 mm concrete wall

Wall plus apron

Fig 4.43 *Construction of perimeter trench*

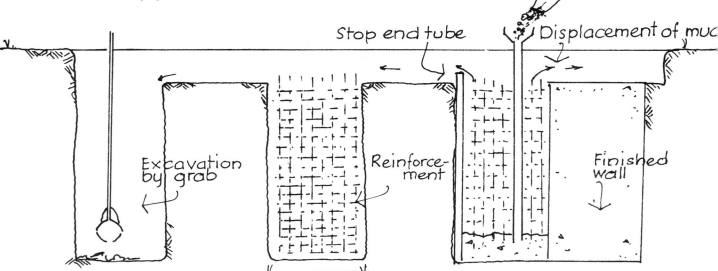

Concreting with tremie pipe

Stop end tube

Displacement of muc

Excavation by grab

Reinforce-ment

Finished wall

5 m

Fig 4.44 *Sequence of operations in constructing diaphragm wall*

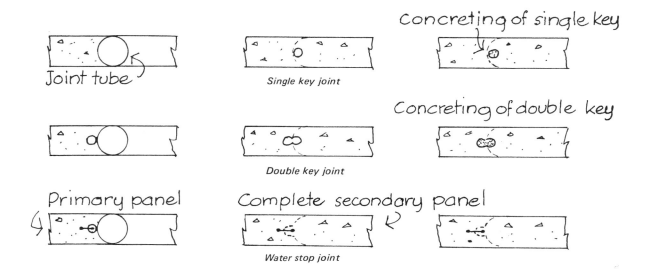

Joint tube

Single key joint

Concreting of single key

Double key joint

Concreting of double key

Primary panel

Complete secondary panel

Water stop joint

Fig 4.45 *Methods of forming joints in diaphragm wall*

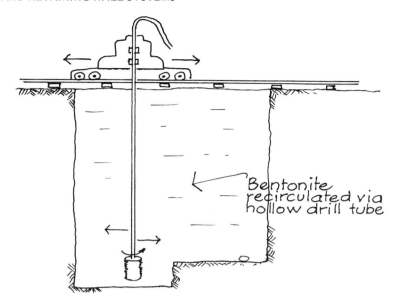

Fig 4.46   *Excavation by rotary drill*

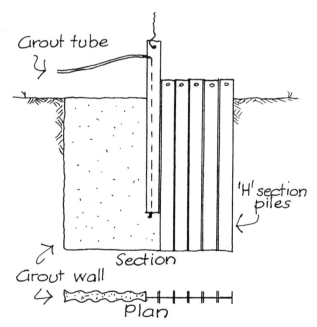

Fig 4.47   *Diaphragm walling by grouting method*

Strip pile diaphragms

These can be used in dry ground to overcome the problem of providing a facing or counterfort support to conventional diaphragm walls. The method consists of sinking strip piles (Fig 4.48) 2 metres to 3 metres in length around the perimeter of the site to the depth required and filling them with reinforced concrete. The main excavation within the perimeter wall is commenced, taking care to remove the soil between the strip piles. The sections between the strip piles are cast as strong reinforced columns which are integral with the beams carrying the basement floor. This eliminates the need for the careful positioning of starter bars for floors, as in normal diaphragms, and gives an appreciable gain in floor area.

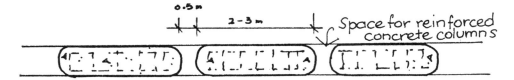

Fig 4.48   *Plan of strip piles*

Diaphragms on legs

Diaphragm walls are often used as part of the permanent structure of a building, as well as forming a permanent water cut-off for excavation purposes. Where the water cut-off can be achieved by a shallow diaphragm, say up to 10 metres deep, the problem left to solve is one of stability or load-bearing capacity. Lateral stability can be achieved by anchors or tie-backs, but this does not necessarily satisfy the load-bearing capacity requirements. Diaphragms on legs may therefore be employed to satisfy all the required conditions of stability. This method involves sinking part of each panel (Fig 4.49) to a depth appropriate to the stability required. Depending on the panel dimensions, one or two such extensions may be required beneath each panel. The reinforcement is continuous with the main diaphragm reinforcement, ensuring transmission of load to lower areas. The method produces a low cost diaphragm for heavily loaded structures.

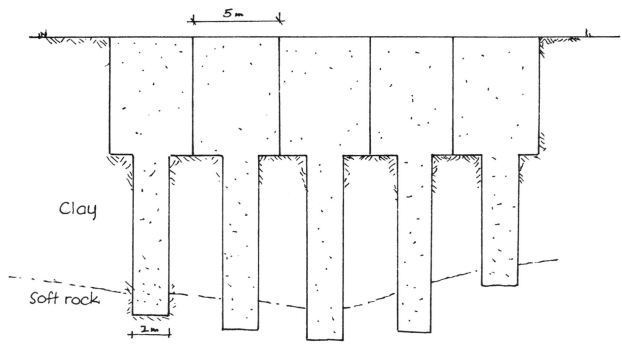

Fig 4.49   *Diaphragm on legs*

Precast diaphragms

The most recent development in diaphragm construction is the precast unit wall. It consists of placing precast units in a grout-filled trench and effectively sealing the joints. The wall units are reinforced concrete units of a plan section which suits the particular perimeter wall. The dimensions of the units or panels are limited only by the site craneage available. For use as retaining walls there are two principal types, namely panel units and beams and slabs. The panel units (Fig 4.50) slot together with tongued and grooved joints, whereas the beam and slab type (Fig 4.51) consists of vertical beams of various sections, which support concrete slabs. In both cases stability is achieved by anchoring the diaphragm back to the soil as the excavation proceeds. Both systems use a conventional slurry-supported trench, which is excavated by methods discussed earlier, but the slurry or grout differs from the ordinary bentonite mud. Experience has shown that it is practically impossible to seal the elements if they are immersed in normal bentonite mud, so a special grout slurry has been developed. The grout used has the properties of retaining fluid during excavation and also for the period of time during which the elements are placed, but it then acquires sufficient strength within a few days to allow excavation to take place close to the installed panel. The grout must not be so strong as to prevent its removal from the face of the panels. A cement and bentonite grout is used, containing retardants to regulate the setting time. After the trench has been excavated, the pre-fabricated elements are placed in position above the trench. They are coated with a special compound on the outer face, to ensure clean removal of the grout at the excavation stage, and are then lowered into the ground (Fig 4.52). Final positioning is achieved by trench guides which hold the units in place until the grout sets.

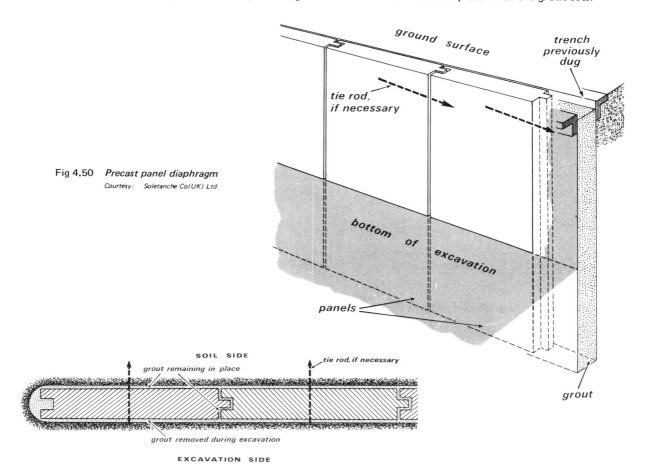

Fig 4.50   *Precast panel diaphragm*
Courtesy: Soletanche Co(UK) Ltd

Other pre-fabricated units (Fig 4.53) are available for use in conjunction with conventional cast in-situ walls or other forms of construction. The method shown in Fig 4.54 consists of precast column units, with continuity steel protruding, being lowered into boreholes supported by cementitious mud. When the mud has hardened the soil between the columns is excavated, along with the main excavation, to a depth of 2 metres, and an in-situ wall is cast between the columns. This is one sure method of obtaining continuity in the horizontal reinforcement. With all types and forms of diaphragms there is an increasing tendency to use anchors for lateral stability. These are discussed in section 4.5.

Contiguous piling

This is an alternative solution to diaphragm walling (section 4.4.1), in which the soil is removed by boring. Care must be taken to ensure that the piles touch for their full length, otherwise grouting will be necessary to make an effective seal between the piles. The thickness of these walls will depend on the resistance they have to provide when they are exposed by excavation; they can vary in thickness from 375 mm to 600 mm. In this method the boreholes may be supported by temporary linings or bentonite until the concrete has been placed. Special cutting tools or a heavy cutting shoe may be used to cut a slot in the newly cast piles to form a key for the intermediate piles. If the pile wall is to be part of the permanent structure, it can be lined with mesh reinforcement and sprayed with concrete to provide a smooth finish. This process is known as the Gunite process (see section 8.1.6). Another method of finishing the pile wall is to cast a concrete facing wall and capping beam on the inside face of the piles (Fig 4.55). In all cases the piles are reinforced.

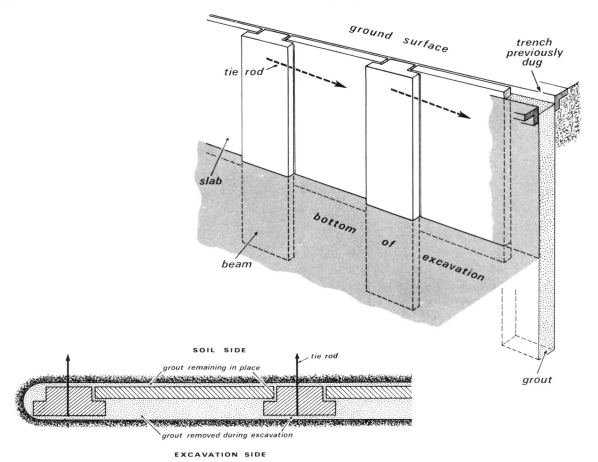

Fig 4.51 (a)   *Beam and slab diaphragm* (Soletanche Co(UK) Ltd)

Fig 4.51 (b)   *Beam being lowered into position* (Soletanche Co(UK) Ltd)

(a) *Plain unit*

(b) *Corner unit*

Fig 4.52   *Precast diaphragms*
(Soletanche Co(UK) Ltd)

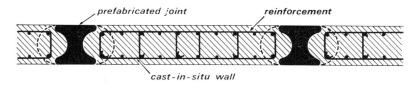

Fig 4.53

Precast units in conjunction with in-situ or precast panels

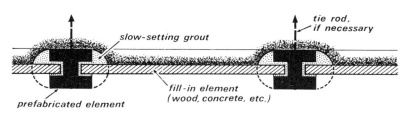

Fig 4.54

Method of construction giving continuity of reinforcement

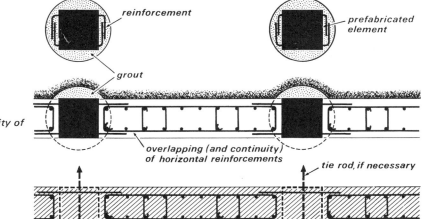

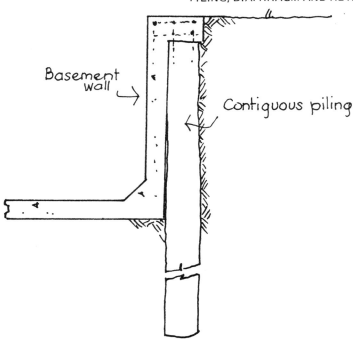

Fig 4.55   *Facing wall and capping beam to contiguous piling*

4.4.3   Plant and equipment

The plant used for excavating the trench is normally of a very special nature, as discussed below, but it is possible to use any of the powerful back-acting machines for trenches up to 10 metres deep. The specialised machines range from grabs to sophisticated drilling equipment, but they fall into three main categories:

Percussion methods

Hydraulic methods

Rotary boring or drilling methods.

The percussion method was one of the first to be used in this form of construction. It consists of a grab, which operates by gravity, suspended and controlled by steel ropes from a special rig (Fig 4.56). If obstructions are met during excavation they are broken up percussively with a heavy chisel and then removed by the grab. A heavier form of grab has been developed by the Nuttall-Bachy company (Fig 4.57). This particular grab was used for excavating deep diaphragms for the Portbury Dock in Bristol. It is suspended and controlled from heavy crawler-mounted cranes (Fig 4.58).

Hydraulic excavators (Fig 4.59) have a very positive digging action and can dig to depths of 36 metres. The specially developed grab is operated from a standard crane by means of a purpose-designed attachment, including a kelly bar and kelly bar guide. The kelly bar ensures correct alignment and verticality of excavation.

Rotary boring or drilling methods are very suitable for excavating hard compact soils. This method of excavation is linked with a bentonite circulation system, called 'reverse circulation system' or 'counter-flow system'. The cutting tool is cylindrical and its diameter is equal to the width of the diaphragm wall. The rig carrying the cutting tool (Fig 4.46) is mounted on rail track to facilitate horizontal movement, which allows elongation of the slot as the excavation progresses. The drill pipe, which is hollow for the circulation of the bentonite, extends horizontally from the centrifugal pump mounted on the chassis and then rises 3 metres to a U-bend and down into the trench. As the excavation proceeds, additional pipes are added with flanged and bolted joints. The lowest length of pipe is jointed to a special pipe incorporating the cutting tool; several types of tools are available to suit the ground conditions. The circulatory system is primed by a small vacuum pump which connects to the crown of the U-bend. This type of plant, which is capable of excavating to depths of 70 metres, requires a substantial 'mud station' for the circulatory system. The mud station consists of a sectional tank (Fig 4.60) which will hold 72 000 litres of slurry and a mixing unit comprising a tank about 4 500 litres capacity with a reciprocating mud pump and feed hopper. The units and tanks are connected by a circulation system. The slurry

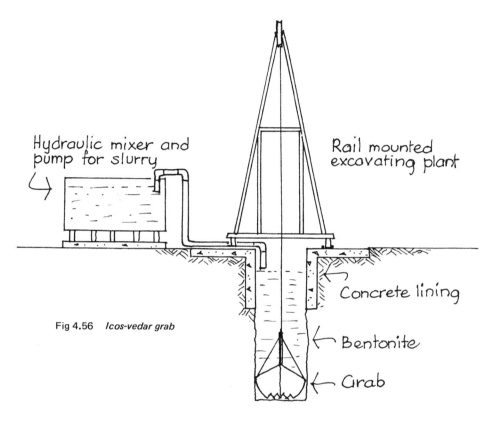

Fig 4.56   *Icos-vedar grab*

leaving the tank passes through a vibrating screen chamber, mounted in an elevated position on the rig, which separates the cuttings into disposal hoppers as the slurry gravitates back to the trench. Silos for bulk storage of bentonite powder, together with small storage tanks, can be seen in Fig 4.61.

The largest rotary drill, developed in Japan, is called the B.W. Longwall Drill (Fig 4.62). The excavator consists of a train of five or seven drill bits operated by two submersible motors, which permit rotary boring while continuously ejecting the slurry produced at the tip of the drill bits. An electrically operated deflection indicator and adjustable guide assembly enable the necessary corrections to be made during operation. The drill employs a combined normal and reverse slurry circulation system. Bentonite is constantly sprayed from the top of the drill bits while the cuttings are ejected by air lift. When the drill reaches the required depth, normal circulation ceases and reverse circulation continues to clear the trench of loose material. This equipment is very suitable for excavation in soft rock.

4.4.4   Economic factors

The economic selection of diaphragm walling methods and equipment will depend on factors such as the function of the diaphragm, whether load bearing or cut-off; the depth of diaphragm required; and the type of soil to be excavated. Some types of equipment are limited in that they have to operate a minimum of 1 metre away from existing buildings, so reducing the maximum plan area of excavation. Contiguous piling and the precast column with in-situ panel are not suitable for waterbearing soils, since grouting would prove expensive and the construction method difficult. Precast units are generally cheaper for shallow to medium depth diaphragms, say 4 metres to 10 metres deep.

Fig 4.57   *Excavation of diaphragm wall with Nuttall-Bachy grab*

Fig 4.59   *Hydraulic trenching plant*
(Cementation Piling and Foundations Limited)

Fig 4. 58   *General view of excavating and concreting of diaphragm walls*   (Port of Bristol Authority
Contractor: Nuttall-Bachy & Company Limited
Engineer: W.J. Sivewright M A CEng FICE
Consulting Engineers: Rendel Palmer and Tritton)

Fig 4.60
Bentonite tanks and pipeline
(Cementation Piling and Foundations Limited)

Fig 4.61
*View showing bentonite storage silos
with a group of 4 powder silos and
a group of 6 slurry silos*

(Port of Bristol Authority
Contractor: Nuttal-Bachy & Company Limited
Engineer: W.J. Sivewright MA CEng FICE
Consulting Engineers: Rendel Palmer and Tritton)

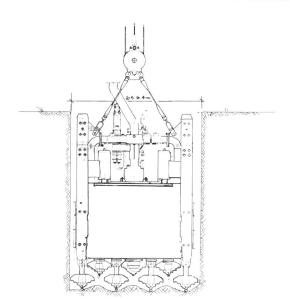

Fig 4.62   *Multi-spindle drill trench excavator*

A specification for cast-in-place concrete diaphragm walling has been produced and is re-printed here by courtesy of the Federation of Piling Specialists.

Specification for Cast in Place Concrete Diaphragm Walling

Design

1. All work shall be carried out in accordance with good engineering practice and related to an adequate site investigation. The recommendations of the codes of practice CECP. No. 2: EARTH RETAINING STRUC-TURES and CP.2004: FOUNDATIONS, shall be followed in so far as they are applicable to the construction of diaphragm walling.

(Note for guidance: The site investigation should be designed to give the information required for the design of diaphragm walling and needs to be fully comprehensive).

(Note for guidance: All references to Codes of Practice and British Standards shall refer to the latest edition in print).

2. The maximum compressive stress in the concrete of a wall shall be that given in CP.114: REINFORCED CONCRETE, for the appropriate conditions of use (or CP.110: STRUCTURAL USE OF CONCRETE). Except with the approval of the Engineer, permanent direct compressive stress shall be limited to a value of less than 7.0 N/mm^2 and compressive stress due to combined bending and direct stress to 9.0 N/mm^2.

3. Steel reinforcement for use in diaphragm walls shall be designed in accordance with the recommendations of CP.114: REINFORCED CONCRETE (or CP.110: STRUCTURAL USE OF CONCRETE) except that if using deformed bars the increases allowed in permissible bond stress in the Codes may not be applied but a 10 per cent increase over equivalent plain bars may be allowed.

4. The minimum cover to the main bars of steel reinforcement is to be 75 mm and the minimum clear spacing between main bars shall be 100 mm.

5. The design of the wall shall take account of the stresses due to active and passive soil pressures, due to surcharges, due to the combined horizontal and vertical forces induced by ground anchors used to maintain stability of the wall, due to retained ground water where applicable, and due to the worst conditions arising in the stages of subsequent excavation, propping and anchoring and to other special conditions. The design shall take into account both the permanent and temporary states of stress which will arise during the life of the structure.

6. The assumptions made and the factors of safety which have been used in the design of the wall are to be stated.

7. All the imposed loads including those arising from the soil taken into account in the design are to be clearly stated.

8. The design shall take into account the deflection of the wall. Consideration shall be given to the need for any underpinning, grouting or soil treatment required to maintain the stability of adjacent foundations during the construction and exposure of the diaphragm wall.

9. Walls constructed by diaphragm wall techniques may be used for the retention of earth, the provision of reaction to applied lateral forces and the support of vertical loads simultaneously, provided that evidence can be produced by testing or otherwise, that such loads can be supported in the ground conditions known to exist on the site.

(Note for guidance: Friction or adhesion on that part of any wall above the related main excavation level or where the contact between the soil and the wall face could be lost as a result of deflection should not be taken as contributing to the capacity of the wall to carry imposed structural loads).

10. All the panels in any continuous length of wall should be designed according to compatible principles.

(Note for guidance: For example, the use of panels spanning horizontally between alternate cantilever panels is generally to be avoided unless shear transference can be verified).

11. The thickness of wall and the provisional panel lengths required are to be as detailed on the drawings. Provision is to be made for all recesses, anchorage positions, inserts and special details as shown on the drawings, and steel reinforcement shall be fixed to accommodate these items.

(Note for guidance: Where close to adjacent structures the soil retained by a diaphragm wall is subject to surcharge loads, careful consideration should be given to the use of reduced panel lengths in order to increase the factor of safety and decrease the possibility of trench wall failures. The maximum panel excavation length acceptable should be stated by the Engineer in the tender documents. The minimum panel excavation length required to accommodate the excavating equipment should be stated by the Specialist Contractor with the tender. The effects of deflection of the wall on both adjacent structures and services must be considered).

(Note for guidance: Where boxes are required in a wall for the formation of recesses, consideration must be given to the effect of the boxes on the strength of the wall, the placing of rein-

flow of concrete during placing. Boxes must be positioned so as torcement through the boxes, and the effect of the boxes on the to pass into the panel excavation with a clearance).

12. Guide walls are to be designed with continuous reinforcement and are to be constructed to comply with the drawings. They are to be cast on and against firm ground or alternatively, where it is desired to shutter both faces of the guide wall, all back-filling behind the wall is to be done using an approved lean mix concrete unless otherwise agreed by the Engineer.

(Note for guidance: The top of the guide wall should, preferably, be not less than 1.5 m above any standing ground water level, and guide walls must be capable of being constructed in the dry).

Materials

Concrete

13. Cement shall be Ordinary Portland cement complying with BS.12 or Sulphate Resisting cement complying with BS.4027.

14. Aggregates shall comply with BS.882. The shell content shall not be greater than the limits given in the table:

Nominal max. size of aggregate	Shell content max. per cent
40 mm	2
20 mm	5
Sand	30

The chloride ion content of the aggregate shall be such that the chloride ion content of the mixed concrete shall not exceed 1.2 per cent for unreinforced concrete or 0.2 per cent for reinforced or prestressed concrete.

(Note for guidance: Aggregate of a size in excess of 20 mm will normally only be used in non-reinforced concrete diaphragm walls).

15. Clean water, free from acids and other impurities and in accordance with the BS.3148 shall be used in the making of concrete.

16. The slump of the concrete shall normally be in accordance with the following standard:

Minimum slump   150 mm
Range   150 mm to collapse

Unless otherwise approved by the Engineer, a minimum cement content of 400 kg/m³ is to be employed in making concrete which is to be placed by tremie methods under a bentonite slurry, in accordance with CP.2004.

The concrete mix shall flow easily in the tremie pipe and shall be designed to give a dense concrete when placed by the tremie method.

Aggregates shall comply with gradings of Zones 2, 3 or 4 of BS.882 and shall preferably be of naturally rounded gravel and sand.

Water cement ratio shall not exceed 0.60.

(Note for guidance: The desirable range of slump is from 175 mm to 200 mm).

17. Any additive used in the concrete must be stated.

18. Ready mixed concrete may be used and shall comply with BS.1926.

(Note for guidance: BRMCA Reprint 71-1: "The Specification and Use of Ready Mixed Concrete for Cast in Place Piling" gives some useful information regarding the use of ready mixed concrete which is to be placed through a tremie pipe).

19. Test cubes shall be prepared and tested in accordance with BS.1881 as required in the contract.
(Note for guidance: Opinions vary as to the number of test cubes which should be required on a diaphragm wall contract but it is suggested that 4 cubes be taken for every panel).

20. In cold weather, ice and snow shall be excluded from the materials used in the manufacture of concrete for use in diaphragm walls.

Aggregates must not be heated to more than 38 deg. C, and the concrete when placed must have a minimum temperature of 5 deg. C.

Reinforcement

21. All reinforcing steel shall be in accordance with the appropriate British Standard unless otherwise agreed.

22. The welding of steel reinforcement required in the works shall be carried out only by techniques which can be shown to maintain the full strength of the structural reinforcement.

(Note for guidance: The drawings should show all the steel reinforcement necessary including that required for lifting stiffening and splicing. They should also show clearly the type of steel required. Mild Steel and High Tensile Steel of similar diameters and type should be avoided. The drawings should also indicate clearly the orientation of the cage in relation to the earth face and the excavated face. It may be advisable to leave the preparation of detail drawings of reinforcement, which should take into account all the tolerances stated in Clause 34, until after acceptance of tender when actual methods of construction are known).

23. The steel reinforcing cage shall be clearly marked to indicate its correct orientation for proper insertion into the trench.

Bentonite

24. Bentonite, as supplied to the site and prior to mixing, shall be in accordance with specification No. DFCP.4 of the Oil Companies Materials Association, London.

A certificate is to be obtained by the Specialist Contractor from the manufacturer of the bentonite powder, stating from which manufacturer's consignment the material delivered to site has been taken, and showing properties of the consignment as determined by the manufacturer. This certificate shall be made available to the Engineer on request.

(Note for guidance: The properties which should normally be given by the manufacturer are the apparent viscosity range (centipoises) and the gel strength range (N/m²) for solids in water).

25. The bentonite powder shall be mixed thoroughly with clean fresh water. The percentage of bentonite used to make the slurry shall be such as to maintain the stability of the trench excavation.

(Note for guidance: In the case of certain estuarine clays of very low strength, it may not be possible to produce a slurry which alone will maintain the stability of trenches. Care also needs to be taken in very permeable ground).

26. Control tests are to be carried out on the bentonite slurry using suitable apparatus, to determine the following parameters:

(a) **Freshly mixed bentonite slurry**

The density of the freshly mixed bentonite slurry shall be measured daily as a check on the quality of the slurry being formed. The measuring device is to be calibrated to read within ± 0.005 g/ml.

(Note for guidance: A satisfactory way of measuring the density of a bentonite slurry is by means of a mud balance.

The following table shows the relationship between the concentration, expressed as a percentage by weight, and the density:

Concentration per cent	Density g/ml
3	1.017
4	1.023
5	1.028
6	1.034

These figures relate to a typical bentonite material of British origin).

(b) Bentonite slurry supplied to trench excavation

In average soil conditions the following tests shall be applied to the bentonite supplied to the trench, and the results shall generally be within the ranges stated in the table below:

Item to be measured	Range of results at 20 deg C	Test method
Density	Less than 1.10 g/ml	Mud density balance
Viscosity	30–90 seconds	Marsh Cone method
Shear strength (10 min gel strength)	1.4 to 10 N/m^2	Shearometer
pH	9.5–12	pH indicator paper strips

Tests to determine density, viscosity, shear strength and pH value shall be carried out initially until a consistant working pattern has been established, taking into account the mixing process, any blending of freshly mixed bentonite slurry and previously used bentonite slurry, and any process which may be employed to remove impurities from previously used bentonite slurry.

When the results show consistent behaviour, the tests for shear strength and pH value may be discontinued, and tests to determine density and viscosity only shall be carried out as agreed with the Engineer. In the event of a change in the established working pattern, the additional tests for shear strength and pH value shall be reintroduced for a period if required by the Engineer.

(Note for guidance: Freshly mixed bentonite slurry should comply with the requirements of the table consistently, provided a normal concentration has been selected. Where bentonite slurry is used once only and then discarded, the tests set out in the table should not be necessary beyond a short initial period, unless some alteration is made to the concentration or mixing procedure.

Where bentonite slurry is re-used, and possibly blended with freshly mixed slurry, or has chemical additions made to preserve its properties, there will be a need for routine checking throughout the work, particularly in regard to the tests for density and viscosity. The frequency of testing may initially need to be on a panel by panel basis where bentonite slurry becomes heavily contaminated during its first use (eg fine sand soil conditions) and may in other cases (eg mainly clay soil conditions) be on a daily basis where contamination is slight. Subsequent frequency will need to be agreed between the Engineer and Specialist Contractor in the light of the test results obtained.

In those cases where a mechanical process is employed to remove contaminating solids from the slurry, the frequency of testing will depend on the circumstances and the equipment employed. The Specialist Contractor should indicate to the Engineer prior to the commencement of the contract, that he intends to employ such a method, and tests should be carried out as for re-used and blended slurries).

(c) Bentonite slurry in trench prior to placing concrete

Prior to placing concrete in any panel, the Specialist Contractor shall ensure that heavily contaminated bentonite slurry, which could impair the free flow of concrete from the tremie pipe, has not accumulated in the bottom of the trench. The proposed method for checking this item is to be stated with the tender, and is to be agreed with the Engineer prior to the commencement of the contract. If the bentonite slurry is found to exhibit properties outside the agreed appropriate range, then it shall be modified or replaced until the required agreed condition is achieved.

(Note for guidance: One method of identifying contaminated bentonite slurry is to take a sample of the slurry from near the bottom of the trench excavation (say about 0.2 m above the base of the trench) and to carry out a density test on this using a Mud Balance. Where this method is employed, the density determined should not be greater than 1.3 g/ml to enable satisfactory concrete placing).

(Note for guidance: Details of apparatus and test methods referred to in Clause 26 may be obtained from the following publication:

Recommended Practice: Standard by American Petroleum Institute, New York City, 1957. Ref. API RP29. Sections I, II and VI relate to the above mentioned tests).

(Note for guidance: The result of tests on bentonite slurry referred to in Clause 26 should be related to a temperature of 20 deg C approximately).

27. The temperature of the water used in mixing bentonite slurry, and of the slurry supplied to the trench excavation, is to be not less than 5 deg C.

28. During construction the level of bentonite slurry in the trench shall be maintained within the depth of the guide walls, and at a level not less than 1.0 m above the level of external standing ground water.

23. In the event of a sudden loss of bentonite slurry, the trench shall be backfilled without delay and the instructions of the Engineer shall be obtained.

30. Where saline or chemically contaminated ground water occurs, special measures shall be taken as required by the Engineer to modify the bentonite slurry.

(Note for guidance: The modification required depends on the nature of the contamination. In saline conditions it is frequently necessary to ensure that the bentonite is fully hydrated in fresh water before supplying it to the trench).

31. All reasonable steps shall be taken to prevent spillage of bentonite slurry on the site away from the immediate vicinity of the wall. Discarded bentonite slurry which has been pumped from the trench is to be removed promptly from the site.

Construction

32. The proposed method of excavation is to be stated by the Specialist Contractor at the time of tendering

(Note for guidance: The use of chiselling to overcome obstructions may cause difficulty in maintaining the stability of the trench and it is therefore an item to be treated with caution. It should also be allowed for in preparing the Bill of Quantities, where the possibility of its use is apparent).

33. Steps are to be taken to avoid damage to panels which have recently been cast. In deciding the sequence of panel construction, the Specialist Contractor shall take this into account.

(Note for guidance: If the Engineer requires some specific sequence of panel construction, this should be made known to the Specialist Contractor in the tender documents).

34. The construction shall be carried out in accordance with the following normal tolerances:

The finished face of the guide wall towards the trench and on the side of the trench nearest to any subsequent main excavation shall be vertical and shall represent the reference line. There shall be no ridges or abrupt changes on the face and its variation from a straight line or specified profile shall not exceed ±15 mm in 3 m.

From this face the minimum clear distance between the faces of the guide walls shall be the specified diaphragm wall thickness plus 25 mm, and the maximum distance shall be the specified diaphragm wall thickness plus 50 mm.

(Note for guidance: Where curved walls are to be constructed, the clearance distance between the guide wall faces may have to be increased).

The wall face to be exposed and the ends of panels shall be vertical to within a tolerance of 1 : 80. In addition to this tolerance, a tolerance of 100 mm shall be allowed for protrusions resulting from irregularities in the ground as excavated, beyond the general face of the wall.

(Note for guidance: It should be borne in mind that, within the limits of the verticality tolerance specified, a wall panel may show an angular deviation at any level when viewed in plan. Such a deviation is usually only important in regard to the exposed face of the wall and will be a function of depth.

Tolerances are not normally necessary for this item, but where they are considered to be essential they should be agreed with the Engineer, taking into account the above factors, the panel length and the panel position, in relation to the particular site circumstances.)

(Note for guidance: Designers should have in mind that diaphragm walls normally consist of a series of panels and, especially in the case of deep walls, the wall thickness should be carefully considered in relation to the permitted tolerances for excavation).

(Note for guidance: The protrusion tolerance of 100 mm refers to . homogeneous clays. In highly fissured clays, sands, gravels or loose or soft grounds the tolerance should be increased. Unless this tolerance has been taken into account in the design and setting out, provision needs to be made in preparing the Bill of Quantities for any cutting back required).

Where recesses are to be formed by inserts in the wall, they shall be positioned within vertical and horizontal tolerances of 150 mm.

(Note for guidance: Horizontal inserts cannot be placed continuously between panels in normal diaphragm wall construction, but must be curtailed at the end of the reinforcing cage).

The tolerances in positioning reinforcement shall be as follows:
Longitudinal tolerance of cage head at the top of the guide wall and measured along the trench: ± 75 mm.
Vertical tolerance at cage head in relation to top of guide wall: ± 50 mm.
The reinforcement shall be maintained in position during the casting of each panel.

(Note for guidance: In the design of diaphragm walls, the distance between reinforcement cages in adjacent panels must take into account both the longitudinal positional tolerance and the shape of the stop end in relation to the shape of the cage).

35. Stop ends, inserted prior to placing concrete in a panel shall be clean and have a smooth regular surface. They shall be adequately restrained to prevent horizontal movement during concreting.

36. Safety precautions shall be taken throughout the construction of diaphragm walls in accordance with the statutory requirements listed in CP.2004: FOUNDATIONS.

Concrete placing

37. Concrete shall be placed continuously by one or more tremie pipes, and care shall be taken during placing to avoid contamination of the concrete. Where two or more pipes are used in the same panel simultaneously, care shall be taken to ensure that the concrete level at each pipe position is maintained nearly equal.

38. The tremie pipe shall be clean, watertight and of adequate diameter to allow the free flow of concrete. The tremie shall extend to the bottom of the trench excavation prior to the commencement of concrete pouring, and care shall be taken to ensure that all bentonite slurry is expelled from the tube during the initial charging process. Sufficient embedment of the tremie pipe in concrete shall be maintained throughout concrete pouring to prevent re-entry of bentonite slurry into the pipe.

39. The concrete pour for any diaphragm wall panel shall be completed in such a manner and within such time that the concrete above the foot of the tremie remains workable until the casting of the panel is complete.

40. The effective trimmed final wall level shall generally be taken as 250 mm below the top of the guide wall when concrete is cast to the top of the trench.

For trimmed final wall levels below this level the tolerance of the cast concrete profile shall be a minimum of 150 mm and a maximum of 600 mm above the specified wall level plus an additional allowance of 150 mm over the maximum tolerance for each one metre of final wall depth specified below the top of the guide wall.

(Note for guidance: Special problems occur with deep specified final wall levels, when it becomes difficult to locate adjacent panels precisely and when backfill over previously completed panels cannot be retained without special measures such as backfilling above final wall level using lean concrete mixes. Such circumstances require appropriate items to be included in the Bill of Quantities).

41. The extraction of stop ends shall be carried out at such a time and in such a manner as to avoid causing damage to concrete placed against it.

42. The method of forming joints and the equipment used shall be such that all solids are removed from the end of the adjacent panel by the excavating equipment. The Specialist Contractor shall be responsible for the repair of any joint where, on full exposure of the wall, visible water leaks resulting from faulty materials or workmanship are found.

(Note for guidance: Seepage which may result from differential wall deflections or the installation of anchor points, are not considered to be included under this item. A provisional item should be included in the Bill of Quantities to allow for any special measures necessary to deal with such seepages).

Records

43. The following records shall be kept for each panel completed:

Panel number
Top of guide wall level
Bottom of guide wall level
Top level of wall as cast in relation to top of guide wall
Depth of base of panel from top of guide wall
Date panel excavated
Date panel concreted
Length of panel
Thickness of wall
Strata log
Cubes taken
Volume of concrete used
Details of steel reinforcement (cage type)
Details of any obstructions encountered and time spent in overcoming them.

4.5 RETAINING WALLS

4.5.1 Types of walls

There are two main types of retaining wall: the gravity retaining wall and the cantilever retaining wall. The former is mainly used for the support of solids such as soil, fuel, chemical and waste materials. The latter may be used for both solids and liquids. Reservoir walls are often constructed in a cantilever form. In some cases the wall may be designed to support dead loads in addition to the normal lateral loads, but essentially these walls are designed to resist lateral movement. Both types of retaining wall must be designed to resist the following factors:

Overturning

Overstressing of the material in the wall

Forward sliding

Settlement due to overstressing of soil under the wall

Circular slip.

These possible factors of failure are shown diagramatically in Fig 4.63. Gravity retaining walls depend on their dead weight for strength and stability. They are limited in height to approximately 3 metres if inclined, or 2 metres if the wall is vertical. Over these heights the thickness of wall, to comply with the safe height/thickness ratio, would make the construction uneconomical. They are designed so that the width of wall is sufficient to distribute the resultant loads of the wall and the earth pressure to the soil below the base of the wall without undue settlement. High tensile stresses at the back of the wall can be offset by designing the width of the wall so that the resultant force is kept within the middle third of the base. A suitable width of base can be taken as between one-quarter and one-half of the wall height. The width at the top of the wall can be taken as one-seventh of the wall height.

Cantilever walls are used for retaining walls up to 7 metres in height without counterforts, and if counterforted can be designed for greater heights without being excessively thick. The wall shape may vary to suit the loading and the material to be supported. The walling material is normally reinforced concrete, although pre-stressed concrete may be used for liquid-retaining structures. The form shown in Fig 4.64 (a) is used in situations where the wall is to support soil and where it is not possible to excavate behind the wall. The form in (b) may be used where excavation behind the wall is necessary; this type makes use of the backfill for stability. When the height exceeds 7 metres the extra thickness of the wall must be considered against the cost of constructing counterforts. The forms in Fig 4.64 (c) and (d) show the use of counterforts; (c) shows a buried counterfort which reduces the cost of finished concrete (since it can be cast from rough shuttering without any finishing work) whereas (d) produces a very strong buttressed retaining wall which is not dependent on the weight of backfill material. Other forms and types of retaining walls can be used, such as:

Diaphragm walls — Section 4.4

Steel sheet piling — Section 4.1

Concrete crib walls

Contiguous piling — Section 3.2.4

Anchored walls.

4.5.2 Methods of construction

There are four basic factors for consideration in the construction of retaining walls:

Retention of the soil, if excavation is necessary, while the wall is being constructed

The actual constructional form and materials to be used

Control of ground water

Backfilling the structure.

The retention of soil during excavation is covered fully in Chapter 3, but will depend a great deal on the proximity of other structures and the amount of excavated material that can be freely removed without danger to plant and equipment; this can be achieved by battering the sides of the excavation giving clear working space.

Where the excavation has to be limited but space allows steel sheet piling to be used, the wall can be constructed without disturbing the compacted soil behind the wall. Where loads and structures in close proximity prevent the driving of sheet piling and excavation as outlined above, a diaphragm walling technique should be considered.

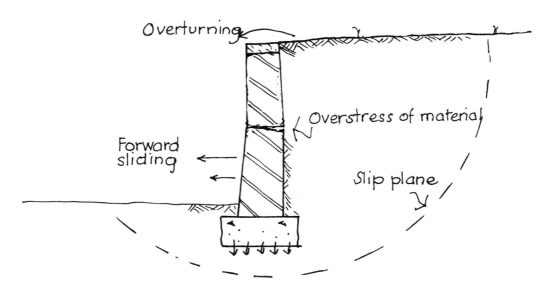

Fig 4.63   *Possible failures in retaining walls*

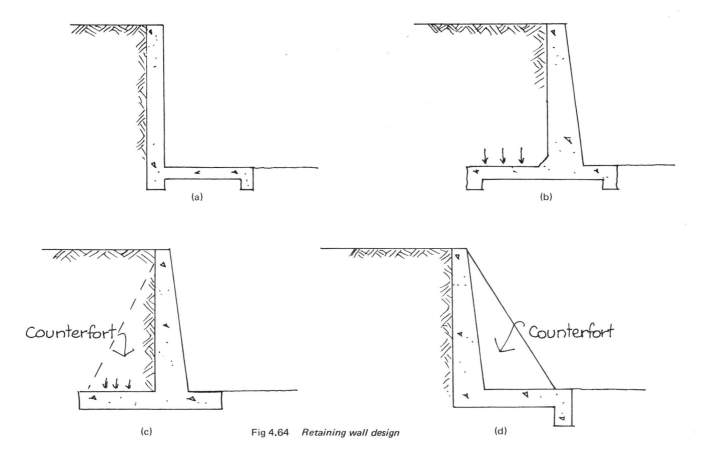

Fig 4.64   *Retaining wall design*

The shape of the retaining wall should be such as to provide economic use of formwork, where in-situ concrete is used. In some cases the forms may be track-mounted for long walls, giving rapid turn-round in stripping and fixing. Some plan shapes may present difficulties in achieving the rapid turn-round of wall forms (Fig 4.65). The materials used in retaining walls may include brick and stone but in the main are constructed of reinforced concrete either in-situ or in the form of concrete blocks or units. Pre-stressed retaining walls are of particular value in basement structures, reservoir construction and dam construction. Anchored retaining walls are very suitable for deep basement work where the retaining wall can be designed as a deep narrow strip without the toe element (Fig 4.66).

Anchorage for retaining walls may take three different forms depending on the soil conditions behind the wall. The three types of anchorage used can be classified as:

Clay anchors

Injection anchors

Rock anchors and rock bolts.

Clay anchors are formed by under-ream drilling and grouting. The under-reamed cones (Fig 4.67) are cut with a special expanding cutter bit at the bottom of the borehole, and after placing the high tensile steel tendon the borehole is pressure-grouted.

Injection anchors are formed in non-cohesive soils which would not otherwise be strong enough to afford sufficient anchorage. The granular material of these soils permits the grout to penetrate into large or irregular zones along the length of the drilled hole (Fig 4.68).

Rock anchors are constructed in the same way as clay anchors, by under-reaming the rock at the base of a borehole. Single anchors in sound rock have been tested to 200 tonnes, multiple anchors being used when excessive loads are required. Rock bolts, which are used extensively in tunnelling, provide a fixing into rock and are commonly secured with a resin fill which flows around the anchor bolt (Fig 4.69). The resin and catalyst are contained in a single capsule which is inserted into the hole and mixed by rotating the bolt. The resin has a higher compressive strength than surrounding materials and therefore bolts perform exactly as if they were cast insitu.

Concrete crib retaining walls (Fig 4.70) consist of a series of concrete lintols or beams which are stacked in a grillage pattern, usually interlocking, and filled with earth or rock. They are constructed to a batter of 1 in 6 or 1 in 8 and are very suitable for retaining embankments to motorways.

Control of ground water: if water is allowed to build up behind a retaining wall not specially designed for liquid retention, then there is a danger either of the wall being overstressed by water pressure, or of the water creating a slip plane under the wall. This type of danger can be eliminated by placing agricultural pipes behind the wall at a low point, and connecting the drainage line to weep-holes through the wall. The area directly above the land drain should be filled with granular material and the level below the invert of the pipes should be concreted.

Backfilling retaining walls should be carried out with great care to prevent undue stresses being placed on the wall. The materials used should be of the quality which the designer has assumed in the earth pressure calculations. Inferior material, such as soft wet clay, can treble the pressure exerted against the wall compared with a dense dry fill. The materials used should be well graded granular fill which will compact easily by mechanical means.

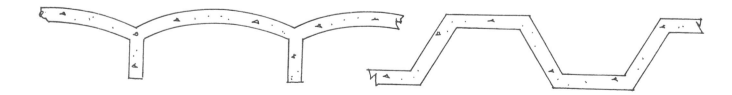

Fig 4.65   *Possible plan shapes of retaining walls*

Fig 4.66   *Anchored retaining wall*   (Cementation Piling and Foundations Limited)

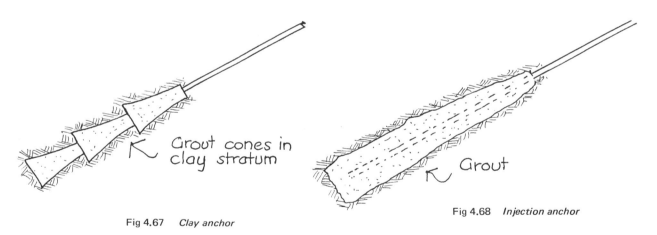

Grout cones in
clay stratum

Fig 4.67   *Clay anchor*

Grout

Fig 4.68   *Injection anchor*

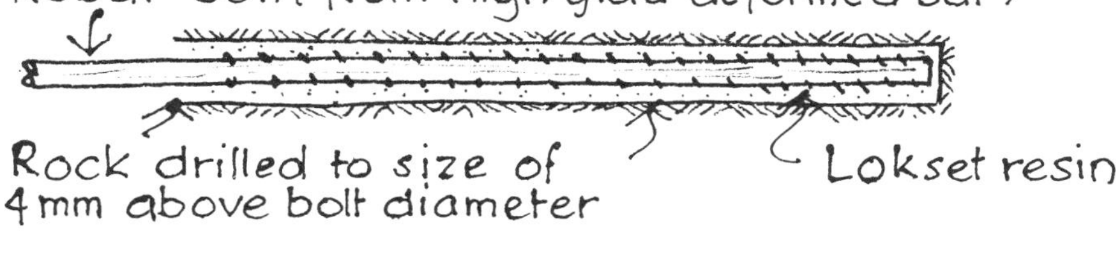

Rebar bolt (from high yield deformed bar)

Rock drilled to size of
4mm above bolt diameter

Lokset resin

Fig 4.69   *Lokset Rebar Bolt*

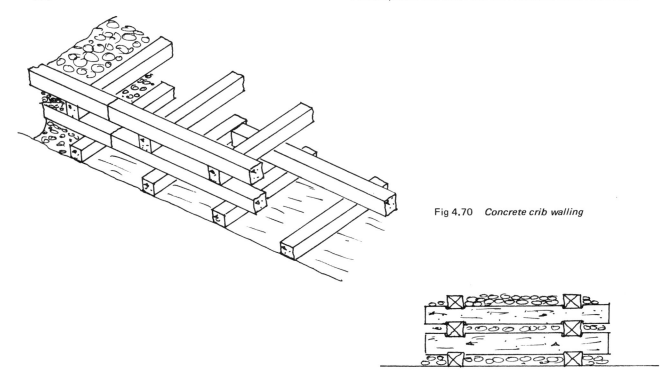

Fig 4.70   *Concrete crib walling*

4.5.3 Waterproofing

Retaining walls must be waterproofed to prevent unsightly efflorescence appearing on the face of the wall. This can be achieved in two ways:

By using good quality vibrated concrete, with or without additives, depending on the quality of work

By applying some form of waterproof membrane to the face of the wall.

With the latter method of waterproofing, if excavation is possible the membrane will be applied to the earth-side of the wall against a protective backing of concrete blocks. If this method of construction is not possible the membrane can be applied to the free face of the wall; in that case a supporting skin of brickwork or masonry must be built in front of the membrane to prevent the membrane being pushed off the face of the wall. Where retaining walls form part of a basement the construction may have to be vapour-proof in addition to being water-proof. This is best achieved by using an applied membrane rather than vibrated concrete. Expansion and construction joints may be formed incorporating a PVC waterbar.

Chapter 5

Tunnelling and Underpinning

5.1 TUNNELLING

5.1.1 General considerations

Before tunnelling operations can commence there are numerous factors that require detailed investigation. These factors include:

The purpose of tunnelling

The type of ground

The method of construction

Removal of debris

Control of ground water.

Purpose of tunnelling

Tunnels are constructed for various purposes, such as road and rail transport, conveyance of water or sewage, access to mines, power houses and other underground structures, and ventilation of underground structures.

In the majority of cases the purpose will affect the size and shape of the tunnel, but small and medium-sized tunnels may involve driving a larger cross-section than the ultimate size, simply to provide room to manoeuvre equipment and materials. Therefore the economic design of a tunnel for a specific purpose must involve consideration to constructional method. The purpose of a tunnel will affect the shape in the following ways. Where the tunnel is to carry liquids the frictional surface should be at a minimum; this may lead to egg-shaped sewers or circular sewers, depending on their volume of flow. Ventilation tunnels of circular cross-section give minimum surface area and provide a form most suitable for resisting internal and external pressures. Tunnels to be used for transport may be rectangular or horseshoe in section if a reasonably level floor can be maintained; however, circular cross-sections have the greatest resistance to stress, and are therefore more usual. These will require a suspended floor for the carriageway, this having the advantage of providing space for services (see Fig 5.18).

Type of ground

Detailed investigation of the ground will be necessary to ascertain the type of soil or rock, whether the ground is water-bearing and the extent, if any, of defects in the strata. Tunnelling in rock and soft ground are discussed fully in Sections 5.1.3 and 5.1.4, but it should be readily appreciated that the type of ground affects the method of construction and choice of equipment. It may also affect the location of the tunnel, both its horizontal level and its lateral position. This may occur where the ground contains badly-faulted rock or variable ground in the vicinity of much more reliable ground for tunnelling operations. The final location of the tunnel will depend on the economics of dealing with ground conditions and obstructions. The problem of tunnelling in the vicinity of major obstructions, such as large sewers, underground railways and similar services, can be greatly reduced by preparing models of the proposed tunnel in relation to existing obstructions. Relevant details can be obtained from surveys and from information held by local authorities.

Method of construction

This will depend on the type of tunnel, on ground conditions, on the length of tunnel to be driven and on the time available for construction. In the main, tunnelling can be placed in two categories: (i) those in rock; which require blasting and generally need lining, weak places being temporarily supported until permanent lining is carried out; and (ii) those in soft ground where permanent structural lining must be installed as driving proceeds and where excavation does not require the use of explosives. Spoil handling methods depend chiefly on the size of the tunnel and the type of ground; wherever practicable mechanical means are employed.

A discontinuous working cycle is employed for the construction of most tunnels. In rock tunnels the cycle is: drill, fire, clear smoke, load away debris and erect any temporary support needed. In all but the largest rock tunnels the permanent lining is a separate operation carried out when the driving has been completed. Soft-ground tunnels follow a different cycle, excavation and disposal being immediately followed by the erection of prefabricated linings to support the ground, the space between the excavation and the outside of the lining being filled by grouting with cement or other material after one or more cycles. In both cases several cycles may be completed in twenty-four hours.

Removal of debris

The method employed for the removal of debris (or 'mucking out') depends on the size and length of the tunnel. In rock tunnels, where blasting is employed, loading is by mechanical shovel; the type of mechanical shovel depends on the size of tunnel. Face shovels, tyred and tracked-loading shovels and specially developed rocker shovels (Fig 5.1) and backacters have all been used. In small, soft-ground tunnels hand-loading is still used but conveyors are increasingly used to raise the material high enough to load it into 'tubs' or wagons. Mechanical excavation of soft ground is generally based on some form of hydraulic backhoe.

In both rock and soft-ground tunnels transportation of debris along the tunnel can be achieved by independent trucks (large tunnels only), by rail-mounted wagons or by conveyor. It should be noted that, particularly with long tunnels, progress is frequently governed by how fast the debris can be removed.

Control of water

Tunnelling, whether in soft ground or rock, is always made more difficult if water is present. Various methods have been employed to control water; pumping is the most common. Other methods include lowering the water table, grouting, freezing and the use of compressed air.

5.1.2   Methods of tunnelling

Methods of tunnelling vary according to the purpose of the tunnel and the problems encountered in its formation. Most tunnels are formed by cutting and boring the ground and lining the tunnel as work proceeds. However, two other methods of construction are also used, which purists might argue are not tunnelling at all: they are the 'open-cut' method and the 'immersed-tube' method. The first method is suitable for shallow tunnels in both water and dry ground, whereas the immersed-tube method is suitable for tunnels crossing deep water.

The open-cut method (Fig 5.2), sometimes called 'cut and cover', may involve the construction of a deep trench supported by diaphragm walling or, in the case of underwater construction, may consist of placing fabricated sections into a trench dredged in the water-bed and backfilling the trench. A variant of the open-cut method is the pre-deck method (Fig 5.3) which is suitable for high level tunnels, such as pedestrian tunnels: the tunnel walls are sunk by the diaphragm walling method and the upper surface of the ground is removed to allow the positioning of the tunnel deck. When the deck has been positioned and water-proofed, backfilling and reinstatement is then completed. Tunnel excavation can then continue from both ends of the tunnel without fear of collapse and with minimum disturbance to traffic and services.

The immersed-tube system, known also as a submerged-tube tunnel, consists of lowering prefabricated tunnel sections into a prepared foundation pad at sea or river-bed level. The tunnel sections may be either concrete or steel and are prefabricated, usually in a dry dock (Fig 5.4), before floating them out to their final position. Sections are then carefully lowered into place from pontoons, guided by anchor cables (Fig 5.5) and joined together prior to trench filling. When the tubes have been joined together, they can be de-watered to allow work to proceed internally.

Conventional tunnelling, in which tunnels are formed by cutting through the ground and forming the tunnel profile as the cutting proceeds, varies in method of construction depending on the nature of the ground and the length of diameter of the tunnel. The selection of a system or method of tunnelling will involve three important components, namely excavation equipment, muck-loading and muck-haulage equipment. In rock conditions, the excavating method will vary from drilling and blasting to mechanical rock cutting, whereas in soft ground a tunnel shield is generally used with excavation by machine or by hand-held pneumatic tools. These methods are discussed fully in the Sections 5.1.3 and 5.1.4.

Fig 5.1   *Rocker shovel* *(EIMCO (Great Britain))*

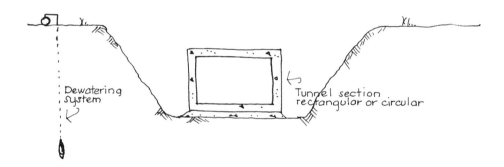

Fig 5.2   *Open-cut tunnelling*

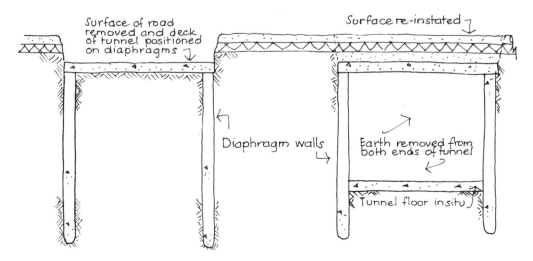

Fig 5.3   *Pre-deck method of tunnelling*

Pipe-jacking

This is a tunnelling technique that has been used in the UK since the late 1950s. The method consists in forming a pit at both ends of the proposed tunnel or pipeline and jacking sections of steel or concrete tube from one pit to the other. The equipment for jacking the tube consists of hydraulic cylinders (Fig 5.6) which thrust against a reaction wall and distribute their load to the tube via a thrust-ring. This method of tunnelling is very suitable for taking services under canals, railway embankments and roads without creating a disturbance to traffic or to the ground. A pit of the required length to accommodate the jacking equipment and tube sections is dug, followed by the construction of a thrust wall or thrust platform (Fig 5.7). The jacking equipment is installed at the desired gradient and the process commences by excavating and positioning the first section of the pipe with a drive shield. Excavation is carried out by conventional mining techniques, the drive shield controlling the working face. The excavated material is brought out through the unit, usually in special trucks which are designed to run on the invert of the tunnel. Recent developments involve the casting of the complete tunnel lining on the thrust base; this is suitable for short to medium distance jacking. The method eliminates craneage problems in handling large sections and allows greater flexibility in size because transportation of units no longer limits the designer. The slotted thrust base is employed as a reaction for the hydraulic jacks.

Fig 5.4   *Construction of tunnel units in dry dock*

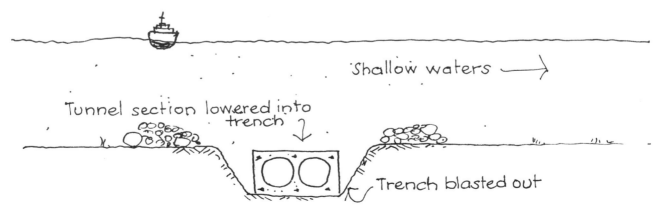

Fig 5.5   *Submerged tunnel for shallow waters*

Fig 5.6   *Pipe-jacking equipment*   (Westfalia Lunen)

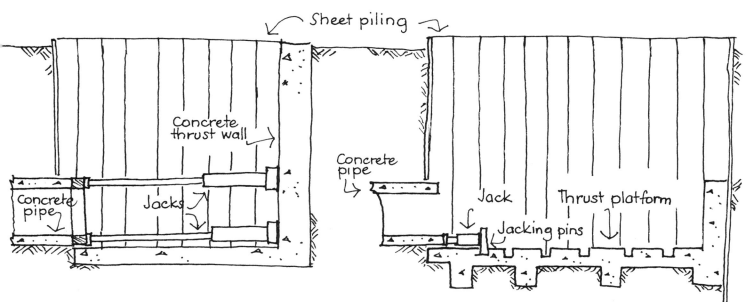

Fig 5.7   *Thrust wall and thrust platform for jacking*

In the early days this method of tunnelling was limited to jacking pipe diameters of up to 2 metres, but improved jacking equipment can cope with tubes up to 4 metres diameter and box sections of a size up to 7 x 4 metres. Where the larger section unit creates problems in providing suitable jacking reaction, a modified system of jacking can be employed. This system introduces a sleeve, carrying supplementary jacks, into the line of units being jacked. The line is then jacked forward in a caterpillar fashion (Fig 5.8), jacking the first section forward, then using the jacks in the intermediate position, followed by jacking from the pit to close the line. Alternatively, bentonite can be introduced from the rear of the driving shield to reduce friction during jacking.

Drive or thrust-shafts are generally 2 metres longer and 1 metre wider than the unit being jacked. Where the thrust-shaft is in excess of 7 metres deep, the jacking can take place from a bolted segmental shaft with an underground chamber for the jacking equipment. Reception shafts should be of sufficient size to recover the driving shield.

Fig 5.8   *Jacks at an intermediate stage using the first section of the tunnel as a jacking base*   (Westfalia Lunen)

Auger-boring

This is another method of tunnelling that can be used in difficult situations, such as those discussed under the pipe-jacking system. The principle of forming pits and thrust walls is similar to the pipe-jacking technique, but there the similarities cease. The tube is held and located by a rail-mounted machine which augers the soil as it pushes the sleeve or tube into the ground. The auger (Fig 5.9) turns and cuts the face of the borehole and transports the excavated spoil back down the sleeve into the shaft for disposal. When the machine has inserted a length of sleeve, complete with auger, into the ground, the machine is withdrawn and another length of sleeve is welded on and the auger flight extended. This process is repeated until the desired length has been installed in the ground. For sewer pipes the base of the pit is constructed to the desired gradient of the proposed sewer. Whereas pipe-jacking methods are capable of driving large-section units through the soil, this system is limited to a diameter of 750 mm and is therefore most suited to small sewers and pipelines up to 600 mm diameter. The finished pipe-line may be threaded through the sleeve by means of roller-mounted spacing legs (Fig 5.10) and the annular space between the sleeve and pipeline can be grouted with a PFA cement-bentonite mixture.

Mini-Tunnels

This tunnelling system, introduced by the Rees Group, is suitable for the diameter range of 1000 to 1300 mm and is particularly suitable for sewer schemes. In principle the technique is similar to the pipe-jacking method, but the jacking equipment is housed in the driving shield. The tunnel is constructed with concrete rings, each having three identical un-reinforced concrete segments per ring. The ring is built within the rear section of the shield, using a purpose-designed erector. The shield (Fig 5.11) is driven forward by six hydraulic jacks, each having a working capacity of 15 tonnes, controlled by aerohydraulic pumps within the shield. The rams are mounted within the shield on front and rear-thrust rings, the latter bearing against the last segment of tunnel that has been placed. The front ring transmits the load from the segment, via the jacks, to the shield and so drives the equipment forward. The front and rear rings, together with the jacks, can be moved as a complete rig by releasing spring-loaded catches, to provide extra work space during excavation or assembly of the concrete segments. The tunnel invert is protected during the construction period by special rail tracks mounted on sleepers formed to the radius of the tunnel, the shaped sleepers distributing the heavy wheel loads of the muck skip. The rail tracks are pulled along the invert of the tunnel by the shield as the work proceeds and extra lengths of track are added at the access pit. The shield cuts an overbreak of about 6% of the tunnel diameter and the space is filled with pea gravel, injected under pressure through holes in the concrete segments. This gravel surround, which is grouted, gives immediate support to the ground as work progresses. The gravel is fed from a pressurised hopper (Fig 5.11) and injector, which is positioned at the access pit. Construction joints are of the knuckle male and female type and are sealed by attaching, to the female section, a sealant tape; this tape is extended over the whole width of the knuckles by ram pressure on the circumferential joints and by earth pressure on the longitudinal joints. (See photo of segments in Fig 5.12.)

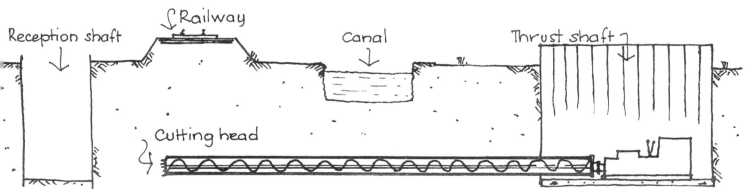

Fig 5.9   *Longitudinal section showing auger boring under obstructions*

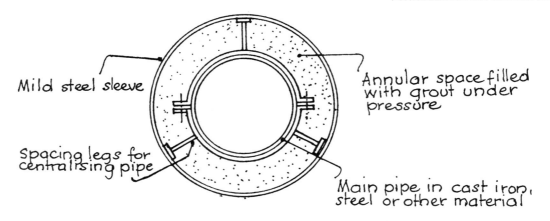

Mild steel sleeve

Annular space filled with grout under pressure

Spacing legs for centralising pipe

Main pipe in cast iron, steel or other material

Fig 5.10   *Permanent pipe line within auger sleeve*

Fig 5.11   *Typical pipe jacking shield incorporating sliding face boards* (Rees Hough Limited)

Fig 5.12   *General view of access pit showing hopper containing pea gravel for tunnel surround* (Underground Services)

5.1.3   Tunnelling in rock

Detailed investigation of the rock will allow the designer and contractor to classify the rock in terms of construction method. This classification would be:

Hard rock — unsupported or lightly supported

Hard rock — heavily supported

Soft rock — unsupported or lightly supported

Soft rock — heavily supported

Soft rock containing hard intrusions.

Hard rock tunnels are driven through rock with a minimum compressive strength of 100 N/mm^2. There are two methods of driving tunnels in hard rock: whole face boring, and conventional drilling and blasting.

Whole face boring employs a machine which is specially designed to suit the particular cross-section required (Fig 5.13). The disadvantage is the high capital cost involved in the original purchase of the machine, together with the specialist maintenance required; the advantages are that fewer men are employed and high rates of progress are possible. The debris from this type of machine would normally be removed from the tunnel face by conveyor. Whole face borers are capable of cutting rock which has a compressive strength in excess of 300 N/mm^2; however, it is usually uneconomical to employ whole face boring equipment on rocks that have a strength exceeding 130 N/mm^2. The disadvantage of this method of driving is the inflexibility of the machine to corrections in alignment and changes of direction. The cross-section is always circular, 'overbreak' is minimal and hence only the theoretical amount of concrete is required when lining. Whole face machines do not perform well in badly broken ground such as fault zones.

Conventional methods of driving tunnels have four stages of operation: drilling, blasting, mucking out and supporting. Drilling is achieved by percussive or rotary percussive methods. In order to reduce health hazard, the dust is suppressed by means of water or by dry extraction. The drilling equipment may be mounted on main line trolleys or gantry type 'jumbos' (Fig 5.14), depending on the tunnel diameter.

Fig 5.13   *Whole face boring machine* (Robert L. Priestley)

Fig 5.14   *Gantry Jumbo with seven rock drills mounted in a fixed pattern*

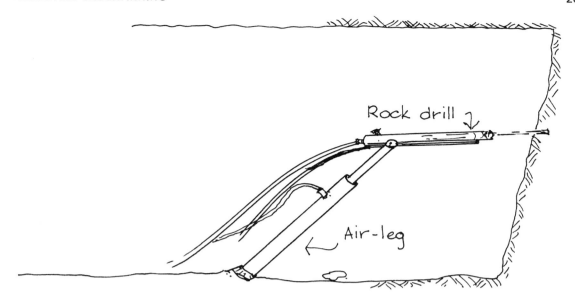

Fig 5.15   *Rock drill supported by an air-leg*

Small diameter tunnels and headings may be advanced by a light drilling machine supported by an 'air leg' (Fig 5.15). The compressed air cylinder of the air leg lies back behind the drill, carrying the weight and exerting a forward thrust to the rock face.

Hard rock tunnels which are heavily supported require a reduced round length (length of blasted rock face) to eliminate rock fall. The amount of time involved in supporting the tunnel before another section can be drilled and blasted makes it uneconomical to employ a large heading gang, so the gang size and mucking equipment is arranged to suit the progress of tunnel support. Most hard rock tunnels are bored by an almost identical process; the rock face is drilled to a drilling pattern which will best suit the quantity of rock to be moved, and charged with the necessary explosive. The pattern, depth and direction of the drilling depends on the size and shape of the tunnel and on the type of rock encountered. The explosive used may be one of the types described in Section 1.3.3. The charges are detonated in a pre-arranged sequence, working from the centre to the circumference. When the charges have been laid and fused, the drilling equipment and men are moved to a safe place and the charges are fired electrically. Smoke, dust and fumes are rapidly cleared by an auxilliary ventilation system which ventilates the tunnel by displacement at a rate of 100 m^3 per minute per square metre of face.

Spoil removal may commence when it is safe for the men to return to the face after blasting (see 5.1.6 Safety aspects). The dust may be quickly settled by spraying the area with water at frequent intervals during mucking (spoil removal).

The equipment for mucking will vary according to the cross-section of the tunnel. In small tunnels muck cars and appropriate loading equipment may be used, whereas in large cross-sectioned tunnels conventional track or tyre-mounted shovels are used to load dumpers or tunnel waggons. An alternative method of transporting the spoil, providing the haul distance in one direction is limited to approximately 400 metres, is by low haul dump machines; these machines are particularly useful at tunnel intersections.

Soft rock tunnels which require little or no support can be efficiently excavated with a tunnel-boring machine, or at less capital cost a 'roadheader' type of machine may be used (Fig 5.16). If supports other than roof bolts are required, the machine should be equipped with a shield which will not hinder the placing of supports.

Where the rock is badly broken or folded, thereby requiring continuous support, the tunnel-boring equipment may be an uneconomical means of excavation. The tunnel may then best be excavated with a 'road-header'. The spoil is ripped out of the tunnel face and fed on to a conveyor which in turn loads the muck cars.

If the soft rock contains hard intrusions which are a source of damage to bits and wheel cutters, it may be necessary to resort to drill-and-blast methods as with hard rocks.

Fig 5.16   *Roadheader* (Anderson Strathclyde plc)

5.1.4   Tunnelling in soft ground

One definition of soft ground in this context is 'that ground which requires continuous immediate structural support to enable tunnelling to advance'. This includes material ranging from gravels and hard clays, through sands to silts. The amount of water present in the ground will have a great effect on the difficulty and manner of operations. For example, some clays and dense dry gravels will stand unsupported over a short span for a limited time, whereas waterlogged silts will immediately find a way through the smallest opening in the support. A tunnelling shield is normally used for work in soft ground (Fig 5.17). The essential parts are a hollow cylindrical skin supported by substantial diaphragms, a cutting edge, and a system of hydraulic jacks.

The diaphragms have openings to give access to the face and house the jacks which thrust against the completed lining to force the shield forward; the cutting edge trims the ground to an accurate shape.

For most types of ground the lining is prefabricated in sections and erected under the protection of the shield's 'tail'. Excavation through the diaphragm opening can be executed by hand or by various types of mechanical excavator if the ground is able to stand unsupported for a short time. Loose dry sands and gravels will require temporary support at the face to control the amount of ground-flow into the tunnel. Waterlogged ground can be tunnelled by the use of compressed air techniques in which the working chamber is sealed and the internal air pressure raised to balance the pressure of the ground water; access for men and materials is achieved by air locks. The effect of this process is to prevent water from entering the tunnel and to stabilise the ground. Grouting such ground, in advance of the tunnel excavation, can also make the work less hazardous by increasing the strength and reducing the permeability of the ground.

Disposal of debris is generally achieved by some form of mine car, mounted on rails in the case of smaller tunnels. Loading these cars is either done manually or mechanically; commonly some form of conveyor is used to raise the excavated material and load it into the car. Conveyors have been used as an alternative to mine cars and track. Few soft-ground tunnels are large enough to use tyred or track-laying equipment.

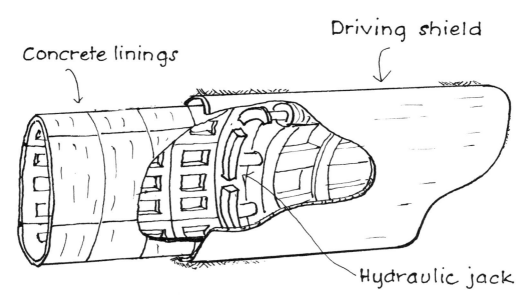

Fig 5.17   *Tunnelling shield showing hydraulic jacks*

Tunnel linings

In addition to supporting the loads which are imposed by the ground, the lining of a tunnel may have to withstand the jacking pressures from a shield. They may have to resist water pressure, at the same time having qualities which permit ease of handling and construction. All these factors, together with the cost and speed of construction, have led to the use of pre-formed linings as opposed to in-situ linings (Fig 5.18). However, slip-form techniques are being used to offset the time factor in tunnels which do not need temporary or early support by the linings. Cast in-situ lining is rarely practicable in small diameter tunnels until excavation is complete.

A popular form of lining used in soft ground is the segmental cast-iron type; it is very durable, resistant to corrosion and strong in compression. It is used in complicated and difficult conditions or where point loads are expected. Pre-cast concrete linings are more popular because they are less expensive, but they are more difficult than cast iron to make watertight. Cast steel, pressed steel and welded pre-fabricated steel linings are also used in soft ground. The cast iron lining can be caulked with lead or asbestos-cement compounds to make the lining completely impervious. If the tunnel is formed in hard ground the lining may take the form of sprayed concrete. These linings may be sprayed on to mesh which has been fixed to the rock face, or sprayed between steel ribs. Further details of this technique are discussed in Section 8.1.6. The greatest problem to the surveyor is one of billing such work. The cost of ribs and lagging is proportional to the length of tunnel supported, but sprayed linings involve a high cost in setting up the equipment in proportion to the cost of forming the lining itself. The amount of interference between phases of the work should be taken into consideration. Important economies when employing this technique include an undulating lining following the rock face as distinct from filling to a shutter line: the thickness can be varied to suit rock conditions, and rock bolting may be eliminated.

Pre-stressed linings may be used, but their use has been rather limited in the UK. One such system, developed by the French engineer Freyssinet, consists of a thin precast concrete lining which is pre-stressed by pressure-grouting. The lining takes the form of planks and segments which are pre-stressed by injecting colloidal mortar into the space between the lining and the excavation. The mortar is injected under very high pressure, which results in high pre-stress in the precast lining and the expulsion of excess water. On completion of a section of tunnel lining, the void is pressure-grouted to provide a solid support which allows equal distribution of stresses.

Expanding tunnel linings can be used in ground that is self-supporting and has been cut to a true circular section. The linings are inserted behind the tunnelling shield, which has been pushed forward to leave an unsupported space. The lining, which consists of precast segments, is erected and expanded against the ground to a pre-determined pressure. This type of lining does not require grouting.

In-situ tunnel linings differ from other forms in that the process gives a smooth lining without undulation, at the same time giving full support to the surrounding earth without further grouting. The lining may be installed by a continuous process, such as the slip-form technique, or by traditional forms mounted on rail tracks. In the former method of construction, the driving shield is connected to a 60 metre long box-frame which supports the forms and carries away the spoil. The long box-frame is mounted on tracks for easy movement but is supported by legs during concreting. The excavated spoil is transported by conveyor through the box-frame and out through the completed tunnel.

Fig 5.18   *Sectional tunnel linings and floor units, the latter forming service ducts* (Balfour Beatty & Company Limited)

5.1.5   Use of compressed air

The health hazards encountered in the use of compressed air are discussed in Chapter 1, Section 1.2.8 on Safety, and compressed air plant is discussed in Chapter 2. There are three basic uses for compressed air in tunnelling:

The safety of the workman

The safety of the property above the tunnel, and

Adequate progress in otherwise troublesome ground.

When excavation in water-bearing ground can be undertaken in a confined space, e.g. in tunnelling, shafts and caissons, it is possible to exclude the water by increasing the pressure within the working space. This technique of dealing with ground water is a traditional method of undertaking underground construction work where soil conditions are difficult because of the presence of water. It is especially suitable for excluding water from fine silts or soft clays which may be difficult or expensive to treat by chemical injection processes. It is also suitable for work in water-bearing rock where there is too much water for pumping methods to handle. In some cases the use of compressed air may be combined with other techniques, such as dewatering: the air pressure can then be reduced in the working chamber if the surrounding ground water level is reduced. In other cases ground treatment may be necessary to prevent excessive loss of pressure at the face; when air escapes through zones of weak soil and reaches the atmosphere or residual air at lower pressures, serious adverse conditions may arise over a short period of time. One method of sealing the face of excavation against air loss, if the soil is very fine, is to spray the face with bentonite; this immediately seals the ground and thereby reduces air losses. Alternatively, polythene sheeting may be used. A great deal of air is also lost through tunnel linings, owing partly to cracked segments and partly to the use of pervious materials. Caulking should be carried out as near to the face as possible to prevent excessive loss of air in the tunnel. Unfortunately, caulking in compressed air conditions may lead to re-caulking in free air, since the former conditions do not show leaks. It is also essential to have sufficient ground cover to balance pressures in the excavation; particular attention must be given to this problem when tunnelling below or adjacent to free water, buried channels or culverts and old pile foundations: any or all of these obstacles can cause sudden loss of air. In cases where the ground cover is insufficient to balance the air pressure, it will be necessary to load the ground surface to give suitable protection.

The limiting factors of using compressed air on its own are the pressure in which men can be allowed to work and the loss of air pressure through the working face, which may prove economically excessive.

As mentioned above, compressed air can be used in conjunction with chemical grouting and other forms of water cut-off, which allow air pressures to be reduced.

The pressure under which miners can safely work can be as high as 340 kN/m^2 (3.4 bar), but normal pressures for working in compressed air are below 2 bar. At a pressure of 2 bar the decompression time, based on the Medical Code of Practice for Work in Compressed Air, is 106 minutes for a three hour shift and 136 minutes for over a four hour shift. Although there is no restriction on the length of the working period in Regulations covering compressed air working, experience has shown that men with no previous experience or who have not recently worked in compressed air should not exceed shifts of four hours under pressure. Guidance for exposure times are given in the Medical Code of Practice.* The supply of fresh air to the working chamber should be at least 300 litres per minute for each man in the chamber and the air temperature should not exceed 21 °C. The maximum working temperature in a chamber should not exceed 27 °C on a wet bulb thermometer.

5.1.6   Safety aspects

Safety aspects in tunnel construction may be divided into two sections, namely safety in soft ground and safety in hard rock.

Safety in soft ground

Having dealt with compressed air in the section above and also in Chapter 1, we now go on to consider other aspects. The face of every tunnel and base and crown of every shaft requires inspection by a competent person at the commencement of every shift. Materials for supporting the ground must be examined by a competent person before use and the erection and dismantling of supports must be directed by a competent person.

*Published by CIRIA

These and other regulations apply to all types of tunnelling work. One of the main hazards in soft ground is movement of soil; this may cause pipelines to settle and fracture, creating dangerous conditions above or in the tunnel. The development of high-pressure jacking equipment has brought about hazards of spilt oil and high-pressure blowouts. The design of temporary works for holding the face of a tunnel requires special attention: all timbers should fit in position without adjustment being necessary; this reduces the time that the face is left open. Many accidents occur during the mucking operation and it is therefore essential that adequate illumination be provided at the working face and protection given against moving muck-waggons or conveyor belts. Provision should be made, if room allows, for the walkway to be separated from the haulway. Spillage of soft material can create slippery conditions and precautions should be taken to eliminate this hazard so far as is practicable. Where laser equipment is being used for alignment of tunnels workmen must be protected from the rays emitted.

A final note on safety in compressed air working concerns the hazard of fire: this hazard is very high because of the excess oxygen in the working chamber. Whilst it is easy to prevent smoking it is not so easy to eliminate burning and welding operations. Fire extinguishers are of no use in high pressures since they operate on a pressure basis and their pressure is insufficient to overcome the pressure in the working chamber. The best method of dealing with a fire in such conditions is to smother it.

Safety in hard rock tunnels

The hazards peculiar to tunnelling in rock can be summarised as follows:

Rock falls

Blasting and use of explosives

Dust and fumes

Noise

Movement of heavy plant.

Small rock falls may occur in large tunnels during scaling operations, or when scaling-down, after blasting has not cleared away all loose material. The decision to support the rock depends a great deal on the rock condition, and the type of support depends on the availability of plant and material, together with economic considerations.

Explosives must be used only by experienced men; however, even then dangerous practices can develop. Failure to remove sources of electric power, checking the circuits at the face instead of from the blasting position, and smoking at the face, are practices which are not uncommon. When dealing with 'misfires' these must be washed out with water, or a relief hole drilled at least 0.5m away.

Dust and fumes can only be dealt with by efficient ventilation (see Section 5.1.7 on Ventilation). The concentration of dust and fumes should be checked regularly: there is immediate danger from fumes if men return to the face too soon after blasting, whereas dust is a long-term hazard which could give rise to Pneumocosis. It is recommended that twenty minutes should elapse between blasting and a return to work but tests should be made for the presence of carbon monoxide and carbon dioxide.

Noise created by heavy plant and drilling machines produces a short-term problem of poor communications which can lead to accidents. In the long term it can have a serious effect on the hearing. These problems can be overcome by wearing protective ear plugs or muffs.

Movement of plant, especially plant concerned with muck moving, is responsible for many accidents in tunnelling. Particular problems may arise when coupling and uncoupling skips and when re-railing skips which have jumped the lines. A common accident which occurs with hand drilling machines is that if the steel breaks, the operator can fall forward and sustain an injury.

5.1.7 Ventilation and lighting

Tunnelling work requires efficient ventilation to clear the dust and fumes, or simply to provide fresh air at the working face.

Mechanical ventilation is usually supplied to the face by electrically driven fans which blow fresh air into or exhaust foul air from the tunnel. In the former case the air is blown through a lightweight pipe or fabric duct:

in the exhaust system it is necessary to use rigid ducting to prevent its collapse under conditions of partial vacuum. Some installations use both systems; this is achieved by a two-way valve and duct arrangement which can be changed to suit conditions. The quantity of fresh air per man should be based on a minimum of 8.33 m^3/min: for a team of eight men this would call for 67 m^3 of fresh air per minute at the tunnel face. In addition allowance must be made for any diesel-operated plant at the rate of 4 m^3/min per kW.

Since the amount of air required for clearing blasting fumes is much greater than the amount required for normal working conditions, the ventilation system should be equipped with variable-load fans to remove quickly the dangerous fumes.

In the blown-air system, air is released at the face and the pressure carries the foul air back down the tunnel, which may be detrimental to workers in other parts of the tunnel. The exhaust system draws the foul air and dust into the duct near the working face, thereby causing fresh air to flow the full length of the tunnel. As mentioned above, a combined system may be used; this has the advantage of exhausting the noxious fumes after blasting before reverting to the blowing method. Care must be taken to avoid 'dead' areas in long tunnels.

Economy in ventilating depends on the airtightness and resistance of the duct: loss of volume or a drop in pressure lead to high running costs.

Adequate lighting in tunnels is a pre-requisite to efficient working. A light intensity of 250 lux in the working area is necessary if men are required to work at maximum efficiency. This service is further complicated by the fact that lamps should be withdrawn from the face prior to blasting and then returned for working. The size and spacing of lights depends upon factors such as tunnel dimensions and rock conditions. In addition to the normal lighting, an emergency reserve circuit, supplied by batteries or a generator, is desirable.

5.2 UNDERPINNING

This section on underpinning deals mainly with heavy construction and structures such as those found in civil engineering. Although some of the methods discussed apply equally to the underpinning of lighter structures, it is suggested that such work be studied as part of building construction as distinct from civil engineering.

5.2.1 General considerations

Before underpinning is resorted to, a full investigation should take place to ascertain its feasibility. The object of underpinning is to transfer foundation loads from existing levels to new levels at greater depths. The operation may be carried out for one or all of the following reasons:

To allow the adjacent ground level to be lowered

To increase the load-bearing capacity of the foundation

To arrest settlement of a foundation.

Investigation of the ground below the structure is essential before work commences; such an investigation will assist in the determination of:

Conditions responsible for settlement

The nature of ground and its load-bearing capacity

The depth at which the new foundation can be established.

The structural stability of the building being underpinned must be checked for inherent weaknesses which may develop during the underpinning operations. Precautions should be taken to reduce the load on the structures being underpinned; this can be achieved by propping, shoring and removal of live loads within the structure. High walls should be checked for plumb before and during the underpinning work; datum levels should be established and checked frequently as the work proceeds.

Before excavation of supporting ground is commenced, the support of the excavated face must be carefully planned. This could take the form of chemical injection or pressure grouting with cement; alternatively, normal timbering may be employed. The underpinning should be executed in stages which allow a gradual transfer of load without risk of settlement.

5.2.2 Methods of underpinning

The method of underpinning chosen will vary with the need for underpinning. The following examples will be considered:

Underpinning of settlement due to shallow-seated faults

Underpinning of settlement due to mining subsidence

Underpinning against the effects of adjacent excavation

Underpinning to move structures.

Settlement due to shallow-seated faults, such as compressible soil, is easily arrested when compared with mining subsidence. The foundation can be supported by beams and piles (Fig 5.19(a); if access is not available to the inside face of the wall the concrete beam may be cantilevered as in Fig 5.19(b). In all cases the piles will be taken down to a load-bearing stratum. An alternative method to the cantilevered beam is the 'jacked pile' (Fig 5.20), in which short sections of precast pile are jacked down to a load-bearing stratum; in this method the foundation is used as a reaction for the jacking process.

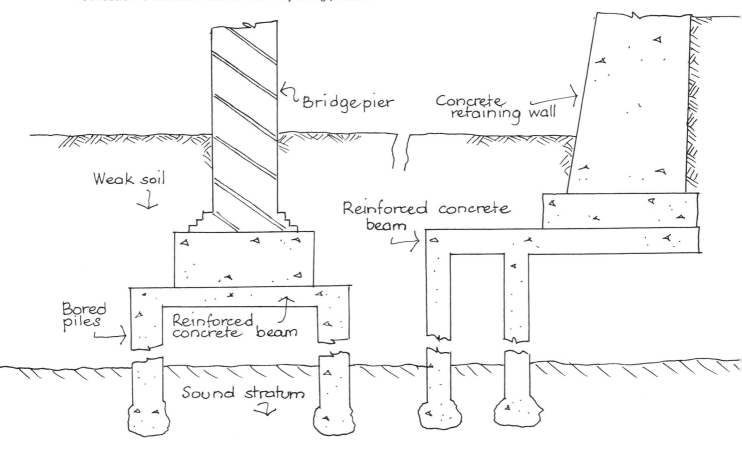

Fig 5.19(a)   *Underpinning with piles and beams*   Fig 5.19(b)   *Cantilever beams*

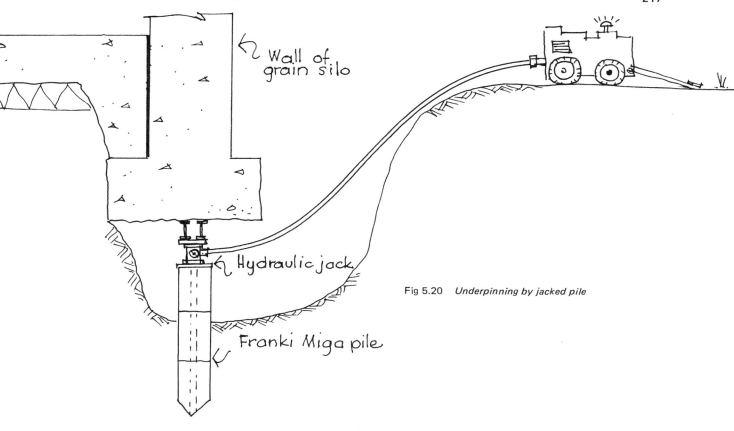

Fig 5.20   *Underpinning by jacked pile*

Underpinning for mining subsidence differs from traditional underpinning in that it is uneconomical to sink a foundation to a stratum which is not subject to settlement. There are two broad methods of dealing with this problem: firstly, to form a raft or series of continuous beams under the building, thereby distributing the load over a large area and thus preventing local fracture due to ground movement; and secondly, to construct jacking points under the building so as to permit jacking back to the vertical and horizontal positions. The latter method has been used in the construction of large industrial complexes in which settlement due to coal mining is inevitable. The pedatifid raft system, installed by Pynford (Southern) Limited, has been successfully used on a large automatic plant near Nottingham. The structure was built on a slab approximately 49 x 18 metres. Jacking positions were arranged in four rows which divide the slab into three equal areas. The jacking points, known as 'pedatifid pockets', are in pairs spaced at 2.4 metres centres along the rows (Fig 5.21) which are parallel to the longer axis. The overall depth of the movable slab is 600 mm and a series of longitudinal beams, cross-beams and covering slab form a waffle plate design (Fig 5.22) around the jacks. The waffle-plate slab, which stands in a recessed sub-base, has its top surface level with the adjoining factory floor. When the floor requires re-levelling, the space beneath the raft is sealed so that an air pressure of 7 kN/m^2 can be used to reduce the weight of the slab on the jacks. After lifting the slab to the required level it is permanently supported at all the pockets.

The pedatifid system is designed so that access to the jacking positions can be obtained from above the raft level by removing steel plates in the floor. These plates are bolted down to the raft with substantial bolts anchored into the slab; the jacks are arranged in pairs so that either one can carry the full load at the pocket during lifting operations. To lift the slab jacks are placed mounted on top of short columns passed down through the slab to the sub-slab; the main slab is then jacked to the desired level and supported by short columns which have been cut to fit between the jacking point and the sub-slab. The jacks are then removed in sequence and the cover plates are bolted down to hold the slab.

The principal advantage of this system is that it is not necessary to provide a shallow basement beneath the slab to give access to the jacks and jacking positions. Another advantage is that due to the small size of the pockets and the fact that they can be placed anywhere to suit access above floor level it is possible to provide many points of support thus reducing the depth of the floor beams.

Fig 5.21   *Pedatifid pockets in pairs* (Pynford Design Limited)

Fig 5.22   *Formation of waffle plate around pedatifid pockets* (Pynford Design Limited)

Underpinning against the effects of adjacent excavation can be accomplished by several methods:

Traditional underpinning executed in sections	(Fig 5.23)
Piling, using contiguous piles	(Fig 5.24)
Diaphragm walling	(Fig 5.25)
Chemical injection	(Fig 5.29)

The disadvantage of using traditional methods of underpinning (as shown in Fig 5.23) is two-fold. Firstly, the soil at the back of the proposed underpinning is subject to slip during the underpinning excavation, which could lead to settlement of floors within the existing building. Secondly, the actual pinning against the existing foundation is very difficult to achieve without some minor settlement; methods of minimising this settlement include 'Pretest' underpinning and the use of Freyssinet 'flat-jacks'.

The 'Pretest' method is used in conjunction with normal underpinning in which 'legs' of brickwork or concrete are brought up to a required level and after hardening are used to support jacks and concrete beams. The beams support a layer of wet concrete which, when jacked up against the existing foundation, squeezes into and around all the projections. After this concrete has hardened, the space between the legs and concrete beam is filled (Fig 5.26).

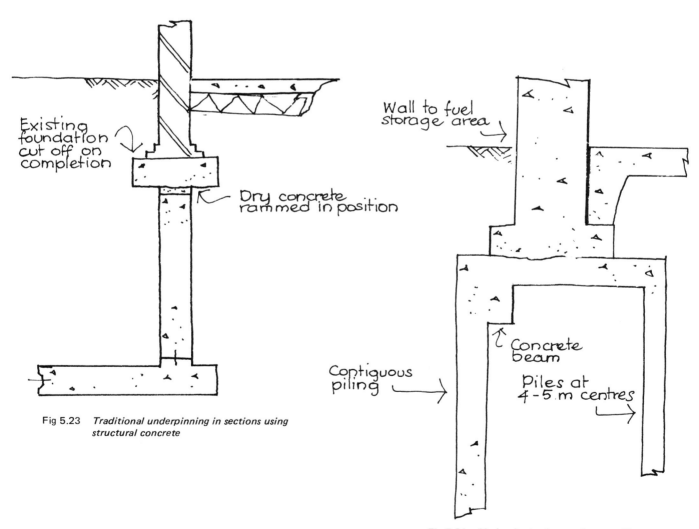

Fig 5.23 *Traditional underpinning in sections using structural concrete*

Fig 5.24 *Underpinning by contiguous piling*

The Freyssinet 'flat-jack' method works on the following principle: the jacks, which consist of hollow light-gauge metal canisters approximately 250 mm in diameter, are placed between the legs of underpinning and the existing foundation. Oil is introduced under pressure and the jack expands to stress the new foundation against the existing. When the desired stress has been reached an epoxy resin is then introduced and the injector pressure pipe is sealed off. The space between the legs and the existing foundation is then rammed with dry concrete (Fig 5.27).

A further method of underpinning by an expanding system is one using an adjustable pile head (Fig 5.28). This device was used for supporting tunnel sections in the River Maas at Rotterdam. The problem was one of ensuring that the submerged tunnel sections were sitting evenly on the pile foundations. The grout pressure lifts the head of the pile until it supports the desired load.

Chemical injection is very suitable for underpinning ground of a gravelly nature. The soil is removed to the level of the top of the existing foundation and grout tubes or drill holes are inserted. The grout is injected under pressure to form a wall of solid soil which both supports the existing foundation and allows excavation without complicated shoring. This method of underpinning has been used by the Central Electricity Generating Board to strengthen the foundations of cooling towers (Fig 5.29). A two-shot silicate-based process was used, sodium silicate being injected as the lances or injection tubes were driven in and calcium chloride being added during withdrawal (see Section 3.3.5).

Underpinning to move structures

This form of underpinning is employed when structures require moving without resorting to extensive demolition. The weight of the building is transferred from the foundations to a series of wheeled carriages: this is achieved by a system of beams which penetrate and support the walls. The carriages are mounted on rails which are laid in the required direction of movement: changes in direction can be achieved by relieving any carriage of its load and swinging the rails into correct alignment. Such operations are carried out by specialist firms who carefully survey and brace the structure to prevent damage during the operation. New foundations are prepared to receive the structure when it has been re-positioned and the structure is carefully lowered on to the foundation by means of jacks.

This method of underpinning has been used for moving framed buildings up to five storeys high for a distance of 0.4 km.

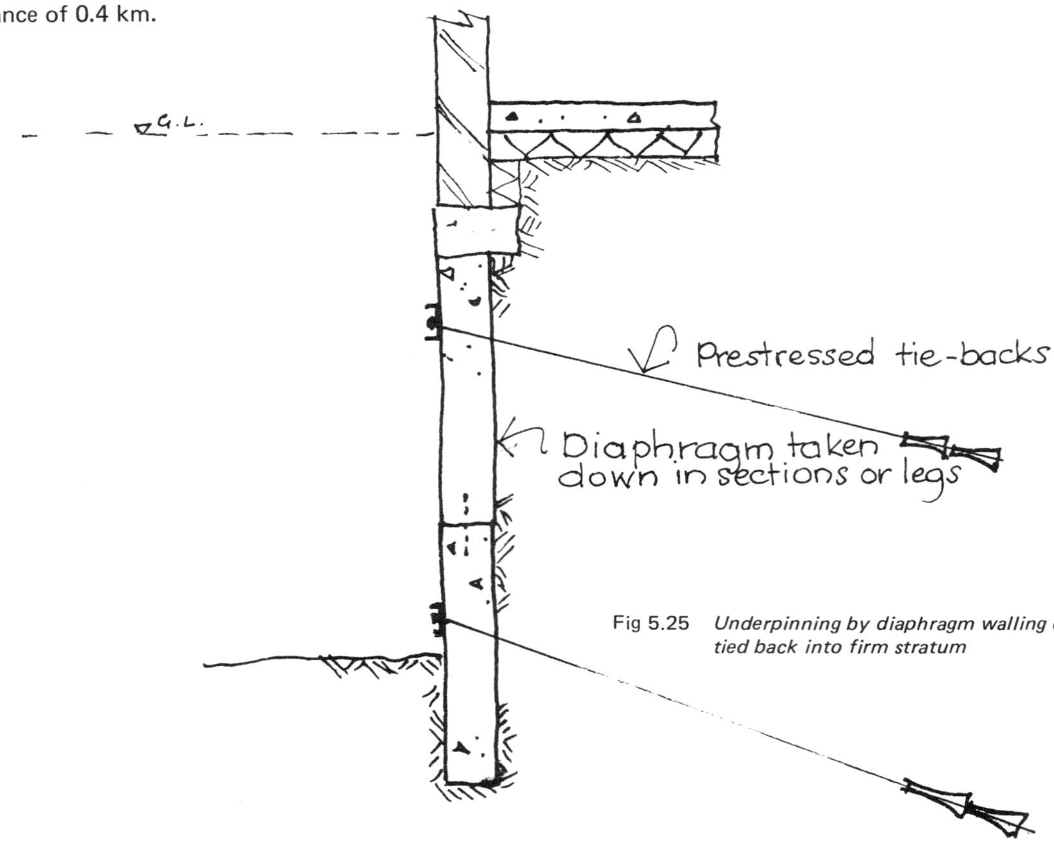

Fig 5.25 *Underpinning by diaphragm walling each section tied back into firm stratum*

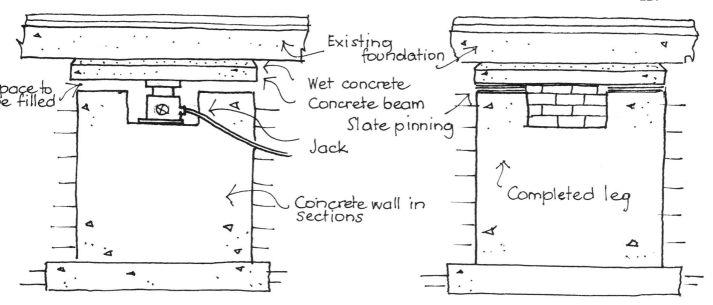

Fig 5.26   *'Pretest' method of underpinning*

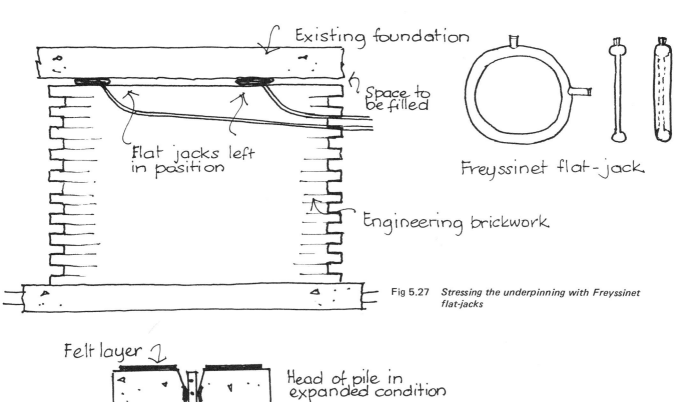

Fig 5.27   *Stressing the underpinning with Freyssinet flat-jacks*

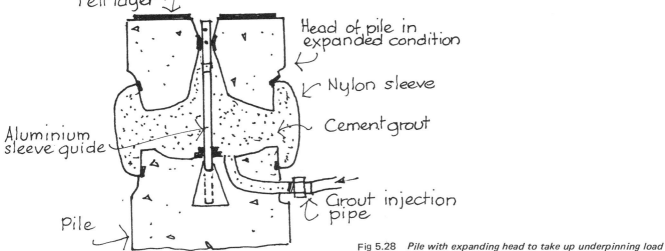

Fig 5.28   *Pile with expanding head to take up underpinning load*

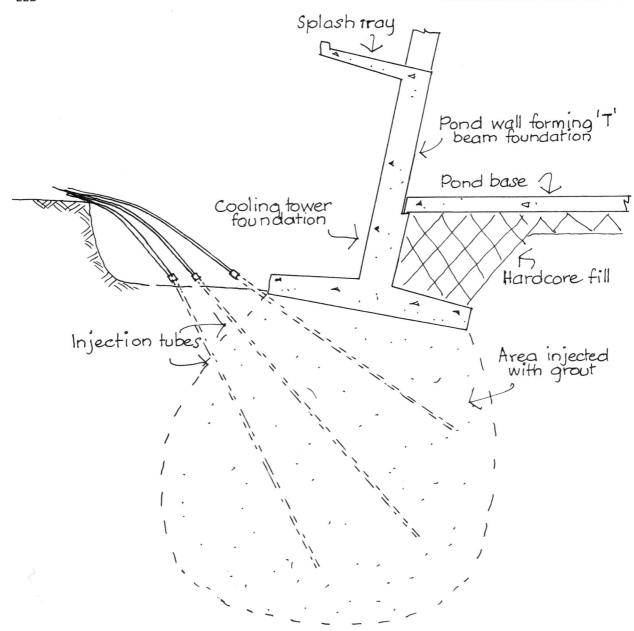

Splash tray

Pond wall forming 'T' beam foundation

Pond base

Cooling tower foundation

Hardcore fill

Injection tubes

Area injected with grout

Fig 5.29   *Underpinning by injection to cooling tower foundation*

Chapter 6

Marine and Other Works Associated with
River or Groundwater Environments

6.1 COFFERDAMS

6.1.1 Introduction

Cofferdams are usually temporary structures which may be employed to assist in the formation of foundations. Their function is to provide a working area at foundation level from which ground and water is excluded sufficiently to permit safe working. It should be noted that cofferdams do not necessarily exclude all water, since it would be uneconomical to attempt to do so.

It is common practice to use steel sheet piling for cofferdams, but although this material is ideally suited, being strong and relatively watertight, it is not the only suitable material, especially with the increased use of diaphragm walling. Material used in the construction of cofferdams should suit design requirements and these may involve earth, rock, steel or concrete.

The choice of material and type of cofferdam will depend upon the following conditions:

Location of cofferdam, e.g. onshore, estuarine, offshore

Depth of and size of excavation

Type of overburden and substrata

Volume of water, velocity of flow, tide levels

Availability of materials

Accessibility of site.

If the head of water is low, then an earthfill cofferdam may suffice; if the water is likely to erode or undermine the dam, a face of impervious material may be used to protect the earthfill, the fill giving weight and support to the face material. Before selecting the type of cofferdam to be used, a full site investigation should be carried out. Borings should be made and samples of soil tested, in relation to both permanent and temporary works. It is essential when constructing cofferdams to assess the insitu permeability and strength of the soil: this will assist in determining the depth to which the cofferdam sheeting can be driven to prevent 'blow' or 'boiling' (a 'blow' or 'boil' is caused by the flow of water and soil, usually fine silt, into the bottom of an excavation, due to the water pressure outside the excavation being greater than that inside). When cofferdams are constructed in fast-flowing rivers the site investigation should assess the problems which may occur due to current-velocities and wave action. Reinforced concrete should be of a quality to satisfy the CP 114: 1969; the stress limits for temporary works that are only temporarily subjected to loading may be increased, at the discretion of the engineer, above the allowable stress limits, but in no circumstances to more than 33 $^1/_3$% above the stresses specified in the Code.

Steel used in cofferdams should comply with the requirements of BS 4360 and BS 449 or the equivalent foreign standards, with a permissible increase up to 25% where the loading can be assessed with confidence (ref: CP 2004: 1972) and where the works are of a temporary nature.

6.1.2   Types of cofferdams and methods of construction

The main types of cofferdams are shown in Fig 6.1, the upper part of the chart showing the usual types, the lower part showing those which utilise steel sheet piling. It will be seen from Fig 6.1 that certain types are suitable for both water and land cofferdams whereas others are suited only to one or other; for this reason the selection of the type to be used requires detailed consideration, and for this a full site investigation report is necessary.

Selection of cofferdams

When selecting a suitable cofferdam for a specific problem the following factors should be considered:

Site investigation report

Whether the cofferdam is required on land or in water

The size of the working area required inside the cofferdam

The nature of the permanent works to be built

The amount of water or soil to be excluded whilst work proceeds in the cofferdam

Soil conditions

Water conditions, i.e. strength of flow, wave action, tide or groundwater range

Availability of materials and plant

Possible effect of the cofferdam construction on adjacent structures

Possible methods of constructing the cofferdam

Cost in comparison with other solutions.

The final choice may result in a combination of cofferdam types, e.g. sheet piling and ground stabilisation, or even in a change in mode of support, e.g. choosing a caisson rather than a cofferdam.

Gravity Cofferdams

Earth and rockfill cofferdams are the most common gravity type (Fig 6.1). They are enclosures formed by banks of soil or rock. They are very suitable for protecting large areas of excavation against flood waters and are best constructed in the dry during low-water periods. If the velocity or water is small and the head of pressure low, then earth fill is suitable (see Section 3.2.5); if the velocity is likely to be high, rock fill offers better resistance to scouring if founded on similar material. The side slopes of the dam will depend upon the size and shape of stones; where rock of sufficient size is not available, a quantity of smaller rocks may be enclosed in wire-mesh nets or baskets (see Section 6.6 for 'Gabions'). The water at high tide or flood level may be controlled by sealing the dam with clay or other suitable fine material (Fig 6.2). Water that flows beneath the dam can be intercepted by a ditch and drained away.

Sheeted cofferdams

Sheet piling has gradually replaced timber sheeting but where timber is readily available it can be used economically in low-head dams. A combination of H-beam piles and timber sheeting is very suitable for supporting deep excavations in waterlogged ground but only if ground water lowering methods are also employed inside and outside the cofferdam.

Crib cofferdams (Fig 6.3) are formed by a framework of heavy timbers or precast concrete units which are laced together in a criss-cross fashion to form pockets up to 3.5 metres square. The units are secured to each other by bolts and the pockets are filled with rock for stability. The water-face of the crib can be made watertight by driving a single line of steel sheet piling along the face. A water cut-off is formed by driving the sheet piling to an impervious stratum. The use of this type of cofferdam in the UK is now rare.

Concrete sheeting includes precast sheet piles, precast or cast in-situ panels or slabs, contiguous bored piles and conventional diaphragm walling (see Section 4.4 on Diaphragm Walling). The two most popular methods of concrete sheeting are contiguous piling (Fig 6.4) and diaphragm walling (Fig 6.5). It should be noted that although these forms of structure are permanent, in that they are not demolished or dismantled on completion of the works, they are not necessarily an integral part of the permanent works but can be designed as such.

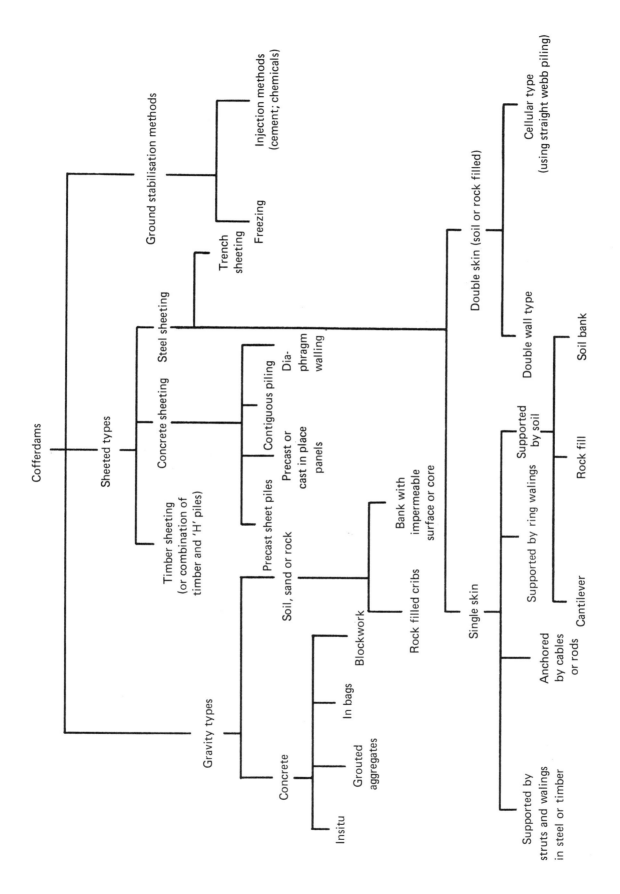

Fig 6.1 *Cofferdam types*

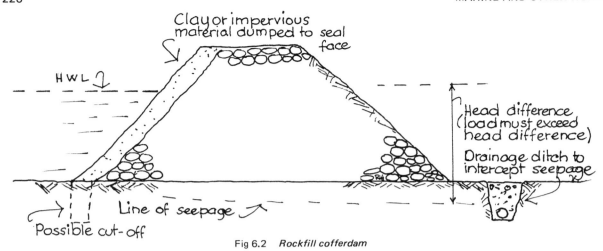

Fig 6.2   *Rockfill cofferdam*

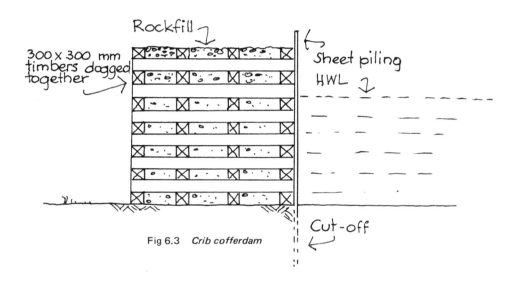

Fig 6.3   *Crib cofferdam*

Contiguous piling may be used where headroom or vibration prevents the driving of steel sheet piling. Where boulders would hamper the driving of sheet piling, special measures are necessary.

Diaphragm walling is particularly suitable for large cofferdams in weak or waterlogged ground, because the great stresses involved can be resisted by increasing the thickness and depth of the diaphragm.

Steel sheeting can be divided into two distinct types: single-skin, which has one or more vertical stages, and double-skin, which consists of two lines of sheet piles or circular cells of sheeting filled with rock or other material.

Single-skin sheet pile cofferdams: steel sheet piling, of dimensions suitable to withstand the external pressures, is driven into an impermeable stratum and, if required, supported above the cantilevered end by struts, walings, or anchors. The amount and type of support will depend on the external pressures. Figs 6.6 to 6.9 show the various types of support. The construction of sheet steel piled cofferdams will be the same as that of other forms of sheet piling, which are fully described in Section 4.1.

Double-skin cofferdams: these are self-supporting gravity structures, of either the parallel-sided double-wall or the cellular cofferdam type (Figs 6.10 and 6.11). The stability of these dams depends on the fill material and on the arrangement of the sheet piling. The width of the dam should not normally be less than 0.8 times the height of retained water and/or soil. Cofferdams which exclude water must be provided with sluice gates to allow the works to be flooded (if the nature of the work inside the cofferdam allows flooding) to equalise the external pressures during storm conditions.

Fig 6.4   *Contiguous piling in cofferdam work* (Soil Mechanics Limited)

Fig 6.5   *Circular cofferdam using diaphragm walling (the walls are 1 metre thick and 30 metres deep) for pump house*
(C.O.S. Engineering Limited)

Fig 6.6   *Steel sheet cofferdams (supported by steel struts and walings)* (Edmund Nuttall Limited)

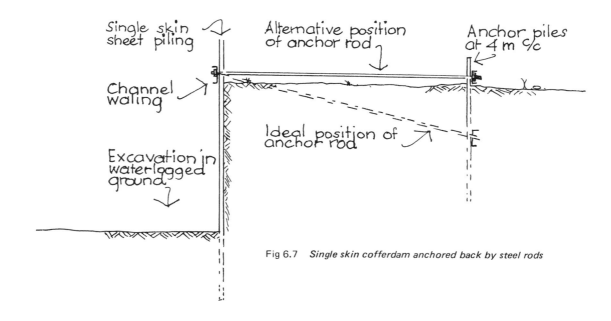

Fig 6.7   *Single skin cofferdam anchored back by steel rods*

Fig 6.8 *Circular cofferdam supported by ring walings* (Gleeson Civil Engineering Limited)

Fig 6.9 *Single skin cofferdam supported by soil*

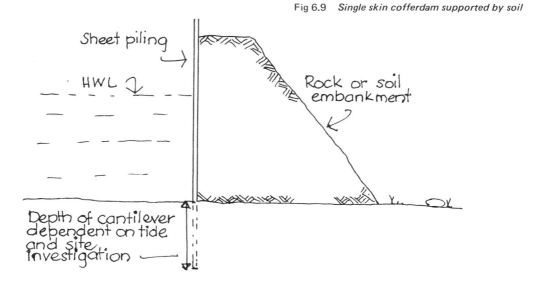

Cellular cofferdams are constructed from straight-web steel sheet piling (see Section 4.1). The piling is interlocked and driven to form cells; the fill material develops high circumferential tensile forces in the piling which straight-web piling is best able to resist; for this reason trough-shaped sections are rarely used. Cellular cofferdams are suitable for resisting the considerable head differences which are encountered in harbour and dock works. The piling does not have to penetrate the hard stratum for stability, although some penetration is necessary to prevent seepage under the dam. Cellular cofferdams can be used on irregular beds of rock when the sheet piles are cut to fit the rock profile.

Double-wall cofferdams consist of two parallel lines of sheet piling connected by walings and tie rods at one or more levels; the space between the walls is filled with material to give stability. The inner line of piling is designed as a retaining wall suitably keyed into solid strata, and the outer line as anchorage. Ordinary steel pile sections are preferable for these structures.

Ground stabilisation

This may also be used in cofferdam construction, the practical methods being chemical or cement injection and freezing techniques. These methods of dealing with ground conditions are described in Chapter 3.

It should be stated that whatever type and method of construction employed, cofferdams may be billed in two different ways: either as part of temporary works, or in detail from a specific engineer's design.

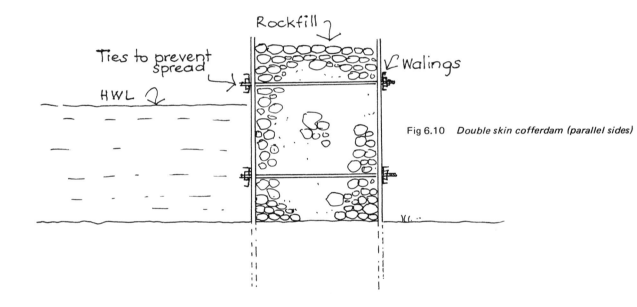

Fig 6.10   *Double skin cofferdam (parallel sides)*

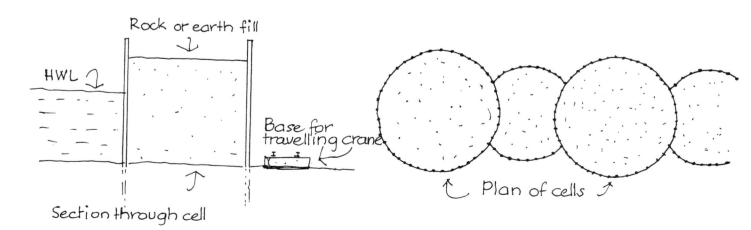

Fig 6.11 (a)   *Cellular cofferdam*

Fig 6.11(b)   *Cellular cofferdams for Leigth Harbour Development*   (Edmund Nuttall Limited)

6.1.3   Economic factors

The factors for consideration in this section are the same as those mentioned in Section 6.1.2 under the heading of 'Selection'. The design for a cofferdam may be executed in various ways and in different materials, but a cost 'break-even' point can be established for the various solutions. The main economic limitations are size and depth of cofferdam; above a certain size shoring becomes prohibitive with thin wall dams and thick diaphragm walling may well prove more economic. A diaphragm wall may be sunk to depths to which steel sheet piling cannot be driven and so deep cut-off walls can best be formed by this method. However, for cofferdams of shallow depth, i.e. up to 10 metres, steel sheet piling is usually the least expensive. Earth and rockfill are even cheaper than steel sheet piling for very large shallow cofferdams. The nature of the permanent works and method and sequence of excavating may affect the amount of strutting and shoring needed in the cofferdam and thus influence both the design and the cost. Safety is also of paramount importance, since many accidents have occurred in cofferdams.

6.2 CAISSONS

6.2.1 Introduction

Caissons are structures which are sunk through ground or water to provide working space for the purpose of excavating and executing work at a prescribed depth, and which subsequently become an integral part of the permanent work. They may be constructed of steel, cast iron segments or reinforced concrete, or a combination of these materials. The plan area of the caisson in relation to that of the superstructure should be sufficient to provide for some deviation from its precise position during sinking.

Choice between cofferdams and caissons

Since the usual difference between a cofferdam and a caisson is one of temporary enclosure and incorporation with final works, the type of structure being erected within the enclosure will indicate whether a permanent enclosure is economically viable. The chief factors influencing the choice between the two enclosures are ground conditions and the depth to which the work is to be taken. If the sinking of the enclosure requires compressed air working, a caisson may be used, although it is possible to fit cofferdams with air-decks. Generally, cofferdams are suitable for depths of up to 18 metres below high water level, while for greater depths caissons should be employed. Caissons are restricted, if compressed air working is employed, to a maximum pressure of 340 kN m^2 (3.4 bar).

Design

The design of a caisson (usually contractor design) will be determined by several factors, such as proposed method of sinking, size of caisson and nature of the permanent works. The sides of the caisson should be free from bulges and constructed so as not to lose their shape during sinking; in some cases steel caissons are strengthened by insitu concrete between inner and outer walls to prevent buckling and to add weight to prevent floating. The bottom of a caisson is fitted with a shoe or cutting edge which projects beyond the face of the caisson: this allows the shoe to cleave a hole larger than the caisson and so reduces skin friction. Skin friction of between 10 kN/m^2 to 25 kN/m^2 can be assumed when the caisson is moving, although much greater friction has to be overcome to start movement. This friction can be greatly reduced by using water jets or bentonite as lubrication, additional kentledge or concrete being added to maintain movement.

6.2.2 Caisson types and forms of construction

There are four main types of caisson:

Box caissons

Open caissons

Compressed air caissons

Monoliths.

Box caissons are prefabricated boxes, usually in concrete, with sides and a bottom, which are set down on a prepared base. The box is then filled with concrete to form a massive foundation for a pier or similar structure (Fig 6.12). They are, however, unsuitable where foundations may be subject to erosion by fast moving water; this can be solved by setting the caisson on a piled foundation if the sub-strata permit the driving of piles; the piles also act as anchorage against buoyancy.

Excavation of the site is carried out by dredger or grab in normal conditions, i.e. gravel or mud bed, and a layer of crushed rock is levelled on the bed of the sea or river to receive the caisson. If the sub-stratum is rock, it should be levelled off, by blasting, before laying the crushed rock base. Setting of the caisson is covered in Section 6.2.3.

The box caisson may be concreted by one of three methods: tremie pipe, pump, or bottom-opening skip, the first being the most common method in recent years. Box caissons must be anchored or ballasted to prevent flotation before the concrete fill has been placed.

Negative buoyancy required at all times

Dredged base

Rock blanket over fissured base

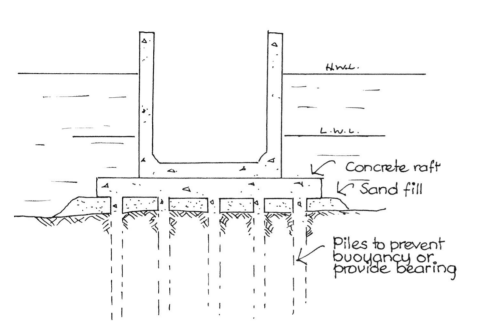

Concrete raft

Sand fill

Piles to prevent buoyancy or provide bearing

Piled foundation

Fig 6.12   Box caisson

Open caissons are structures which are open at both top and bottom and are suitable for foundations in waterways where the sub-stratum is soft clay or silt and therefore easily excavated by grab or air lift. They are also suitable for deep foundations in water where compressed air working would require air pressures above 340 kN/m^2 (3.4 bar): men cannot work in pressures greater than this. Open caissons are not suitable for sinking through ground containing obstructions, e.g. large boulders, unless the depth permits their removal by divers or by compressed air working. The caisson (Fig 6.13) is sunk by grabbing the soil through the open wells. When the caisson has reached the desired depth, the bottom is plugged with a layer of concrete and the well is pumped dry. The foundation is completed by filling the well with concrete or hearting ballast. Care must be taken to ensure that the caisson is sufficiently loaded to resist flotation when it is pumped out.

Compressed air caissons (Fig 6.14) are suitable for sinking foundations in troublesome ground, e.g. ground containing obstacles that require moving by hand. The caisson is positioned and sunk (see Section 6.2.3) and is then lowered into the soil as the soil is removed from within it. Men excavate the soil by hand with aid of pneumatic tools, and load the spoil into skips for hoisting up through the muck-lock. This method of sinking is very suitable for foundations which by other methods might result in the settlement of adjacent structures. The advantages include dry working conditions and accurate levelling and testing of the foundation bed, together with ideal conditions for the placing of concrete. However, the rate of sinking is very

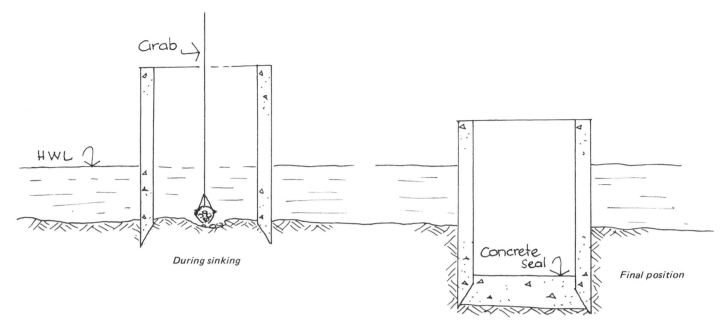

Fig 6.13   *Open caisson*

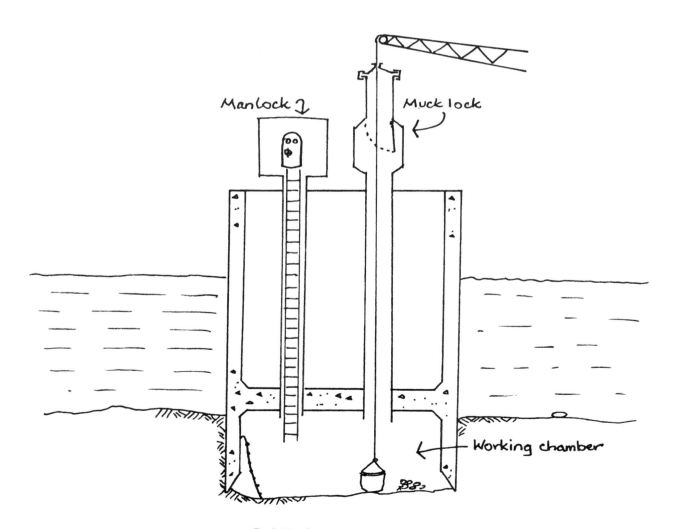

Fig 6.14   *Compressed air caisson*

slow because the manual labour and the depth to which these caissons can be sunk in water is limited by the air pressures required. When the roof of the working chamber is to form part of the structure, the concrete, as ballast filling, should be carefully placed to ensure that no void is formed against the roof. Grout pipes should be incorporated in the roof structure to facilitate the grouting of any spaces formed by shrinkage or by incomplete filling of concrete. Air locks should be located at a height that will not descend below the highest water level during sinking. If the depth of sinking is great it may be necessary to extend the air shaft at various stages of sinking.

In some cases it is possible to design a caisson which can be sunk partly by open grabbing and partly by compressed air. When caissons are to be sunk wholly by compressed air working, the working chamber can occupy the whole area of the caisson rather than a series of separate cells; this will allow freedom of movement for men and materials and also facilitate easier control over sinking. Explosives may be used in the working chamber for removing large obstacles or for levelling rock formation, but special precautions should be taken (ref: CP 2004: 1972).

Monoliths are similar to open caissons with kentledge but differ in that they are much heavier. The monolith consists of reinforced concrete walls of substantial thickness to provide sufficient weight to prevent overturning: for this reason they are often used for quay walls which have to resist great impact forces from ships coming in to berth. Their great weight makes them unsuitable for sinking through very soft deposits because it would be difficult to control the verticality of the structure. With both open caissons and monoliths it is common practice to increase the height and weight of the caisson by casting, insitu, further sections as the structure sinks into the ground. Air decks can be fitted to monoliths and open caissons to permit compressed air working.

6.2.3   Positioning and sinking of caissons

If the caisson is to be founded in a river or sea, it may be partly constructed in dry dock and towed to the site. If this is the case, the shoe of the caisson, which may incorporate 10 to 30 metres of caisson wall, is constructed and then completed when in position. An alternative method of launching the shoe can be seen in Fig 6.15 where the shoe is winched down a slipway into the water. If the caisson is being sunk on land the shoe will be constructed in position on a weak concrete base and the insitu or prefabricated walls will be constructed as excavation proceeds.

Box caissons are designed to be floated to the site and sunk in place, so normal dry dock construction is most suited. These caissons have permanent bottoms which provide the necessary seal for buoyancy and are sunk at low tide and anchored or loaded before high tide. Open caissons have to be fitted with watertight diaphragms.

The caissons are towed out to the site by tugs and are positioned by one of the following methods:

Piling enclosure or dolphins

Wire cables to submerged anchors

Anchored pontoons or barges

Radio buoys and beacons.

A further method of positioning caissons is known as the 'sand island' method (described below).

Piling enclosures or dolphin support: piling, in the form of H-sections or tube sections, is driven into the river or sea bed to form a three-sided enclosure. The piles are linked with welded beams to form fender rails, a further line of piles being driven outside the enclosure to provide support for a working platform. When the platform has been constructed (Fig 6.16), the caisson is towed into the enclosure and the opening in the enclosure is sealed with a connecting truss beam. The clearance between the fender rails and caisson will depend on the size of caisson and the proposed accuracy of sinking, but will be in the region of 300 mm on plan. Dolphins, normally used for mooring ships in estuaries or rivers, are usually formed with raking piles and concrete platforms.

Wire cables to submerged anchors: where the tides or currents are not very strong the caisson may be positioned and lowered into place by winching from submerged anchors. The anchors must be heavy enough to withstand the winching operation: in some cases H-piles are driven down below the mud line to act as anchors.

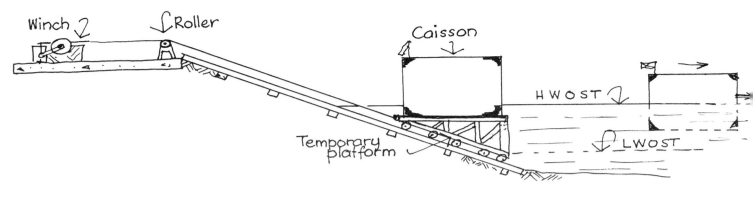

Fig 6.15   *Launching caisson by means of slipway*

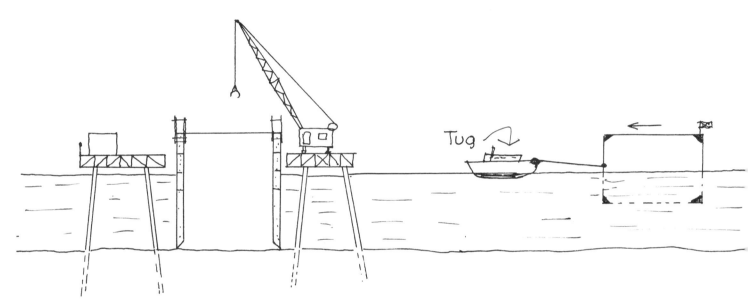

Fig 6.16   *Temporary platform for positioning and sinking caisson*

Floating pontoons, barges or camels (large hollow steel floats) are the simplest forms of guide platform to construct in tidal water. The pontoons are anchored to form a three-sided enclosure (Fig 6.17) and are joined by a heavy truss to form the fourth side when the caisson is in position. The pontoons should be large enough to carry all the construction equipment needed to extend the caisson and excavate the soil.

Sand islands are used for sinking caissons in fast flowing water which would create difficulties for the anchorage of pontoons or for floating a caisson to the site. The island is formed over the proposed site with dredged sand or gravel; steel sheet piling may be used to contain the material. The caisson is constructed on the island and sunk through the sand to the bed. The disadvantage of this method of caisson positioning in rivers and estuaries is the possibility of bed and river bank scouring: the island (Fig 6.18) reduces the width of river and causes the flow of water to scour the adjacent banks and bed planes. In some instances, this has resulted in complete failure of the island.

The sinking of caissons can be achieved by one of the following methods:

Free sinking or jacking down between anchored pontoons

Lowering by block and tackle or cranes from anchored pontoons

Winching from submerged anchors

Controlled sinking, using air domes, and ballasting within lateral control, usually radio beacons.

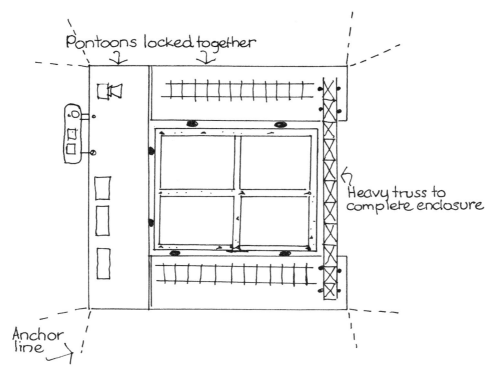

Fig 6.17   *Caisson in position between anchored pontoons*

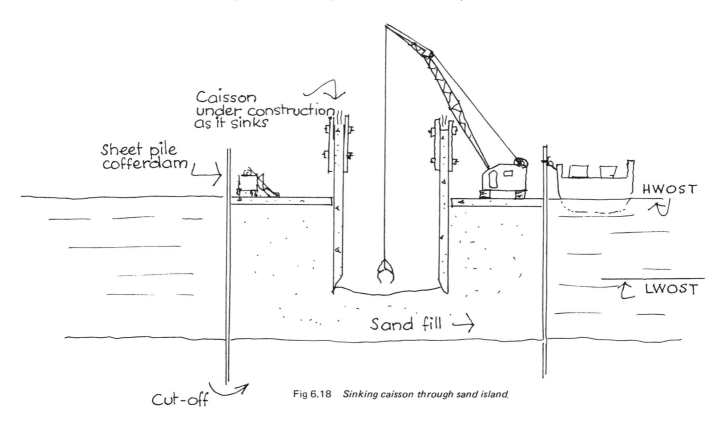

Fig 6.18   *Sinking caisson through sand island*

The initial rate of sinking will depend on the amount of insitu walling to be completed. The top of the caisson should maintain a minimum of 10 metres (in very rough conditions 25 metres) above high water level to receive the extension of the walls. The caisson sinking is accomplished by weighting, or in the case of compressed air caissons and open caissons which have false bottom plates, by controlled flooding. Large open caissons usually have double skin walls, which make them buoyant for towing into position: the cavity between the skins is then filled with concrete for the purpose of sinking.

The final sinking through the silt and mud is normally achieved by grabbing, although ejectors may be used. The ejectors, operated by compressed air or water, churn up the soil which is drawn through an ejector pipe. Compressed air caissons, as stated before, are sunk to their final position by hand excavation. If skin friction prevents the sinking of compressed air caissons a process called 'blowing down' may be used. This process involves removal of men from the working chamber and a rapid reduction of air pressure to increase the effective weight of the caisson.

Land caissons which do not require compressed air to combat ground water are sunk by conventional methods of excavation within the caisson. The toe of the caisson can be rebated to carry a skin of bentonite slurry (Fig 6.19), which reduces the skin friction on the sides of the caisson to a minimum. The caisson shoe is cast or assembled in position and excavators remove the ground under the toe of the shoe and allow the structure to move slowly into the ground. As the excavation and caisson construction continues, the annular space outside the caisson, created by the rebated shoe, is filled with bentonite from pipes carried down inside the wall and out through the shoe. The space may vary from 25 mm to 75 mm in width, depending on the depth of sinking and on ground conditions.

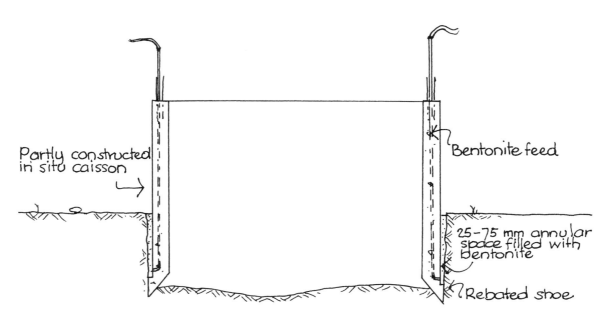

Fig 6.19   *Sinking a caisson on land (with bentonite lubrication)*

6.2.4 Sealing and filling caissons

All loose material should be removed from the bottom of the excavation and the excavation should be level or concave. In some cases it will be necessary for the haunching adjacent to the cutting edge to be removed by hand: this may have to be carried out by a diver.

When sealing open caissons and monoliths the first layer of concrete will have to be placed under water by tremie or bottom opening skip: on completion of the first layer the caisson may be-pumped fully or partially dry for further filling, but if this procedure is followed the caisson must be sufficiently loaded to prevent flotation. Compressed air caissons are concreted in dry conditions. The first layer of concrete, normally 600 mm thick but varying according to the span, seals the floor of the working chamber and is carefully vibrated under the cutting edge of the shoe. Subsequent layers of concrete are placed and vibrated until only a small space is left between the concrete and the roof of the working chamber. The space between concrete fill and the working chamber roof is then pressure grouted with a 1:1 cement-sand grout at 400 kN/m^2 and left for three or four days before the air shafts are finally filled with concrete.

6.3 UNDERWATER FOUNDATION CONSTRUCTION

6.3.1 General considerations

Underwater foundations may have to be constructed in circumstances which prohibit the use of coffer-dams and caissons; the reasons for this are usually the cost and feasibility of the works. Where small-scale or non-repetitive foundation work has to be carried out the cost of constructing a caisson or cofferdam may prove too high, in relation to the permanent works, to be a practical solution. If the stability of cofferdams or caissons is endangered by tides or 'blowing', the cost of 'making safe' may be excessive compared with other construction methods. Long foundation pads to receive precast concrete blocks for harbour wall construction are difficult and costly to form by caisson construction, but insitu methods have proved very successful in calm waters. However, the use of cofferdams in conjunction with underwater construction is common and must not necessarily be considered a separate form of construction.

Some of the problems or limiting factors in this work include:

Transport of men and material; this proves to be difficult in anything but very calm waters

Lifting gear must be carefully positioned and pontoons securely sprung anchored to prevent excessive 'snatching' when lifting loads

Skin divers cannot work efficiently in currents over 2 knots or for long periods in depths of water exceeding 15 metres or in waters where visibility is virtually nil. Hard suit divers can carry out work involving torques, welding etc.

Strong currents cause loss of materials and restrict methods of placing.

6.3.2 Excavation

Excavation is normally carried out by dredgers or grabs, which work off pontoons and load the spoil into barges. Gravel and sand may be excavated by suction dredger or ejector tube, powered by air or water-pressure. Rock formations may be excavated by drill and blast methods, and large boulders reduced by plaster-shooting — see Chapter 3, Section 3.2.2. Foundation trenches should be blasted out in one operation or post jetted to allow a quick follow-up in concreting; slower methods of hand excavation are hampered by silting-up.

Underwater drilling and cutting by jackhammer may be employed on hard rocks where blasting is un-necessary; soft rock may be dredged or broken up by air tool and grabbed.

6.3.3 Formwork

Formwork may be of a temporary or permanent nature. Temporary forms should be made of steel and designed to allow ease of placing by divers. Sand bags may be used to anchor the forms and prevent leakage of concrete under the toe of the form: if an improved seal is required a skirt of plastic sheeting around the forms, suitably anchored with sand bags, may be satisfactory. The effective pressure on the formwork is that due to the submerged weight of the concrete only, but forms can be designed to withstand pressures that occur in normal dry conditions: this provides robust forms which can cope with any underwater conditions. If the concrete foundation is limited in height the forms may consist of bagged cement or concrete placed in layers and left in position on completion. Higher lifts of concrete work may be supported by precast concrete blocks which can form part of the permanent work by using suitable ties: typical formwork sketches are shown in Fig 6.20 and 6.21

6.3.4 Underwater concreting

When a mass of fresh concrete moves through water, or when water flows over the surface of concrete, some of the cement is washed out of the mix. Therefore as much of the concrete as possible should be kept out of contact with the water. This involves maintaining the concrete flow within the initial mass placed, allowing the initial mass to protect the fresh concrete. To achieve the flow of concrete within the mass first placed, the mix must have a high degree of workability. This ensures that the leading edge of the concrete is kept moving forward under the pressure of additional material: a slump of 150 mm is normal. Extra cement over and above the normal requirements for the mix design (typical mix would include 450 kg of cement per m^3 of concrete) must be added to offset loss through water, but too much cement will result in excessive laitance forming on the surface of the concrete.

Fig 6.20   *Temporary formwork for underwater foundation (shallow water only)*

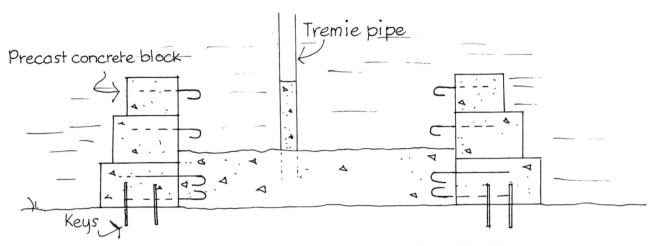

Fig 6.21   *Permanent formwork incorporated with foundation design*

Tolerances in underwater concreting

Dimensional tolerances can approach those for concreting in the dry, but only at great cost and considerable effort. The tolerances specified should be set with due regard to the requirements of the works and the particular conditions under which the work is being constructed. Screeded foundations for precast concrete harbour walls may be laid to a level of 25 mm to 100 mm depending on visibility. Screeding widths of up to 6 metres are possible in good conditions, but smaller widths are to be preferred.

Placing of concrete

This is achieved by three principal methods: tremie, underwater skip and pumping.

Placing by tremie: a tremie (Fig 6.22) is a steel tube suspended in the water from a crane, with a hopper fixed to the top end to receive the concrete. The tube must be watertight, smooth-bored and of adequate diameter for the size of aggregates being used: diameters of 150 mm and 200 mm are commonly used. The tremie is erected vertically over the area to be concreted with the lower end resting on the bottom. A travelling plug, formed from cement bags, foamed plastic or similar material, is placed in the pipe as a barrier between the concrete and water. The water in the pipe is displaced as the weight of concrete forces the plug to the bottom: some plugs float to the surface but if they remain in the concrete their presence is insignificant. After the pipe has been filled with concrete it is raised off the bottom to allow the concrete to flow. Thereafter, the flow should continue to feed the interior of the initial mass. The rate of flow of concrete is controlled by raising and lowering the tremie but care must be taken not to lift the tremie out of the mass. If the bottom of the tremie is lifted out of the mass, the seal will be broken and concrete will be weakened by water as it rushes out of the pipe; seals are often broken when attempting to clear blockages in the pipe. A broken seal may result in a damaged surface to the mass of concrete and consequent removal before work can recommence. Simultaneous placing through more than one tremie is recommended where the concrete cannot be placed from one position: one tremie will serve an area of about 30 m².

Placing by skip: skips used for underwater concreting (see Fig 2.22, Chapter 2) should be of the bottom-opening type which can be operated automatically or manually. The skip should be equipped with a top cover consisting of two loose overlapping canvas flaps, which are kept in position by water pressure; the skip may also be fitted with a skirt to confine the concrete on release. The skip is filled with concrete and the canvas covers are put in position before gently lowering into the water: rapid lowering through the water may disturb the canvas covers and damage the concrete. On reaching the bottom the skip is gently emptied to minimise turbulence of the water around it.

The choice between placing by skip or by tremie rests on economics and on the plant and skills which are available. Placing by skip is the slower but more practical method for thin beds, whereas tremies are suitable for large concrete pours. The continual movement and placing involved with skips makes the concrete subject to a greater loss of strength or damage by exposure to water.

The pumping of concrete is discussed in Chapter 2 and therefore needs no further explanation here; it is used in underwater concreting when very large concrete pours are involved. Other methods, such as re-usable bottom-opening bags (toggle bags), may be used for very small concrete pours.

Injection grouting into coarse aggregate can also be used in underwater concreting. The aggregate, 25 mm or greater, is placed in position and compacted before the grout is pumped into it. The grout should flow from the bottom of the aggregate upwards through the mass. Better-quality concrete can be produced by using 'colloidal grout' (a grout having properties which increases its flow and reduce absorption of water).

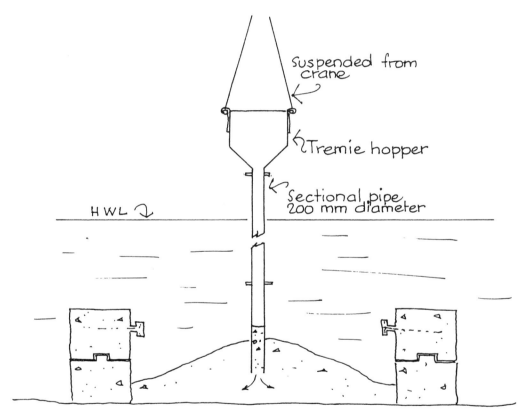

Fig 6.22   *Underwater concreting using tremie pipe*

6.4 SEA WALLS, DOCKS, JETTIES AND OTHER MARINE STRUCTURES

6.4.1 Methods of construction

Sea walls are constructed to resist encroachment by the sea and are often incorporated into the construction of a promenade. They are constructed in various materials, ranging from masonry blocks and precast concrete units to insitu concrete. The design of the wall should minimise the effect of wave action and prevent the underscouring of the foundation (Fig 6.23). Concrete blocks with projecting reinforcement (Fig 6.21) may be used in conjunction with an insitu backing.(See also Section 6.5.3).

Docks may be divided into two types: dry docks and wet docks.

Dry docks differ in design from wet docks in that they have to withstand hydrostatic pressure when the dock is emptied. The walls of the dock should be incorporated with the floor to form a rigid structure and so reduce uplift. If sufficient dead weight cannot be introduced into the construction to prevent buoyancy, a venting system must be provided to relieve the hydrostatic pressure; alternatively anchorage can be used. The walls are normally massive insitu structures which are cast in large, deep trench excavations. The walls are cast in stages of up to 2 metres thick, with stepped construction joints (Fig 6.24). Longitudinal joints should be constructed at intervals of 15 metres; these joints are essentially construction joints with water bars and should be filled with bitumen or other sealing compound. The floor of the dock must, in addition to resisting uplift, be strong enough to distribute a ship's load without settlement or undue deflection. If the loads encountered are very high, a piling support may be adopted, both for supporting a ship's load and resisting uplift. Lock entrance gates, normally of steel construction, may be pivoted or sliding, or consist of floating caisson units.

Wet docks are large areas of water bounded by vertical solid walls against which vessels tie up. The walls must be impermeable to retain the water at high tide level. Locks are provided if entry to the dock is desired at times other than high tide. The walls may be formed by sinking monoliths to a suitable depth and joining them together with insitu concrete: a space of 2 to 3 metres is left between the monoliths to facilitate jointing and finishing. Alternatively, the walls may be constructed with deep diaphragms (Fig 6.25), decking being supported by cross-wall diaphragms.

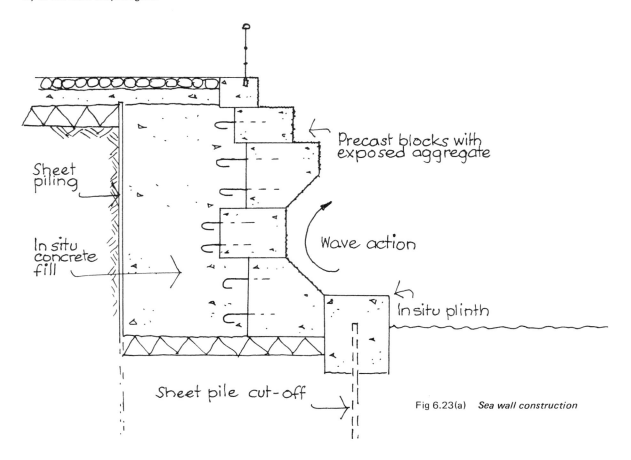

Fig 6.23(a) *Sea wall construction*

Fig 6.23(b)   *Alternative to sea wall. The successive stages of construction in coast defence works*

(Bovis Civil Engineering Limited
Client: Prestatyn UDC
Engineers: Scott, Wilson, Kirkpatrick & Partners)

(Bovis Civil Engineering Limited
Client: Prestatyn UDC
Fig 6.23(c)   *Coast defence work nearing completion*   *Engineers: Scott, Wilson, Kirkpatrick & Partners)*

Fig 6.24   *General view of lock wall construction showing stepped construction joints* (Edmund Nuttall Limited)

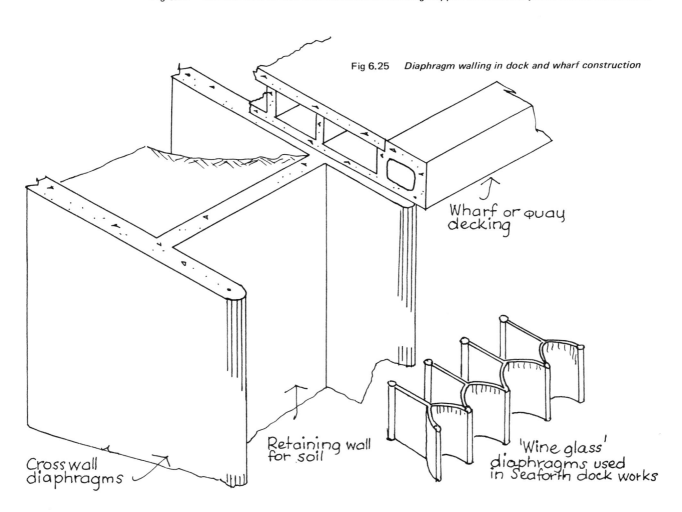

Fig 6.25   *Diaphragm walling in dock and wharf construction*

Wharf or quay decking

Cross wall diaphragms

Retaining wall for soil

'Wine glass' diaphragms used in Seaforth dock works

Wharves are berths for shipping which may retain the surrounding soil or simply provide mooring facilities. Those constructed to retain soil are usually mass concrete walls constructed by means of caisson or diaphragm walling (Fig 6.25). Open wharves, which provide mooring facilities at both sides, can be constructed of piles with concrete decking. An alternative to insitu concrete and caisson construction is the use of precast concrete blocks, which may be dovetail-keyed and weigh anything from 10 tonnes to 30 tonnes each.

Jetties jut out into the sea, usually at right angles to the shore line, although T-shaped and L-shaped jetties are not uncommon. They are open structures, usually of steel tubular or hexagonal piling with a heavy concrete deck (Fig 6.26). They may be used for offloading heavy cargoes, in which case the deck may require extra bracing to the piles; alternatively the jetty may carry pipelines and light lifting gear which do not require heavy bracing. The jetty structure must be designed to withstand impact loads and 'bollard pulls' from berthing ships: this is usually accommodated by raking pile construction and fendering, the latter to avoid holing the ship.

If the sea bed is a rock formation the piling construction will not be economically produced by normal driving methods; holes up to 600 mm diameter may be bored into the sea bed and steel or concrete piles grouted in.

Dolphins are individual mooring points to which vessels may be tied while waiting to enter a wharf or dock. They are also used as a guide to ships entering narrow harbours. Their construction is similar to that of jetties.

Fenders are used in conjunction with all the marine constructions mentioned above. They are used to absorb the kinetic energies produced by berthing vessels. To achieve the necessary absorption, they have to be flexible and may take the form of tubes or springs of metal, rope and plastic. Floating fenders, of rubber and timber, are used to distribute loads over many vertical fenders at the wharf side. If floating fenders are not used the load will normally be applied at deck level and the deck must be suitably braced and protected.

Fig 6.26   *Jetty under construction at Kingsnorth Power Station*   (John Laing & Son Limited)

6.4.2 Other marine structures

Breakwaters or moles

Breakwaters and moles are constructed in the outer harbour area to dampen heavy waves and swell so as to provide easier entrance and exit of vessels. They may be constructed with concrete blocks, rock fill, or a combination of both (Fig 6.27). The choice of material will depend upon the conditions of the site, i.e. depth of water, foundation conditions, range of tides, availability of materials and the anticipated extent of fine weather during construction. Vertical-sided breakwaters are suitable for shallow waters up to 15 metres deep; working in depths above this proves difficult for divers who position the blocks. Where blockwork is used a foundation is prepared by dredging the marine bed and laying a concrete base (see Section 6.3.4 'Underwater Concreting'). Blocks are lowered by cranes operated from pontoons, and are positioned by divers: the location of the blocks is made easier by a dovetailed jointing system (Fig 6.28). As with other large marine structures, caissons are also commonly used for this type of work and are particularly suited to construction of breakwaters in deep waters. The caisson fill may be rock, sand or concrete. Rubble or rock-fill breakwaters are suitable for both shallow and deep waters. The rock fill should contain heavy stones, ranging from 1 to 5 tonnes each in weight, to prevent movement by wave action. The material is transported and placed by bottom-opening barges, some of which have a capacity of 600 m³. Rubble breakwaters require protection against pounding of the deck area by heavy seas and this can be achieved by casting a concrete slab, or by grouting the top layer of rock or laying a precast interlocking deck.

Composite breakwaters for very deep water consist of rock-fill and precast concrete block walls, the walls being taken to a depth of 5 to 10 metres below low water. The concrete blocks for breakwaters of this magnitude should be very heavy, averaging between 20 and 50 tonnes each.

Groynes

Groynes are small section walls of concrete or other suitable material which are built to protect or retain beach material. Steel sheet piling may be used suitably capped and backed with concrete: adequate penetration of the piles prevents underscouring of the structure by wave action.

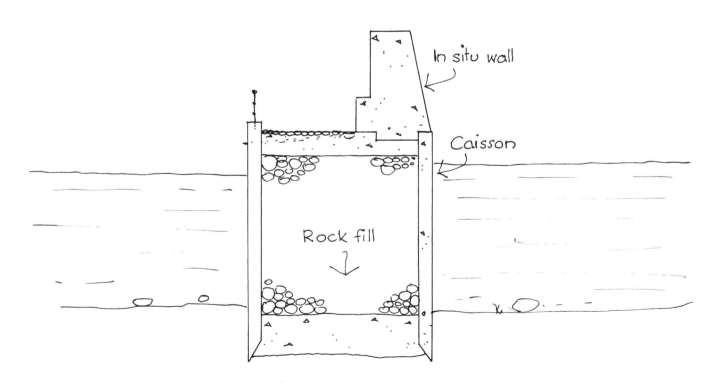

Fig 6.27 *Breakwater or mole construction*

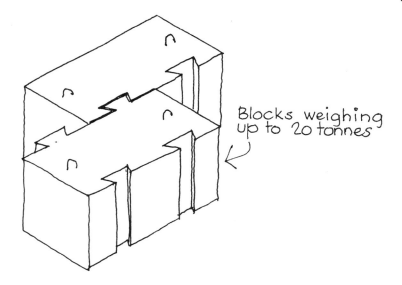

Fig 6.28   *Interlocking concrete blocks*

6.5 DREDGING AND RECLAMATION

6.5.1 General considerations

Definition of and reasons for dredging

Dredging is the process whereby sub-aqueous excavations are carried out by plant located above water level, and may be undertaken for the following reasons:

To lower the bed level to permit the passage of ships

To obtain materials for use in land reclamation

To obtain aggregates which, after desalination, can be used in the manufacture of concrete

To obtain materials for use in the construction of roads and other civil engineering projects

To facilitate the construction of civil engineering works.

Definition of and reasons for reclamation

Reclamation is the process of depositing materials either in the sea or in low-lying swampy areas in such a way that useful areas of land are formed. Almost any type of material can be used for reclamation, depending on the use to which the land is to be put. This will range from agricultural land and land for light industrial uses, which can utilise materials which have low load-bearing capacities, to land for the construction of dock and harbour installations and power stations, which will require high quality incompressible materials.

General considerations in the planning of dredging operations

The one consideration that is common to all types of dredging is the consequence of removing the material. There is little point in dredging in an estuary or harbour or cutting a navigable channel at sea if the void so formed is going to be filled by natural deposition of materials within a very short time. So the first step must be to carry out site investigations and hydrographic surveys to see if the project is feasible from practical, economical and ecological viewpoints. Site investigations are described in greater detail in Chapter 1.

Hydrographic surveys will indicate the characteristics of the seabed and the likely movement of material that will be caused by tides and currents after dredging has taken place. On more important schemes this will be supplemented by a study of scale models which can reproduce marine conditions with great accuracy.

Having established the feasibility of a project, the next stage is to determine the methods of execution, including the necessary plant requirements. Among the more important factors which affect this decision are:

Location of site

Dredging depth

Type of material to be dredged

Disposal of material.

Location of site: the selection of plant and equipment will depend to a large extent on the location of the site; equally the location of the site partially governs the selection of plant and equipment. The dredging of inland waterways such as rivers, canals and lakes will normally require small, easily controllable dredgers such as grabs, cutter suction dredgers or small bucket dredgers. It may even be necessary to use a dredger that can be transported overland. Dredging within harbours or within easy distance of the shore will be done with bucket, trailing suction dredgers or small cutter suction dredgers. Dredging in the open sea calls for large, well-equipped trailing suction dredgers, either with self contained hoppers or serviced by fleets of barges with the necessary tugs, etc.

Dredging depth: navigational requirements can require dredge depths varying from 2 or 3 metres in inland waterways to about 25 metres for very large crude oil carrier (500 000 tonne) approach channels. Underwater pipeline trench excavation will usually require depths within this range also. Dredge depths of up to 60 metres are being presently achieved by the special suction dredgers used for land reclamation with sand in the Ijsselmeer and Maas/Rhine Delta areas of Holland.

Type of material to be dredged: almost any type of material can be dredged. Mud, silt and sand can be removed with bucket or suction dredgers or clam grabs. Harder materials such as clay have to be broken up by bucket or cutter suction dredgers before they can be removed. Hard rock, in some instances, can be excavated by purpose-made rock bucket dredgers, but more often than not will have to be broken up with explosives.

Disposal of material: the vast quantities of material which are removed during dredging operations have to be deposited somewhere else. If there is no area suitable for reclamation, or if the material itself is unsuitable for such a use, the cost of disposal can form a major part of the cost of the operation. Even though the volumes extracted during most inland dredging projects are relatively small, it may still be necessary to employ a fleet of lorries with special water-retaining bodies to transport the material to suitable disposal areas.

The disposal of material dredged from harbours or sea channels presents a greater problem. Depending on whether the material can be utilised or not, it is generally pumped inshore through a pipeline or dumped at sea, but care is required in the selection of the dumping ground. If it is too close inshore it may foul the beaches or silt up a navigation channel. At sea, it must be dumped away from shipping lanes, and in some instances consideration must be given to the possible effect that dumping may have on marine life.

General considerations in the planning of reclamation operations

As with dredging, the prime consideration must be the effect that the project will have on its surroundings. With inland sites, factors which have to be taken into account include the stability of the surrounding land and the effect on existing watercourses. Proper provision must be made to ensure that the run-off from the area can pass round, through or under the area, even at times of flood.

Reclamation of coastal sites, especially on a large scale, can interrupt the natural process by which the foreshore remains stable. This may result in siltation of existing navigable waterways or the undermining of sea defences. It is often necessary to construct scale models with simulated tides and currents to study the effects that a reclamation scheme might have on its surroundings.

Having established the feasibility of the project, the planning stage will involve consideration of:

Location of the site

Type of material

Transport of materials.

The location of the site: for inland sites the question of access is all-important. If necessary, road and/or rail access must be provided, although these will usually also be required as part of the permanent works when the site is developed. Coastal reclamation sites, in addition to the above, may require access from the sea, i.e. a navigable channel. The material from this channel may itself be used in the reclamation.

Type of material: for most coastal sites there is rarely any problem about the material to be used. Sand is not only the easiest and cheapest to win but is also suitable for supporting most types of development; however, the haul distance can be an economic factor. With regard to inland sites, material availability will depend on the location of the site. Excavated material, rock, shale, pulverised fuel ash, even household refuse, can be used for reclamation. The uses to which the site is to be put may rule out some of the more compressible materials, but generally speaking it would be uneconomic to locate a reclamation site in an area where suitable material was not available.

Transport of materials will involve the mobilisation of large amounts of plant. The plant used will determine the rate at which reclamation can be carried out and a great deal of planning will be required to determine the best combination of equipment. The loading of transporting plant — be it dredgers or lorries — the cycle time, the size of the vessels, the placing requirements, will all need to be carefully calculated, as it is their efficiency which will have the greatest effect on the economy of the scheme.

6.5.2 Plant and equipment

Dredging plant

Dredging plant may be broadly described under two main heads:

Digging dredgers

Suction dredgers.

The following is a brief description of the more important types of dredging plant.

Digging dredgers

A bucket dredger (Fig 6.29) is usually a dumb mobile craft with an endless chain of buckets on a ladder similar in action to a trenching machine. Its ladder can be raised and lowered mechanically to the required level and the buckets will discharge either direct into a barge or, more usually, into a hopper within the craft. The former is preferable as it enables the dredger to operate without interruption while dumping takes place.

The maximum depth at which a bucket dredger can work is about 30 metres and its capacity is fairly low. It is, however, easily controlled, being manoeuvred by winches pulling on side, head and stern anchors, and its prime function is river, dock and harbour maintenance. Purpose-made bucket dredgers have been constructed to enable rock and other hard materials to be dredged in this way. The dredging of channels for underwater cables and pipelines can be carried out quickly and accurately with a bucket dredger.

The dragline dredger operates on the same principles as its counterpart on land. Its uses are limited to shallow inland waterways where there are few bridges, and the material dredged from the bed can be dumped on the banks.

The grab dredger, in its simplest form, is a crane with grab attachment mounted on a pontoon. This type requires towing into position and a barge in attendance to receive the grab discharge. At the other end of the scale

is the grab hopper dredger, a self-propelled vessel with multiple cranes which fill its own hopper. The hopper itself
can be self-discharging by means of conveyors or bottom-discharging through opening doors, or it can be emptied
with the same grabs. The grab itself will generally be of the clamshell type to retain mud and silt, but the claw type
is useful for picking up large rock pieces and other debris. The grab dredger is generally used on inland waterways,
docks and harbours, and has special value in the sinking of caissons where it can operate in a confined vertical
space.

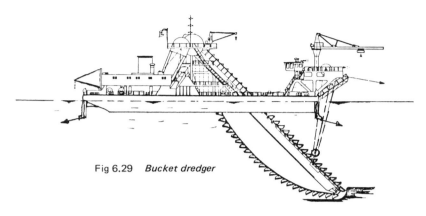

Fig 6.29   *Bucket dredger*

Suction dredgers

This is by far the most common type of dredger in use today.

Trailer suction hopper dredgers (Fig 6.30) comprise a self-propelled hull containing a tank or hopper which
is filled with sand, silt or some clays (depending on the drag head used and the hopper design) by one or two suction
pipes which usually trail alongside the vessel with the suction head dragging along the bed.

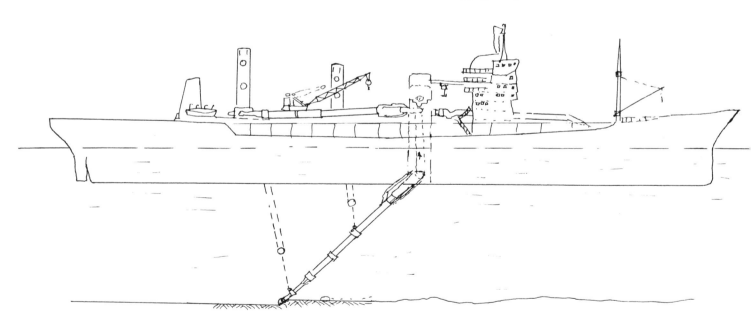

Fig 6.30   *Trailer suction hopper dredger*

The diameter of the suction pipes will be between 400 mm and 1300 mm with a maximum dredging depth
of about 35 metres, and the hopper capacity will be up to 3000 m³ for the smaller vessel and up to 10 000 m³
or larger for the deep-sea type. The suction pipes are raised and lowered by crane or winch and a 500 mm diameter
pipe will deliver approximately 650 m³ of sand into the hopper per hour (this, of course, varies with the concentration and grading of material). This type of dredger has great mobility and loads itself while under way. As soon
as the hopper is full, the ship heads for its unloading point, where the spoil will be dumped.

Discharge is either by bottom dumping, which involves the opening of hydraulically operated doors or valves in the bottom of the hopper, or by a further series of suction pipes which can discharge over the side into barges if the vessel cannot reach the dumping ground itself.

Cutter suction dredgers: (Fig 6.31) whereas the trailer suction dredger can work in sand, silt and light clay conditions, the cutter suction dredger is designed to break up and remove firm and more cohesive materials, including soft rock. The dredger has a central well which houses a rigid ladder which can be raised and lowered by means of a crane. The ladder carries a suction pipe and, at the end of the ladder, a revolving cutting head with teeth which bite into the firm material.

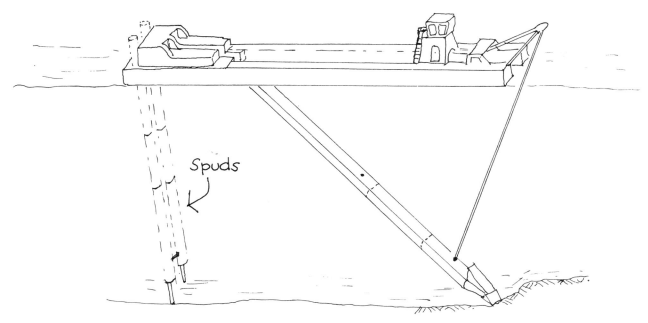

Fig 6.31   *Cutter suction dredger*

To increase the thrust on the cutting head and to enable the dredger to 'walk' ahead into the face, 'spuds' are driven into the sea bed: these are anchor legs which can be raised or lowered hydraulically to suit. Cutter suction dredgers can operate up to a maximum depth of about 40 metres and the material broken up is sucked up the arm and discharged through a floating pipeline or occasionally into barges.

Reclamation dredgers are simple suction dredgers which can be stationed remote from or close to the reclamation area, depending on whether a booster station is used, and transfer sand or silt to barges or via a pipeline to its final location. Water jets remix sand in the barge which is being unloaded, in order to form a pumpable mixture. The reclamation dredger is essentially an inshore craft and will need to be towed to a safe location during storm conditions.

Ancillary dredging equipment

Barges are used to transport materials in situations where it is desired to keep the dredger working full time, where the dredge has no hopper or the draught of the dredger is too great for it to reach the dumping ground, or where a navigational channel between the dredger and spoil reclamation area makes the use of a floating pipeline impractical. Barges can either be dumb, in which case they will be manoeuvered by tugs and towed in strings, or self-propelled. Bottom-dump barges are self-discharging. This can be achieved by having hydraulically or chain-operated doors in the bottom of the hopper, which can be opened when the barge is over the required dumping area.

Another method of bottom dumping is the split discharge barge, which comprises two halves pivoted about hinge points at the top of the superstructure fore and aft. Hydraulic rams force the two halves apart and the sand discharges through the bottom. Inverting barges have also been designed which can be overturned by filling and emptying water tanks in the hull, thus dropping the load.

Well barges are used for transporting material from suction dredgers and bucket dredgers to be unloaded by reclamation dredgers.

Barges have also been designed to transport stone of various sizes. Small stone up to 225 mm in size can be discharged by means of conveyors and hydraulic shovels, while larger rock pieces are transported on trays which can be lifted off bodily at the unloading point.

Booster pumps and pipework: booster pumps are used in delivery pipelines from reclamation dredgers, suction dredgers and cutter suction dredgers, where the combination of pumping distance and material grain size make it necessary to have more horsepower in order to pump the material at an economic production rate through a given size of pipeline. Such booster pumps are nowadays frequently mounted within the dredger (some dredgers have three- or four-stage pumping), while flexibility of planning is maintained by the availability of separate booster stations which may be either skid-mounted for use on land or installed in self-contained dumb pontoons which can be coupled to a pipeline when required.

Reclamation plant and equipment

There is little in the way of reclamation plant which is not described in detail elsewhere in this book, and therefore the following is only a brief resumé of such plant with reference to the relevant section.

Transporting plant

Road: see Section 2.2.3 for dump trucks.

Rail: when materials have to be transported long distances over land, as is often the case with rock, rail will usually be the most convenient and economic solution even when a special unloading terminus has to be constructed. Trains can be loaded at the quarry and moved quickly and regularly at night when there is little other movement on the tracks. For ease of unloading, wagons can be designed to be picked up bodily and turned over with special lifting plant; for stones up to about 200 mm in size, hopper wagons can be used with bottom or side discharge. The best way to handle large rock pieces is to place them on trays which fit on to open wagons. These can be lifted on and off the wagon far more quickly than the grabbing of individual rocks, which is the alternative method.

Sea: see Section 6.5.2 for barges

Placing plant

Apart from the normal earth-moving and compacting plant, which will always be required on a reclamation site and which is discussed in Chapter 2, there are a number of specialised items of equipment which should be considered:

Belt conveyors (see Section 2.2.3)

Cableways (see Section 2.3.3)

Both of these have the advantage of continuous operation interrupted only by mechanical breakdown or extreme weather conditions. They are particularly suitable on reclamation sites where the ground is unable to support heavy vehicles or where there is little room for manoeuvering dump trucks and the like. The use of cableways would be considered for the dumping of heavy materials into water where the depth is insufficient for dumping from floating craft and access is not available from the land, or where high water currents exist. The closing of the gap between the two arms of a sea wall is the most common use for cableways in reclamation.

6.5.3   Construction and materials

Dredging and reclamation with sand

A typical large scale land reclamation project will involve the following:

Site establishment and mobilisation

Dredging of a stockpit (or dump harbour)

Construction of sea walls or bunds

Pumping sand behind sea walls or bunds

Stabilisation of surface.

Site establishment and mobilisation: in addition to the normal requirements, site establishment may involve the bringing of road and rail access to the site to enable vast quantities of materials to be transported economically; the provision of a high voltage electricity supply; the installation of radio and radar communication systems; the installation of conveyor and cableway systems if these are required; the construction of an independent plant yard and offices which may be in use for more than five years; and in remote areas the construction of a labour camp. Mobilisation will often entail the movement of dredgers from various parts of the world, and the timing of these movements will be crucial to the start of the operation.

Dredging of a stockpit: having set up in the site, the first operation will be the construction of a stockpit and any necessary channels. In simple terms this is a pit in the sea bed, located centrally about the area to be reclaimed, into which the dredgers or barges dump their load. A cutter suction dredger (or dredgers), sitting in the middle of the harbour, sucks up the sand which has been previously dumped and pumps it into its final position.

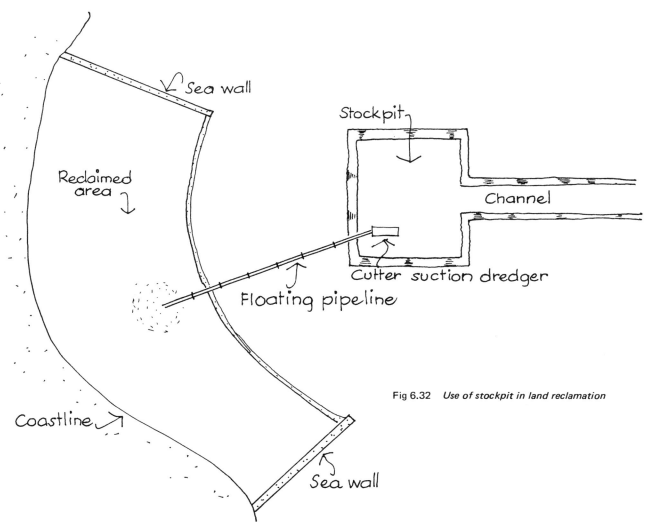

Fig 6.32 *Use of stockpit in land reclamation*

The location and size of the stockpit will depend entirely on individual situations. It should be as close inshore as possible to minimise the pumping distance and afford protection from storms, yet this will be balanced to a certain extent by the need to shorten the length of the approach channel, which might require almost continuous maintenance dredging. Alternatively, the reclaimed material may be loaded into dump or self-propelled well-barges, which travel to a reclamation dredger which then unloads them and pumps the material ashore. This obviates the need for a stockpit, but is a method generally used only in more sheltered waters.

Construction of sea walls: when sand is placed by artificial means on top of an existing beach, the natural action of the sea may tend to wash all the 'foreign' sand away, though this is not always so. Thus in a coastal reclamation scheme it may be necessary to protect the reclaimed area by sea walls. Sea wall construction is discussed in greater depth elsewhere in this chapter and will vary greatly with the availability of material and marine conditions. The design considered for this example may be taken to provide a satisfactory solution for most locations by varying the size of the rock pieces (see Fig 6.33).

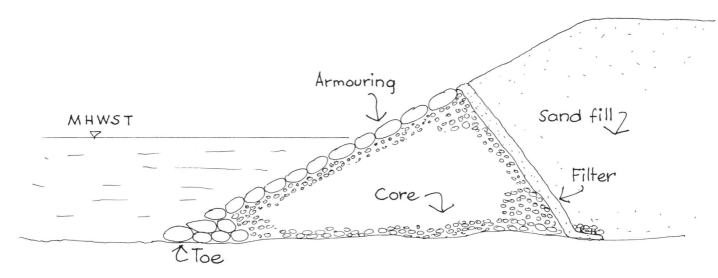

Fig 6.33   *Section through sea wall suitable for protecting reclaimed area*

The construction of the sea wall will vary according to the depth of water. If at some state of the tide there is at least 3 metres of water, it will be possible to place the lower materials by special bottom-dump barges. Elsewhere the material must be placed by transporting out from the land and bulldozing into place.

The main components of this type of sea wall are (see Fig 6.33):

Toe — formed of heavy rock pieces of precast concrete units strong enough to withstand and break up the predicted forces acting upon the foot of the wall.

Core — a graded rock heavy enough to withstand normal seas until the armouring is placed.

Armouring — formed of large rock pieces laid on the face of the wall where wave action can be anticipated. Smaller rock pieces may be used by grouting between the stones with a bitumen binder.

Filters — graded gravel layers or man-made fibre sheeting which prevent the sand behind the wall from getting leeched through the wall (Fig 6.37).

Sand — above the level of the highest predicted storm conditions, the wall can be formed of sand with a thin flexible facing if wave run-up can be anticipated.

The construction of the sea wall must necessarily be carried out in advance of the reclamation, and will be the critical factor in determining the speed at which reclamation takes place. Construction time will be affected by tidal working, storms, the necessity for armouring to follow fairly closely behind the placing of the core and the particular restrictions of the working area. A great deal of planning is needed to enable this sort of operation to be carried out successfully.

Pumping sand behind sea walls: once a protecting arm of sea wall is constructed, it will be practicable to start pumping behind the wall. The dredgers, which may be up to twenty miles away, will deposit their loads either directly or by means of barges into the stockpit. The cutter suction dredgers suck up the sand and pump it through floating pipelines to its final position behind the sea wall. The sea water pumped with the sand runs off through specially constructed temporary sluices and the sand forms a level surface which is finally trimmed by bulldozer and grader.

Stabilisation of the surface: the final operation is the stabilisation of the sand surface. Large areas of dry sand at an exposed coastal location will be prone to sand storms and sand losses of appreciable magnitude. In the short term, a weak bitumen emulsion sprayed on to the sand will bind the surface, while special grasses such as marram grass are becoming established.

Dredging and disposal of materials other than sand

The dredging of materials other than sand will be carried out during the maintenance of inland waterways and harbours, the construction or enlargement of port facilities or the formation of shipping channels at sea. The actual dredging technique adopted will depend on the characteristics of the material dredged, but there is plant available to deal with most conditions that will be met. The only exception to this is likely to be hard rock, which may have to be broken up with underwater explosive before removal by bucket or grab.

The real problem associated with this type of material is one of disposal, and this is discussed in Section 6.5.2.

Reclamation with materials other than sand

As previously stated, reclamation with materials other than sand will generally be carried out at inland sites in areas where the materials themselves are the by-product of other activities, e.g. shale from coal-mining and fly ash from electricity generation.

The sequence of events will be as follows: excavate from stockpile and load; transport; tip and spread; compact. The first three of these, having been fully discussed in previous chapters, require no further comment. Compaction requirements will vary according to the use to which the land will be put. Whilst agricultural land will require little or no compaction, great care must be taken over the compaction of fill materials when the land is to be developed. The various types of compaction plant are fully described in section 2.2.4, and the efficient execution of reclamation works will depend on the selection of sufficient machines of the right type to spread and compact the material as it is delivered. Stock-piling of material adds a further operation to the cycle and this will obviously increase the cost of the project.

6.6 CANALS AND RIVER WORKS

6.6.1 Introduction

The British Waterways Board owns or manages some 3 280 Km of canal and river navigation in England, Wales and Scotland, together with associated works. Apart from the constant upkeep of locks and bridges, an extensive programme of dredging and river bank protection is maintained.

Dredging operations are usually carried out by the Board with their own labour and equipment. Normally dredging operations are undertaken by bucket and grab dredgers, with supporting disposal units.

Larger works, such as bridge building or reconstruction, lock and weir construction and similar works, are carried out by civil engineering firms under contract. A gauging weir and lock under construction at the junction of the Rivers Ouse and Ivel can be seen in Fig 6.34. The photograph shows the river diversion necessary for such work, which was successfully carried out by the use of an earth-fill cofferdam.

Fig 6.34   *A gauging weir and lock under construction at Roxton, Bedfordshire showing earth dam*
(The Dredging & Construction Company Limited)

6.6.2   River-bank protection

River-bank protection or works to control the course of rivers are sometimes called 'training works'. The work involved has two objectives: firstly to prevent damage by erosion, and secondly, to improve the discharge capacity of a river channel or to reduce the natural deterioration of such channels.

The protection may take one of several forms, such as:

Mattresses

Gabions

Steel sheet piling

Stone pitching.

Mattresses (fascines) are particularly valuable for slope protection work on river banks; they are tailor-made (Fig 6.35) from willow branches to the size required — which varies from 3 to 400 square metres. An alternative material for such construction is polypropylene twine; the twine or willow branches are lashed into a grid pattern, one metre square, and covered with brushwood. A further grid is formed over the brushwood and then the upper and lower grids are lashed together to form a mattress approximately 450 mm thick. The mattresses are loaded with rock to sink and hold them in position on the river slope. If the slope is steep the rock is retained by stakes or interwoven willow panels.

An alternative type of mattress, which is likely to supersede all conventional methods, is the Fabripakt flexible nylon mattress. The mattress (Fig 6.36) is an artifical fibre sack, porous to water but not to cement grout, and constructed so that it takes the form of waffle construction when injected with grout. Grout or micro-concrete is injected by means of a special pump at low pressure. The effect of the pressure on the grout within the mattress is to expel any excess vehicle water through the fabric, so increasing the strength of the material and accelerating its initial strength set and rate of increase in strength. An alternative filling material would be bitumen or bentonite cement. Each mattress can be tailored in size to suit the work; mattresses for the River Arun revetment scheme were 33.5 metres long and 13 metres wide. The mattresses are connected together by a ball and

Fig 6.35   *Willow fascines ready for sinking* (The Dredging & Construction Company Limited)

Fig 6.36   *Fabripakt mattresses as revetment to tidal channel* (Intrusion Prepakt (UK) Limited)

socket joint (Fig 6.37) so that individual mattresses can take up settlement without restricting the adjoining panel. Filters are built into the mattresses (Fig 6.37) at 150 mm centres to allow natural drainage of the embankment. The toe of the mattress may be tucked into a trench and backfilled, or anchored with rock fill (Fig 6.38), and the head may be treated in a similar manner.

The name 'Reno mattress' is a trade name for a mattress constructed of galvanised wire mesh and rock fill. The galvanised mesh is PVC coated and supplied to fabricate mattresses 150 mm to 300 mm thick. The merits of the Reno mattress (Fig 6.39) are its extreme flexibility and porosity, together with low cost. For additional strength, the stone fill may be grouted with hot sand bitumen; this may be either partial (surface grouting to a depth of 50 mm) or complete grouting to the full depth, depending on the impermeability required. Special grouting techniques with bitumen may be executed under water. Because the filling material for the Reno mattress is relatively large — 50 mm to 100 mm — compared with the silt of river banks, there is a danger of the finer soil particles being washed out through the mattress. This can be prevented by laying nylon cloth or polythene sheeting under the mattress. The advantage of this type of protection is that silt and plant growth quickly penetrate the structure and bind the stones together, producing an effective permanent wall by the time the wire corrodes.

Gabions (Fig 6.40) are essentially wire boxes filled with small stones to form large blocks. There are two basic types, one consisting of a frame of woven wire covered with PVC and the other of frames fabricated from welded high tensile steel mesh. Gabions are delivered in a folded state and assembled on site, being filled with rock, broken concrete or boulders, and then closed at the top; the whole structure is wired together and lifted into position prior to further wiring to adjacent and underlying gabions. There is no need for any drainage and the boxes are flexible enough to take up settlement without damage. River walls should be of heavy construction if the current is strong or if the bank has to be contained. Protection of the gabion wall against scouring action can be achieved by the use of a flexible apron (Fig 6.41). The apron consists of a mattress 0.5 metres thick, formed with small gabions. As the bed is scoured away under it, the apron folds down, eventually forming a curtain wall which stops further undermining.

Steel sheet piling (Fig 6.42) has been used for bank revetment and protection for many years and its construction is covered fully in Chapter 4 section 4.1.

Stone training work and precast concrete units such as 'Tetrapods' may also be used to counter erosion. The stone work, in the form of pitching of substantial size, is dumped along the river bank and allowed to sink into the silt. The pitching is quickly bound together with silt and forms a strong bank; however, the use of pitching or concrete units is not as aesthetically pleasing as some other forms of revetment.

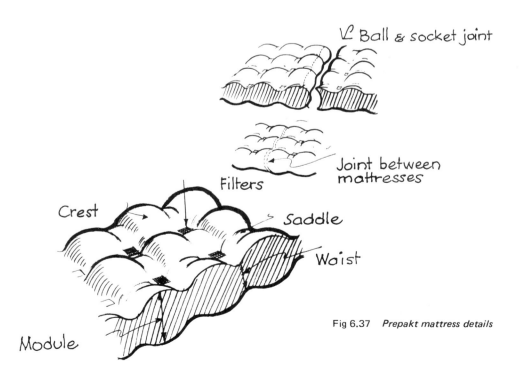

Fig 6.37   *Prepakt mattress details*

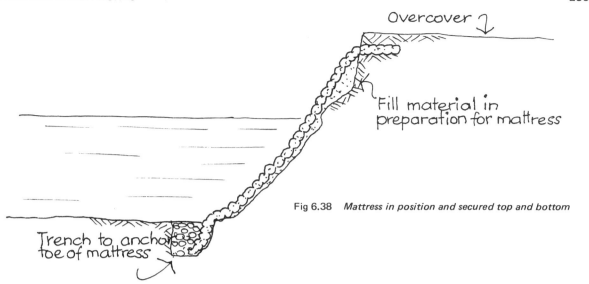

Overcover ↘

Fill material in
preparation for mattress

Trench to anchor
toe of mattress

Fig 6.38   *Mattress in position and secured top and bottom*

.39   *Reno mattresses being constructed to protect bank of open culvert*
(River and Sea Gabions (London) Limited)

Fig 6.40(a)   *Gabion walls shortly after construction*
River and Sea Gabions (London) Limited)

Fig 6.40(b)   *The same walls as Fig 6.40(a) about two years
later. Note the vegetation on the near apron
and the deflection of the far one.*
(River and Sea Gabions (London) Limited

Fig 6.41   *Construction of gabion apron*

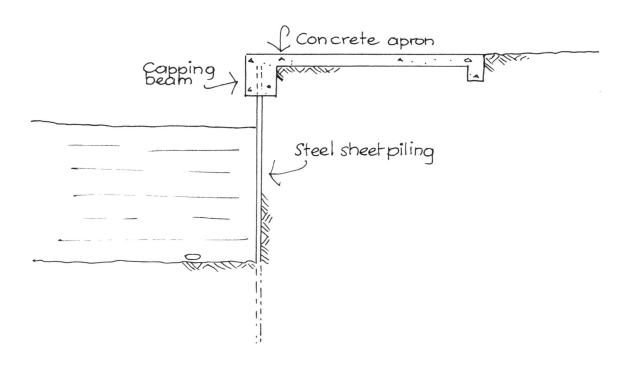

Fig 6.42   *Steel sheet piling in river bank protection*

6.7   RESERVOIRS AND LIQUID-RETAINING TANKS

6.7.1   General considerations

The consideration of reservoirs includes two basic forms: those for the catchment of crude water are referred to as open impounding reservoirs, and those used in the distribution of water are referred to as service reservoirs. The latter are also known as 'covered' service reservoirs because they must be enclosed to protect the water. Liquid-retaining tanks are generally used by industrial or public utility undertakings for the storage of liquid gas, oil products, acids, alkalis and other liquids.

Reservoirs are normally constructed in an elevated position in order to eliminate or reduce the amount of pumping. The ground condition at such levels is normally free from ground water, and the structure, if formed in the ground, can take a very simple form. If, however, the reservoir has to be constructed above ground to give the required head of water, the construction may be very complex. Most gravity schemes consist of a dam across a valley to impound a natural stream. They are all similar in principle in that they all impound the water and have overflow weirs, draw-off points and some form of cut-off walling or other construction to intercept any stray water which may flow under the dam. In addition, of course, they have treatment plants to improve the quality of the water. The design of such structures is undertaken only by Engineers approved by the Home Office. Liquid-retaining tanks must be designed with the following considerations in mind: type of liquid to be stored, temperature of liquid, size of tank, position of tank (i.e. whether in the ground or above ground on columns), type of tank (open or closed, lined or unlined), shape of tank (circular or rectangular). These and other factors will have an influence on the construction and specification of the work to be done (Ref: BS 5337:1976. Code of Practice for the structural use of concrete for retaining aqueous liquids).

6.7.2   Construction

Reservoirs which are designed to impound water — normally dams — can be constructed of earth, rock, concrete, or any combination of these materials. The geological factors, together with the size of the reservoir, will determine the choice; earthen embankments are suitable for clay sites and concrete dams for rocky ground. The earthen embankment must have a watertight face, or a centre core which can be achieved by puddled clay or concrete, although bituminous grout may be used in conjunction with a layer of coarse material (Fig 6.43). Concrete dams may also include cut-off walls or grout-curtains to prevent seepage of water, depending on the geological conditions.

Reservoirs for the distribution of water and those for other liquids are constructed using the same basic design principles, the only difference being that water tanks must be covered, and this involves the construction of a roof structure. The reservoir or tank, when empty, must be designed to prevent flotation or damage to the floor if constructed in waterlogged ground. Consideration must be given to the type of material to be used if constructed in ground which contains injurious chemicals or which is subject to settlement or movement. If tanks are to be constructed in concrete, consideration must be given to the risk of cracking as the concrete cools, especially in thick sections. While overall contraction may be adequately dealt with by the provision of movement joints, the risk of cracking due to differential contraction may require special attention. Construction joints and movements joints can be seen in Fig 6.44. These joints must be provided in the construction if cracking is to be controlled; the spacing of them will depend on the length and thickness of the wall, the cement which is used and its temperature during construction. For maximum spacing, reference should be made to BS 5337:1976. Sliding joints, for the purpose of accommodating expansion or contraction in the walls, are shown in Fig 6.44 (g) — (i); such joints are suitable for tanks containing hot liquids where, therefore, the jointing material must not soften unduly with the heat. Circular tanks may be designed as simple cantilever structures or ring tension structures in which ring reinforcement restricts the outward deflection of the wall (Fig 6.45); the ring-tension structures are usually the cheaper to construct. Rectangular tanks will normally be designed as simple slabs cantilevered from the floor, the corners providing suitable restraints to deflection. For this reason there should be no vertical construction joint at the junction of two straight walls and this fact should be stated in the specification.

Tanks that have roof structures which are connected to the top of the walls may be subject to excessive pressures due to the movement of the roof. Where the tank is surrounded by soil, which can follow the contraction movements, a layer of compressible material, usually foamed plastic, should be placed between the tank walls and the ground (Fig 6.46 (a)); this will allow for wall movement caused by expansion of the roof slab. Alternatively, the roof slab can rest on a sliding joint (Fig 6.46 (b)), the joint being of bituminous material, stainless steel, multilayer rubber or synthetic fabric. If sliding joints are not acceptable, the roof may be cantilevered from columns (Fig 6.46 (c)), allowing roof and walls to move freely.

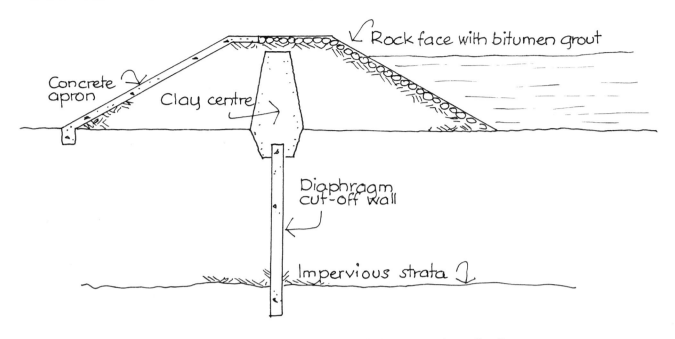

Fig 6.43   *Section through earth dam with clay centre and cut-off wall*

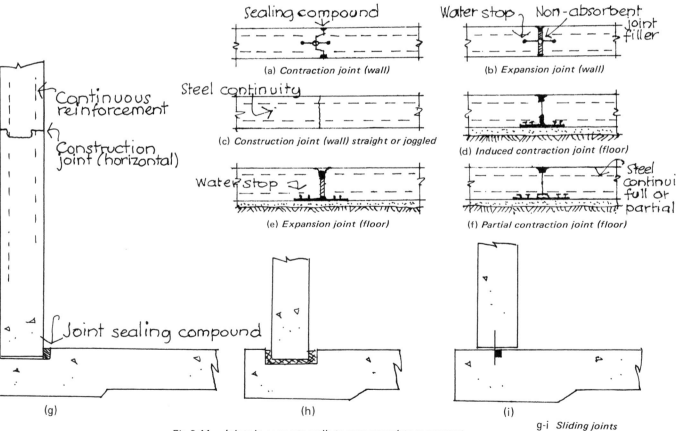

Fig 6.44   *Joints in concrete walls to accommodate movement*

Floors to reservoirs and tanks must be constructed carefully to reduce shrinkage. Laying a floor in alternate bays or in 'chess-board' squares, with seven-day intervals between the placing of alternate bays, will eliminate 50 per cent of the primary cooling shrinkage but will not control the hardening shrinkage. Two schools of thought prevail in the control of shrinkage: the first allows the slab to move freely on a sliding layer of synthetic material, with adequate expansion joints (Fig 6.47 (a)); and the second restrains the slab on a rough concrete sub-floor, thereby restricting shrinkage cracks to a size that will not permit leakage. In the latter case (Fig 6.47 (b)), reinforcing bars give continuity at the joints. Some floors have been laid successfully in two or three layers, each one separated by a waterproof membrane, usually synthetic polymer sheeting. The upper layers cover the joints in the lower layers.

Floors that are suspended, i.e. on columns or on piles, are designed as normal concrete suspended floors.

Tanks below ground should have a roof screeded to falls and covered with granular material to permit drainage of ground water.

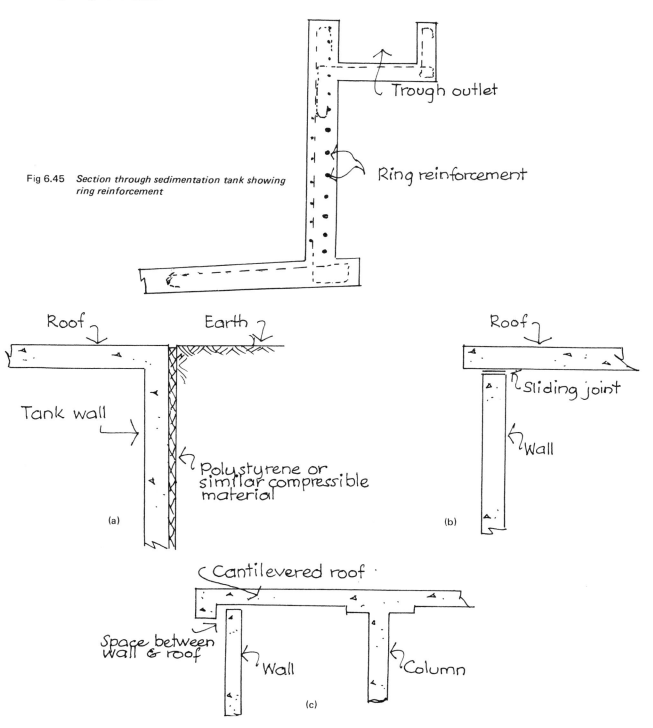

Fig 6.45   *Section through sedimentation tank showing ring reinforcement*

Fig 6.46   *Provision for expansion and contraction of tanks and tank roofs*

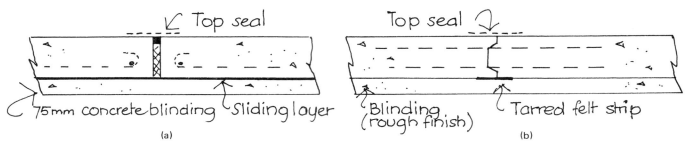

Fig 6.47   *Different treatments to floor slab to counteract movement*

In-ground storage tanks

In-ground storage tanks or reservoirs are used for the storage of liquid natural gas (LNG). The tanks may be lined or unlined, depending on the nature of the soil and the height of the water table. The ground is frozen by the freezing method described in Chapter 3, and when a wall sufficiently strong enough to resist the outer soil pressures has been frozen, the tank is excavated. Since natural gas liquifies at -160°C the temperatures must be kept below this or the gas will 'boil off'. The most suitable soil for unlined tanks of this nature is stiff clay or marl; however, it is recommended that tanks are lined.

Metal-lined tanks with concrete walls and floors (Fig 6.48) are the most practical in construction. The ground is excavated and a concrete tank is cast, to which a metal lining is fixed. The problem of casting concrete against the frozen earth can be overcome by using an efficient insulatory material between the concrete and the ground; the reinforcement should be of nickel steel or other non-brittle steel. Steel with 9 per cent nickel can be used in temperatures down to −200°C. The metal lining is normally nickel-steel or aluminium alloy.

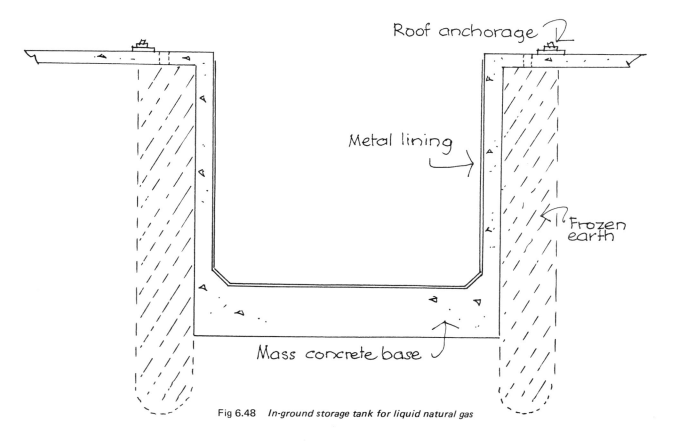

Fig 6.48   *In-ground storage tank for liquid natural gas*

6.7.3   Waterproofing

In considering methods of waterproofing concrete structures, certain major factors must be satisfied: stresses in the concrete and steel must be kept within reasonable limits; the anchorage between steel and concrete must also be adequate; and shrinkage and temperature stresses must be considered.

It should be noted that fine hair cracks can be reduced by using deformed bars in lieu of plain round bars: which highlights the fact that anchorage between steel and concrete can be improved.

Concrete made with rounded shingle makes a more watertight construction than a similar mix using crushed stone aggregate; this is due to a reduction in voids, giving greater impermeability. The concrete mix should be dense and richer in cement than for normal construction; mixes equivalent to 1:1.6:3.2 or 1:1½:3 are frequently specified for impervious tank work.

Integral waterproofing is not favoured by many engineers or authorities, although manufacturers claim great success with their products. A possible risk in the use of admixtures is that of bad workmanship — there is a tendency to rely only on the admixture and so to overlook strict control of concrete batching, mixing and placing. The object of most integral waterproofers is to fill the pores in the concrete, thus making a denser and less permeable material; some admixtures obtain a similar result by chemical action on the cement.

Waterproof linings include asphalt, renderings, plastic sheeting and paints. The oldest, perhaps, is asphalt tanking, which requires no explanation in this book. Waterproof renderings containing a patent waterproofing additive are suitable for tanks which remain filled most of the time. If waterproof renderings are allowed to dry out, and remain too dry for a long time, they may become subject to cracking and spalling.

Plastic sheeting and Butyl hydraulic membrane (a synthetic rubber) have both been used extensively for open reservoirs (Fig 6.49). The membrane is laid over a carpet of sand 100 mm thick, and jointed by vulcanising. The peripheral joints can be formed by sealing the sheeting to a perimeter skirt which in turn is sealed to a water-bar in the toe of the reservoir wall. The Butyl membrane is also suitable for covered storage vessels where the membrane is fixed to the concrete structure with a neoprene-based solvent adhesive. This form of lining is also suitable for the repair of existing tanks.

Fig 6.49   *Butyl sheeting being laid on sand base to provide floor of reservoir* (Butyl Products Limited)

6.7.4 Special linings

Many liquids can be stored in concrete tanks, but there are some groups, especially acids and sulphates, which are extremely harmful to concrete. Concrete must be protected from such liquids and this is done either by lining the tank with a material that will resist corrosion or, alternatively, by lining the tank with a material that can be replaced at suitable intervals of time. The latter method of protection is known as 'sacrificial linings'. Protection linings include silica-of-soda solutions, glass linings, acid-resisting asphalt, wax linings, lead linings, and other soft metal linings. The lining is chosen to resist the corrosive action of the particular liquid.

Sacrificial linings, on the other hand, are linings which do not resist the corrosive action of the liquid but allow an attack to take place over a period of time until the tank requires emptying and the lining renewing. The lining may be rendered in cement mortar or some other relatively cheap form of cover which can be 'sacrificed' to prevent serious attack on the concrete.

Chapter 7

Roadworks, Bridges, Subways and Airfield Construction

7.1 ROADWORKS

Throughout this section reference is made to the Specification for Road and Bridge Works (HMSO 1976*). The individual clause numbers, to which reference is made, may be varied at any time by the originator of the publication and the reader is advised to check the current clause numbers in use. Technical memoranda are also referred to. The reader is also referred to the DOT — Notes for Guidance on the above Specifications.

Traffic is assessed in terms of millions of standard axles (msa) to determine the traffic load when designing pavements. Details of assessment are to be found in the various references quoted.

7.1.1 Earthworks

Road construction can be divided into two distinct phases: first the earthworks, and second the construction of the pavement which overlies the earthworks. The earthworks are concerned with the preparation of the soil to bring it to the correct levels, gradients, profiles, and strength required. The finished level of such earthworks is referred to as the formation level and the soil immediately below that level is known as the subgrade. As discussed in Chapter 1, it is essential that the earthworks are preceded by testing of the soil; this will establish the properties of the soil and assist in the design of an economic subgrade. The formation of embankments is discussed in Chapter 3 and specific reference should be made to Specification for Road and Bridge Works (HMSO 1976). It should be noted that although 'fill' materials are defined as 'suitable or unsuitable', a material that may be suitable for the construction of embankments in a dry state may nevertheless be unsuitable in a wet state. Conversely, material may become unsuitable by compaction with the wrong plant. So it can be seen that the suitability of fill material depends not only on its physical properties but also on the conditions in which it is to be used and on the methods used for compaction (ref: Specification for Road and Bridge Works — Table 6.2 — Compaction Requirements). Since most earthworks are formed by cut-and-fill the relevant considerations are as follows:

Determining side slopes for cuttings and embankments

Treatment of compressible subsoil.

The side slopes of non-cohesive soils are governed by the natural angle of repose of the material, and this can be calculated from site and laboratory tests; a slip-circle analysis is necessary for cohesive soils to take into account the overall height of the bank. Typical ratios for side-slopes in clay embankments range from 1 in 2 to 1 in 4, but the actual ratio must be determined from tests; it is therefore difficult, and in some cases unwise, to produce tables of side-slope ratios without full knowledge of the materials being used (see Chapter 3 — Slopes in embankments).

Compressible subsoil may be removed or stabilised, depending on its quality. Peat and similar materials should be excavated and replaced with granular fill; other methods of removal include bog blasting, overloading and jetting, which are described in Chapter 3 Section 3.2.5 (Construction on soft ground). When the nature of the subsoil material is such that the cost of full or partial excavation cannot be justified and consolidation is likely, or if the embankment itself consists of compacted clay of a very high moisture content, then sand wicks or sand drains may be used. Sand wicks (see Chapter 3 Section 3.3.1) or sand drains are sand-filled bore holes; the sand wick is a sand-filled stocking which is lowered into a borehole. The sand wick decreases the length of the drainage path which the water has to travel and so dissipates pore water pressure and gives greater stability to the soil (Fig 7.1).

*See also 'Roads in Urban Areas' HMSO.

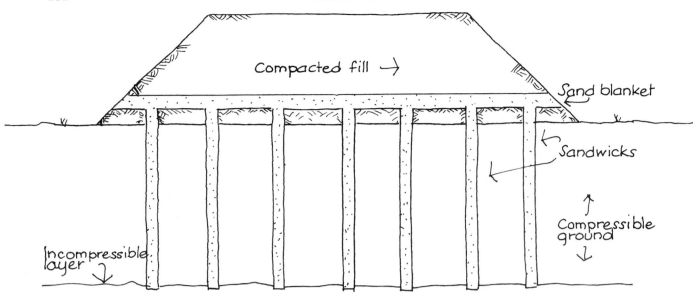

Fig 7.1   *Sand wicks under road embankments*

Subgrade strength

The strength of the subgrade determines the thickness of the pavement needed and should therefore be made as high as possible. The desired subgrade strength can be achieved by:

Removing poor material in cuttings and replacing with selected fill, and using good quality material for forming embankments

Ensuring compaction of the subgrade to a high dry density

Providing adequate subsoil drainage

Avoiding the use of materials subject to frost damage.

The suitability of materials and their compaction have already been discussed.

Subsoil drainage must be provided to deal with:

Seepage through pavement and verges

Seepage from higher ground

Seasonal rise and fall of the water table.

Seepage through pavements is difficult to eliminate, since joints deteriorate over a period of time, and surface materials, which are subject to a very wide range of temperatures, eventually crack, allowing water to penetrate. One satisfactory solution is to apply hot tar or bitumen as a sealing coat to the subgrade; this has the dual purpose of shedding the water to a side drain (Fig 7.2) and also of protecting the subgrade during construction. Moisture seeping through verges and moving into the subgrade, causing swelling and shrinkage of the subgrade, may be intercepted by a subsoil drain situated between the verge and the carriageway, or, in the case of motorways, between the verge and hard shoulder (Fig 7.2).

Seepage from higher ground occurs when a layer of permeable soil overlies an impermeable strata. The water can be intercepted by a cut-off drain, which may be incorporated with the drain at the verge if the impermeable layer is less than 1.2 metres below the surface. Where the impermeable layer is at a lower level, the cut-off drain should be taken to a depth that will keep the seepage water at least 1.2 metres below formation level.

Seasonal fluctuation in the water table should be controlled by drains, as shown in Fig 7.2, so as to keep the water table 1.2 to 1.5 metres below the formation level.

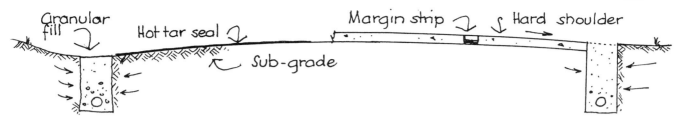

Fig 7.2 *Use of sub-soil drains to intercept ground water*

Frost damage to the subgrade can be expected with certain types of soil which draw and hold moisture in the soil pores. Limestone gravels are likely to be susceptible if the average saturation moisture content of the material exceeds 2 per cent. All crushed chalks are frost susceptible; the magnitude of frost heave increases linearly with the saturation moisture content of the chalk. Burnt colliery shales are very prone to frost heave. For further reference to the frost susceptibility of road materials see DOT TRRL Report LR90.

The final strength of the subgrade is assessed on the California Bearing Ratio (CBR) scale. The correlation between CBR value and soil type is shown in Table 7.1; this table is also used in the calculation of sub-base thickness. The surface treatment of the formation will vary from simple rolling to coating with bituminous materials. If the formation is not immediately covered with sub-base material it should be protected by an impermeable plastic membrane (500 gauge) having laps of 300 mm at the joints. Formation of rock-fill or rock cuttings should be blinded in accordance with Clause 607, 701 or 807 (Specification of Road and Bridge Works 1976).

TABLE 7.1

Estimated laboratory CBR values for British soils compacted at the natural moisture content

Type of soil	Plasticity index (per cent)	CBR (per cent)	
		Depth of water-table below formation level	
		More than 600 mm	600 mm or less
Heavy clay	70	2	1
	60	2	1.5
	50	2.5	2
	40	3	2
Silty clay	30	5	3
Sandy clay	20	6	4
	10	7	5
Silt		2	1
Sand (poorly graded)	non-plastic	20	10
Sand (well graded)	non-plastic	40	15
Well-graded sandy gravel	non-plastic	60	20

(HMSO
Reproduced from Road Note 29)

Soil stabilisation

If the natural properties of the subgrade do not possess the strength required to support and distribute the proposed loading, the subgrade strength may be increased by soil stabilisation.

Stabilisation may be achieved by various agents, which include cement, lime, bitumen and chemicals.

Cement stabilisation is achieved by mixing cement with pulverised soil to form a material which, when compacted and allowed to harden, possesses appreciable strength. The material to be stabilised should not contain sulphates in excess of 1% and it should be graded in accordance with Clause 805 (Specification for Roads and Bridge Works 1976). The thickness of layer to be stabilised should not be less than 75 mm when compacted, and should be compacted in layers of up to 200 mm thick at one pass. Other details on mixing and placing are found in Clauses 805 to 806 of the above Specification. An alternative to cement as a binding material is lime, but its use in the UK is limited because cement is as cheap and produces a stronger material.

Bituminous materials such as cut-back bitumen, and chemicals, have all been used for soil stabilisation in hot dry climates, but since their use in the UK has been on a limited scale, these processes are not dealt with in detail.

7.1.2   Flexible pavements

Flexible pavements (Fig 7.3) consist of a layer system of materials which distribute the wheel-loads to the sub-grade. The thicknesses of individual layers must be such as to distribute the loads without permanent deformation of the material, thereby presenting an uneven running surface.

Sub-base

The required thickness of sub-base is determined from the cumulative number of standard axles to be carried (a standard axle equals 8200 kg; the number of standard axles is that number that has the same damaging power as the actual traffic on the road) and the CBR of the subgrade; this can be obtained from design charts in Road Note No. 29: HMSO, 1970. The sub-base can be formed with stabilised materials but is more commonly formed with granular materials. Free-draining materials, such as quarry overburden or crushed rock, should be used in preference to materials containing large amounts of fines. The material should be graded to the range of grading given in Clause 803; permitted alternative materials and thicknesses are given in Table 8.1 of the DOT Specification 1976 under the heading 'sub-base materials'.

Base materials

Any material that remains stable in water, is unaffected by frost, and has a CBR value of not less than 80% when compacted, can be used for roadbase construction. Suitable materials include crushed stone, blast-furnace slag, dry lean concrete, cement-bound granular material and bituminous-bound materials. Permitted alternative materials and thicknesses can be seen in Table 9.1 of the DOT Specification 1976.

Dry-bound macadam is normally supplied for base construction in two sizes: a single-sized coarse aggregate, nominally 38 mm to 50 mm in size, and a fine graded material, 4 mm to dust, for blinding the surface of the coarse aggregate. The coarse material is laid in a 75 to 100 mm layer and compacted; this is followed by a 25 mm layer of fine material and compaction is continued. Other layers are added in a similar manner until the required base thickness has been achieved.

Wet-mix macadam is prepared by mixing graded crushed rock or crushed slag aggregate normally with 2% to 5% water but subject to Test 13 in BS 1377; an added provision is that the percentage of material passing a No. 200 sieve may be increased to 10%. The material is laid in layers 75 to 150 mm in thickness by a Barber-Greene paver or similar machine, and compacted with either a heavy smooth-wheeled roller or by vibrating roller until the required density is achieved.

Dry lean concrete is similar to normal structural concrete except that the rates of cement to aggregate, by weight, should lie between 1:15 and 1:20; the aggregate may be an all-in aggregate having a maximum nominal size of 40 mm and not less than 20 mm. The water/cement ratio is determined by the compaction requirements but is about 6% of the dry weight of the materials. The strength of the mix is determined by the cement content and should achieve a minimum strength of 10 N/mm^2 at 28 days (one failure allowed per 15 cubes) and a minimum of 11 N/mm^2 at 28 days for any consecutive groups of 15 cubes. The average range of strength for the consecutive groups should not exceed 50% of the overall average 28 day strength of the first 15 cubes; strength at 7 days should be not less than 7 N/mm^2. The concrete can be produced by any normal concreting plant that will give a suitable output, usually in excess of 20 m^3 per hour. The base thickness is built up in layers not exceeding 200 mm compacted thickness; it is spread by mechanical spreader and compacted by smooth-wheeled or vibrating rollers. On completion of the base the surface should be coated with bituminous liquid or polythene sheeting to prevent evaporation.

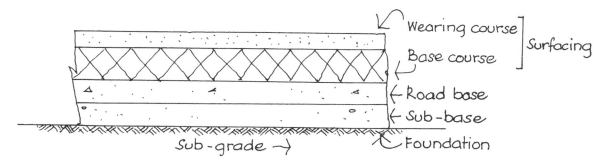

Fig 7.3 *Section through flexible pavement*

Cement-bound granular base material (CBGB) is a high quality cement-stabilised soil consisting of naturally occuring gravel in the 'as-dug' condition mixed with cement. The material is normally mixed in a paddle or pan mixer to prevent excessive segregation of the fines, which may occur in a free-fall mixer. The placing and compaction is the same as for lean concrete.

Bituminous-bound base materials are similar to those used in bituminous surfacings except that the binder content is lower, see DOT Specification 1976, Clauses 810 and 811. The material is laid by a spreading machine and compacted in layers of 50 to 75 mm by a heavy smooth-wheeled roller (8 to 10 tonne).

Surfacing courses

The surfacing layer of a flexible pavement is subjected to a great intensity of stress and must consist of high quality material capable of resisting such stress. It must also provide an impermeable weathering which protects both surface and base materials; in addition to these properties it must also provide a high resistance to skidding.

The types of surfacing material used are numerous, but they are similar in that each consists of an aggregate bound together by tar or bitumen; the difference lies mainly in the type, viscosity and proportion of binder used, and the type and grading of the aggregate. Road tar, which is one of the main binders, is obtained from crude tar refined to BS 76:1974, and bitumen, the other main binder, is produced from crude petroleum or found in natural deposits mixed with mineral aggregate. Asphalt is a mixture of bitumen and mineral matter.

Wearing coat

The wearing coat or course is the upper layer of bituminous material and is usually denser and stronger than the lower layer or base course. The thickness depends upon the specification of the material to be used and the amount of wear expected (see Table 7.2). The main wearing materials are hot rolled asphalt; dense bitumen macadam; dense tar surfacing; open-textured bitumen macadam; cold asphalt; and mastic asphalt. These materials should conform to their relevant BS Specifications and be laid in accordance with the DOT Specification for Road and Bridge Works, 1976.

Base course materials, which should be of a minimum thickness of 60 mm, may consist of rolled asphalt, dense bitumen macadam, dense tarmacadam, or open-textured tarmacadam (see Table 7.2).

The wearing course should be laid on the base course as soon as possible, normally within three days. With the exception of compressed natural rock asphalt and mastic asphalt, laying is carried out by machine. The base course is shaped with the appropriate crossfalls and gradients before the wearing coat is laid; the finished wearing surface being to within ± 6 mm of the true level surface.

Mastic asphalt, although having very durable qualities, is very expensive to lay and hot-rolled asphalt is normally accepted as the next best surfacing material.

7.1.3   Rigid pavements

A rigid pavement consists essentially of a concrete slab resting on a thin granular base. The loads and

TABLE 7.2

Recommended bituminous surfacings for newly constructed flexible pavements (see Note 1)*

Traffic (cumulative number of standard axles) — (msa)

Over 11 millions (1)	*2.5–11 millions* (2)	*0.5–2.5 millions* (3)	*Less than 0.5 million* (4)
Wearing course (crushed rock or slag coarse aggregate only) **Minimum thickness 40 mm** Rolled asphalt to BS 594 (pitch-bitumen binder may be used) (Clause 907)		**Wearing course** **Minimum thickness 20 mm** Rolled asphalt to BS 594 (pitch-bitumen binder may be used) (Clause 907) Dense tar surfacing to BTIA Specification (Clause 909) Cold asphalt to BS 4987 (Clause 910) (see Note 4) Open-textured tarmacadam (Clause 913) (to be surface dressed immediately or as soon as possible — see Note 4) Dense bitumen macadam (Clause 908) (see Note 4) Open-textured bitumen macadam to BS 4987 (Clause 912) (see Note 4)	**Two-course** (a) **Wearing course** **Minimum thickness 20 mm** Cold asphalt to BS 4987 (Clause 910) (See Note 4) or other in column 3 (Clause 913, 912 or 908) (see Notes 2 and 4) (b) **Basecourse** Tarmacadam to BS 4987 or bitumen macadem (Clause 906 or 905) (see Note 2) **Single course** Rolled asphalt to BS 594 (pitch bitumen binder may be used) Dense tar surfacing to BTIA Specification (Clause 909) Open-textured tarmacadam to BS 802 (Clause 913) (to be surface dressed immediately or as soon as possible) (see Note 4) Dense bitumen macadam to BS 4987 (Clause 908) (see Note 4) 60 mm of single-course tarmacadam (Clause 906) (To be surface dressed immediately or as soon as possible (see Note 4) 60 mm of single-course bitumen macadam (Clause 905) (see Note 4)
Basecourse **Minimum thickness 60 mm** Rolled asphalt to BS 594 (Clause 902) (see Note 2) Dense bitumen macadam or dense tarmarcadam (crushed rock or slag only) (Clause 903 or 904)	**Basecourse** Rolled asphalt to BS 594 (Clause 902) (see Note 2) Dense bitumen macadam or dense tarmacadam (Clause 903 or 904) (see Note 3)	**Basecourse** Rolled asphalt to BS 594 (Clause 902) (see Note 2) Dense bitumen macadam or dense tarmacadam (Clause 903 or 904) Single course tarmacadam to BS 4987 (Clause 906) (see Notes 2 and 5) Single-course bitumen macadam to BS 4987 (Clause 905) (see Notes 2 and 5)	

Notes:

1 The thickness of all layers of bituminous surfacings should be consistent with the appropriate British Standard Specification.

2 When gravel, other than limestone, is used, 2% of Portland cement should be added to the mix and the percentage of fine aggregate reduced accordingly.

3 Gravel tarmacadam is not recommended as a basecourse for roads designed to carry more than 2.5 million standard axels.

4 When the wearing course is neither rolled asphalt nor dense tar surfacing and where it is not intended to apply a surface dressing immediately to the wearing course, it is essential to seal the construction against the ingress of water by applying a surface dressing either to the roadbase or to the basecourse.

5 Under a wearing course of rolled asphalt or dense tar surfacing the basecourse should consist of rolled asphalt to BS 594 (Clause 902) or of dense coated macadam (Clause 903 or 904).

See also Design and Performance of Road Pavements, HMSO 1977.

stresses are distributed over a wide area of subgrade by the rigidity and strength of the pavement. The pavement may be reinforced or unreinforced, depending on the designed traffic load.

The subgrade should be compacted and shaped in accordance with the 1976 DOT Specification and can be classed as one of three qualities (see Table 7.3). The subgrade material can be one of those stated in the section on flexible pavements and should be suitably protected against ground water.

Sub-base

The function of the sub-base is to assist drainage, to protect the subgrade against frost, and, in the case of fine-grained soils, to prevent pumping (the ejection of water and silt through joints or cracks caused by the downward movement of the slab due to heavy wheel loads). The materials used are usually granular, e.g. crushed rock, crushed slag, crushed concrete, natural sand, gravels or well-burnt non-plastic shale. The materials should be graded in accordance with the DOT Specification, 1976, Clauses 803 and 804. The thickness of the sub-base depends on the type of subgrade and should follow the recommendation of Road Note No. 29 – see Table 7.3. If the subgrade is susceptible to frost the total thickness of sub base and concrete slab should be a minimum of 450 mm. After the pavement slab has been designed, the thickness of the sub-base should be increased, if necessary, to gain a total pavement thickness of 450 mm.

TABLE 7.3

Classification of subgrades for concrete roads and minimum thicknesses of sub-base required

Type of subgrade	Definition	Minimum thickness of sub-base required
Weak	All subgrades of CBR value 2 per cent or less as defined in Table 3	150 mm
Normal	Subgrades other than those defined by the other categories	80 mm
Very stable	All subgrades of CBR value 15 per cent or more as defined in Table 3 This category includes undistributed foundations of old roads	0

(HMSO
Reproduced from Road Note 29)

Concrete slabs

The concrete used in road slabs (DOT Specification) requires a concrete strength of 2.3 N/mm² at 28 days when using the indirect tensile test. For testing purposes at least one pair of concrete cylinders is prepared for each 75 m run of pavement. The concrete cylinders are 150 mm diameter and 150 mm long. The concrete mix should be designed to ensure that not more than 1% of all tests results fail to reach the standard set; normally 1.8 N/mm² with a standard deviation of 0.4 N/mm². In addition, the water/cement ratio should not exceed 0.55 (see Chapter 8 for further discussion on quality control).

Air-entrainment of the concrete should be specified for either the full depth of slab or for at least the top 50 mm (see Clause 1001–1002 DOT Specification). Air-entrainment increases the resistance of concrete to frost damage and to the destructive action of de-icing salts. The materials used for air-entrainment produces minute bubbles in the hardened concrete which prevent saturation by capillarity and so relieve the stresses which otherwise occur when pore water freezes. Since air-entrainment has the disadvantage of weakening the concrete, the volume of air should be restricted to 4.5% ± 1.5%.

Concrete slab construction

When the base has been prepared, it is common practice to provide a 'sliding-layer' over the base before laying the concrete slab. This layer is normally polythene sheeting, which performs the extra function of preventing grout loss (Fig 7.4 shows a typical preparation prior to slab construction). The slab is normally placed by a concreting train (Fig 7.5) which runs on a heavy duty road form to prevent deflection. The form (Fig 7.6) is bedded in position on the base at least 24 hours prior to concreting the slab. The concrete train usually includes hopper units which feed the concrete on to the base via a conveyor belt; alternatively this operation may be carried out by a screw-type spreader. Concrete is laid to the level of the fabric reinforcement and, following the placing of the fabric, a second spreader and compactor unit completes the slab. The top layer of concrete is placed with a surcharge of up to 25% of the slab thickness to gain maximum compaction; the actual surcharge will depend upon workability of the mix.

An alternative method of laying the slab is by slip-form paver. This machine, which requires no side forms, is mounted on crawler tracks and is capable of laying pavements at speeds in excess of 2 m per minute. The concrete slab is moulded to the required thickness and extruded at the rear of the machine. Line and level is achieved by automatic sensing probes at each corner of the machine; the probes straddle a length of tensioned wire which has been set to the correct gradient. Variations in the level of the base are detected by the probes and the machine level is corrected automatically by hydraulic jacks.

Fig 7.4   *Slab preparation prior to concrete laying*
(Richard Costain Limited)

Fig 7.5(a)   *Concrete train commencing operations*
(Richard Costain Limited)

Fig 7.5(b)   *View of complete concrete train showing work in various stages of progress* (Richard Costain Limited)

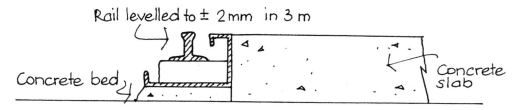

Fig 7.6   *Road form in position*

Reinforcement

Reinforcement may be either steel fabric or bar reinforcement, the latter being deformed and spaced at centres of not more than 150 mm. The diameter of bar to use in lieu of fabric can be established from the DOT (Notes for Guidance) Table 3. Concrete cover to the reinforcement should be 60 mm from the surface, unless slabs are less than 150 mm in thickness in which case 50 mm cover is required. The reinforcement should terminate at least 40 mm and not more than 80 mm from the edge of the slab and from all joints except longitudinal joints. Where two- or three-lane carriageways are constructed in one operation, reinforcing mats with 8 mm transverse wires at 200 mm centres may be used to span the longitudinal joint in place of bars; if so used the 8 mm wires must span at least 500 mm either side of the longitudinal joints. Where three-lane carriageways are constructed in two widths, and where each slab is wider than 4.5 metres, special transverse reinforcement, 600 mm longer than a third of the slab width, should be placed centrally in each slab.

Joint Construction

Joints are formed in concrete slabs for the purpose of allowing and controlling movement; the movements include expansion, contraction and warping. The spacing of joints depends on the amount of reinforcement used, which in turn depends on the proposed traffic intensity; slab thickness; frictional restraint of the sub-grade; and the temperature at which the concrete is placed. Every third joint should be an expansion joint, the remainder being contraction joints. Expansion joints, however, may be replaced by contraction joints, at the discretion of the engineer, when the slab is constructed during summer months. Maximum spacings for expansion joints range from 36 to 73 metres in reinforced slabs and from 27 to 54 metres in unreinforced slabs. Maximum spacing of contraction joints ranges from 12 to 24 metres in reinforced slabs and from 4.5 to 7 metres in unreinforced slabs. Road Note No 29 recommends maximum spacing of expansion joints in unreinforced slabs as 60 metres (if slab thickness is 200 mm or more) and 72 metres if limestone aggregates are used.

Joint-filling and sealing

There are two types of material used in joints: a filler which separates the slabs, and a sealing compound which fills the top 25 mm of the joint, thus resisting the entry of water and grit. Materials suitable for joint filling are softwood (free from knots); impregnated fibre board; cork; sheet bitumen; and rubber.

Softwood filler should be soaked to ensure that it is swollen to near its maximum thickness before installation.

Joint sealing compound must have good adhesion to concrete, extensibility without fracture, resistance to flow in hot weather, and durability. There is no perfect solution to all these requirements but some adequate solutions are:

Straight-run bitumen

Resinous compounds

Rubber-bituminous compounds.

The last has superseded most other types.

Expansion joints (Fig 7.7) must prevent unrestrained horizontal movements of the slabs; to accommodate the movement a compressible material 25 mm thick should be provided between the slab faces. The compressible material must be protected against the ingress of grit by filling the upper part of the joint with sealing compound to a level 5 mm below the surface of the slab. An alternative material to sealing compound is a preformed neoprene compression sealing strip. To prevent movement of the slabs, and at the same time to ensure load-transfer, a system of dowel bars is introduced. The dowel bars are positioned at mid-depth of the slab at centres of 300 mm; the diameter of the bar varies with the thickness of slab, but usually ranges from 20 mm to 30 mm. Free movement of the slab is achieved by providing a plastic sleeve 100 mm long to one end of the dowel; this sleeve should contain a 25 mm pad of compressible material. In addition, the free end of the dowel (the one fitted with the sleeve) should be coated with a bond-breaking compound.

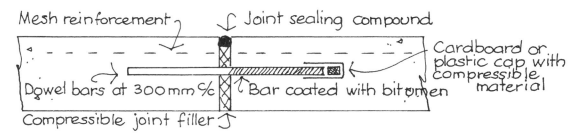

Fig 7.7   *Expansion joint*

Longitudinal joints should have tie-bars 12 mm in diameter by 1 metre long at 600 mm centres; the bars should be fully bonded. Alternatively, a mat of cellular reinforcement fabric may be used in lieu of bars. Difficulties arise when tie-bars are misaligned or when bars require bending aside to allow easier construction; these difficulties may be overcome by casting threaded couplings into the first slab and connecting the bars for the second slab as required (Fig 7.8). In both cases, where dowel bars are used they must be carefully supported by cradles or cages to ensure correct alignment.

Contraction joints

These joints are similar in construction (Fig 7.9) to expansion joints except that the filler material and dowel bar sleeves are omitted. Dowel bars are used to transfer loads across the joints and one half of each bar is coated with a bond-breaking material to allow contraction to take place. In addition, the interface of the slabs may be coated with bitumen before the second slab is cast. For continuous construction 'dummy' joints may be formed (Fig 7.10) by creating planes of weakness at the required spacing. A plane of weakness is induced by means of a timber, plastic or steel fillet, fixed to the surface of the base and cast into the slab. An upper groove is formed by a vibrating plate while the concrete is plastic, or one may be cut with a saw; it is then filled and sealed with a suitable compound. The fillet may be eliminated if the groove is cut to a depth of not less than one-third of the depth of the slab, but in that case the concrete should be made with crushed stone aggregate.

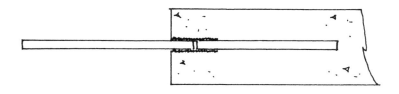

Fig 7.8   *Threaded couplings for longitudinal joints*

Fig 7.9   *Contraction joint*

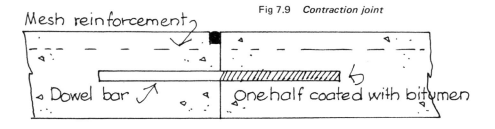

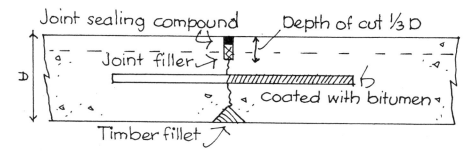

Fig 7.10 *Dummy contraction joint*

Warping joints

Transverse joints are needed in unreinforced concrete slabs to relieve stresses of restraint due to contraction and warping; warping is caused by vertical temperature gradients within the slab, and stresses caused by these may be higher than those caused by contraction. For that reason 'warping' or hinged joints may be used in lieu of the normal contraction joints. These joints, sometimes referred to as tied warping joints, consist essentially of a contraction joint with a special arrangement of reinforcement (Fig 7.11).

Slab finish

On completion, the surface of the slab may be textured by brushing with a wire broom at right angles to the centre line of the carriageway (see Clause 1021 DOT Specification 1969. This gives a better skidding resistance and a uniform appearance. The slab should be cured immediately after brush treatment by spraying with an aluminised curing compound at a rate of 4 m^2 to 5 m^2 per litre.

Pre-stressed concrete slabs may be constructed in lieu of traditional reinforced slabs, giving greater slab lengths without joints; slab lengths of up to 300 metres have been constructed without joints. The disadvantages of this form of construction are lack of continuity in the pouring of concrete, due to jacking; extra cost of supervision during stressing; and problems of maintenance if roads should require cutting for services at a later date.

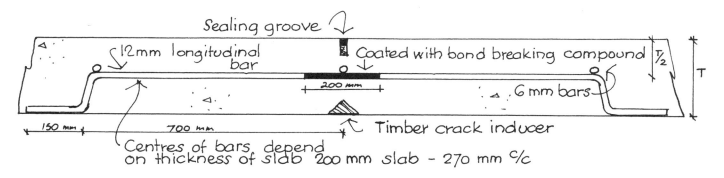

Fig 7.11 *Detail of warping joint*

7.1.4 Composite pavements

In some cases, usually in city streets, a combination of concrete slab and bituminous surfacing may be justified because of its trouble-free performance. It has the advantages of both flexible and rigid pavements in that it gives good riding quality and resists settlement, particularly in roads which are extensively disturbed by excavation for service trenches.

The subgrade, drainage and sub-base follow closely that of normal reinforced concrete, consisting of concrete with a minimum of 28 N/mm^2 at 28 days; the concrete does not require air-entrainment. The thickness of the concrete base varies from 140 mm to 250 mm, depending on the subgrade and traffic intensity.

Reinforcement should be long mesh, not lighter than 5.5 kg/m^2, or longitudinal deformed bar reinforcement of cross-sectional area not less than 650 mm^2 per metre width of road. This heavy reinforcement is recommended in view of the absence of transverse joints. The cover for reinforcement and terminating distances from the slab edges are the same as those for rigid pavements, and the recommendations for reinforcement when constructing two- or three-lane carriageways are also the same as for rigid pavements.

Joints

It is recommended that no transverse joints be introduced except for unavoidable construction joints. Where construction joints are necessary the reinforcement should be allowed to project 700 mm beyond the end of a day's work, and when work is resumed the reinforcement should be overlapped the full 700 mm to minimise joint movement. Longitudinal joints should be provided so that the slabs do not exceed 4.5 metres in width; alternatively, reinforcing mats having transverse wires of 8 mm at 200 mm centres may be used to span the joint. When longitudinal joints are provided they should have tie-bars as described in the section on rigid pavements.

Surfacing (black-top)

The surfacing of a composite pavement should be laid in two courses with a total thickness of not less than 90 mm. Materials should conform to the requirements stated for the surfacing of flexible roads.

7.1.5   Surface water drainage*

The provision of adequate drainage facilities is essential in any pavement design. Drainage facilities must cope with water from the carriageways, hard shoulders, footpath or cycle paths, as well as dealing with water from verges and adjacent catchment areas. The design of surface water drainage is outside the scope of this book, but the reader should be aware that the design will depend on factors such as intensity of rainfall, size of catchment area, duration of storm or time of concentration, and the impermeability factor of the surfaces.

Drainage of urban roads

The surface water is collected into channels at the road-side and discharged through gullies into the storm water sewer. Gullies (Fig 7.12) are positioned at intervals of 25 m to 30 metres, depending on the width of road and nature of the cross-fall. The fall may be in one direction across a lane, or in two directions from a crowned section. The gully should discharge to a storm-sewer under the verge or footpath. The position of the storm-sewer will influence the amount of maintenance work when resurfacing the road; for this reason a storm-sewer under both verges or footpaths is to be preferred but is, of course, expensive. Pavings and verges should be graded towards the road channel to reduce the number of drainage points necessary.

The gully cover may be top opening or side-opening; the latter is preferred because it does not reduce the effective width of road, but it is, however, less efficient for drainage purposes. Gradients for road channels should be the same as the longitudinal road gradients, provided that they are not less than 1 in 250; summit points must be introduced in channels on roads of flatter gradient.

Drainage of roads in open country

If the road is a minor road, the drainage may be achieved by simple openings or channels which feed into ditches or french drains. Most main roads, however, have a system of gullies and piped sewers. If the road has a hard shoulder the kerb is normally kept flush with the road surface and a precast concrete channel is placed at the outside edge of the shoulder to catch water. The channel discharges into gullies and then into a piped sewer or open channel, depending on the elevation of the road and the type of subgrade. An alternative method of retaining water along the edge of the hard shoulder until it flows into the gullies is to provide a raised concrete or mastic asphalt edging 75 to 100 mm high. The practice of providing concrete-lined channels at the toes of cuttings and embankments has been found to be unsatisfactory, firstly because water can penetrate the verge during a storm and affect the properties of the subgrade; and secondly because water flowing down an embankment may cause slip or increase the risk of slip movement.

Road camber

The road camber or cross-fall should be designed to cope with heavy water run-off during a storm; if the cross-fall is insufficient to cope with heavy rainfalls, there will be a danger of skidding or aquaplaning on the water.

*See also Road Note 35 — Guide for Engineers to the Design of Storm Sewer Systems

The standard cross-fall for motorways is now 1:40 compared with an earlier figure of 1:48; this has been increased to eliminate problems that occur with water lying on a flatter road surface.

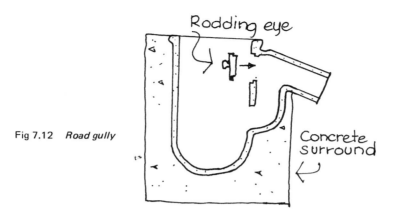

Fig 7.12   *Road gully*

Super-elevation

When a vehicle travels round a bend the horizontal centrifugal force tends to overturn the vehicle or cause a sideways movement, depending on the height and speed of the vehicle. This force can be controlled by banking the road surface at the bend (known as super-elevation). The degree of super-elevation depends on factors such as the type of road surface; speed limits; and radius of bend. The super-elevation can be kept within the recommended limits only if the radius can be increased; in the UK the maximum slope of this work should not exceed 1 in 14.5.

7.1.6   Hard shoulder, kerbs, footpaths and verges*

Hard shoulders are continuous strips of hard standing alongside motorways and other major roads, on to which vehicles may drive during emergencies. They are normally 3 metres wide and constructed in similar materials to the main carriageway, except that a lean concrete or cement-bound granular base is used for the shoulder. The surfacing material consists of 50 mm bitumen macadam or tarmacadam with chippings to give a contrasting colour to that of the carriageway. Alternatively, a concrete hard shoulder with exposed aggregate may be used. Coloured surfacing, consisting of bituminous-coated sand, has also been used to provide a distinctive hard shoulder.

Consideration must be given to whether the shoulder may at some time be incorporated into a carriageway as part of a road-widening scheme. If this is likely to occur the shoulder should be constructed to fulfil the functions of the slow lane. The shoulder is normally separated from the carriageway by a 300 mm wide flush marginal strip contrasting in colour with the road surface.

Kerbs (Fig 7.13) are used to contain the road construction and to define the limits of the carriageway. They may be constructed of concrete or asphalt, vertical or splayed in section, or sometimes level with the carriageway. Concrete kerbs may be either precast or insitu, the latter being laid with an automatic kerbing machine. Asphalt kerbs are also laid with automatic kerbing machines and should be laid as soon as practicable after the completion of the road surface. Vertical kerbs are only necessary where a footpath adjoins the carriageway or where the kerb is used to prevent a vehicle leaving the carriageway at a particular point. For most purposes the top of the kerb should be 100 mm above the road surface; if kerbs are placed too high they induce 'kerb shyness', which effectively reduces the width of the carriageway; flush or level kerbs should be preferred where their use is practicable. Reference should be made to the DOT Specification for Roads and Bridges, 1976 for details of laying .

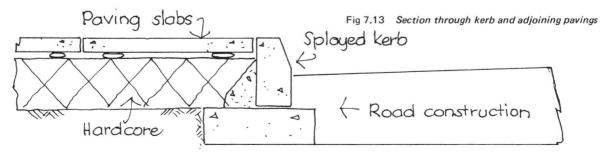

Fig 7.13   *Section through kerb and adjoining pavings*

*See also Design Bulletin No. 32, HMSO 1977

Footpaths and verges

Footpaths may be constructed with concrete slabs or flexible paving. If concrete slabs are used they should be bedded using dabs of lime mortar on a base of ashes or similar material (Fig 7.13). Slabs should be bonded to resist movement. Flexible surfacing conforming to the appropriate BS should be laid to falls on a sub-base of granular material or other suitable material.

Verges should be provided alongside all classified roads in rural areas. They should have a width of 3.5 metres, of which the 1.2 metres adjacent to the carriageway should be free from obstacles. Verges separating cycle tracks from roads should be 2 metres wide; those separating footpaths from roads should be 1 metre wide.

7.2 BRIDGES

7.2.1 Types of construction

There are three basic types of bridge, depending on the form of the load-bearing structure; these forms are flat, convex and concave (Fig 7.14). They are better known as beam, arch, and suspension-type bridges.

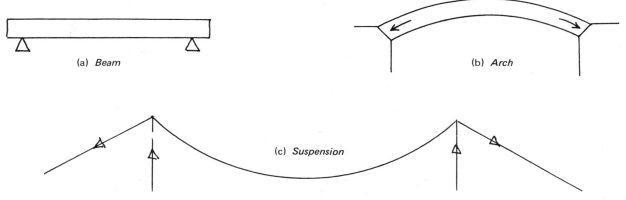

Fig 7.14   *Basic principles in bridge design*

Beam bridges can be divided into two main groups: simple beam and cantilever (Fig 7.15). The simple beam bridge transmits the loads vertically through piers or abutments and is horizontally self-supporting. The cantilever beam transmits its loads through piers which are normally central to the beam; however, when the cantilever is loaded the beam exerts great pressures on the opposite end connection. There are many variations in beam design, ranging from steel truss design to pre-stressed concrete units. The simple beam bridge is very econoᵗ mical for spans of up to 50 metres. The cantilever beam provides a means of producing much greater spans: bridges with spans of up to 540 metres have been constructed.

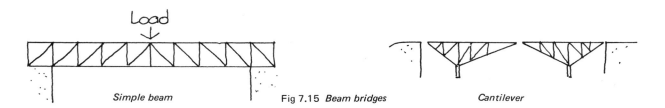

Fig 7.15 *Beam bridges*

The arch bridge can carry greater loads than the beam bridge because the load-carrying member, the arch, is in a state of compression throughout. This makes the design suited to materials which are weak in tension. The arch supports the traffic either above or below (Fig 7.16) the main structural form. The first type of support (that above the arch) is suitable for use where the bridge crosses a gorge and where rock or very hard material is present to resist the thrust. The arch may be hinged or pinned at the ends to eliminate any movement on the foundation. The spandrel of the bridges may be braced or open (Fig 7.16). Roads supported below the arch, by hangers, create a different form of structure in that the deck acts as a tie to the arch and therefore produces a bridge which can be used on foundations that would not resist the thrust of the first arch type. This type of bridge has been used for spans of 496 metres in steel and 305 metres in concrete. The rise/span factor is between 0.15 and 0.25.

The problem inherent in long arch bridges is one of erection; if intermediate piers are impracticable then it often follows that falsework (temporary support) will be impracticable. This means complicated methods of erection, usually involving designing the bridge to withstand stresses which, after erection, it will never have to bear.

A suspension bridge consists of a cable-hung decking supported by towers. The general layout (Fig 7.17) comprises a central suspended span with side spans; the latter may take the form of a simply supported beam over short spans. The towers are secured by main cables which are continuous between anchorages. The foundations of the towers are constructed by caisson or cofferdam methods (see Chapter 6) and the cable anchorages or foundations are taken through anchorage tunnels to suitable ground.

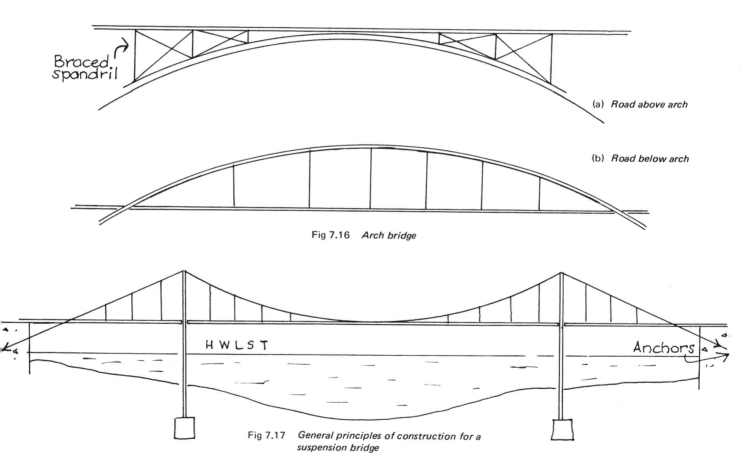

Braced spandril

(a) *Road above arch*

(b) *Road below arch*

Fig 7.16   *Arch bridge*

H W L S T

Anchors

Fig 7.17   *General principles of construction for a suspension bridge*

The deck of the bridge (Fig 7.18) must be stiffened to prevent undue deflection and to provide aero-dynamic stability; this is achieved either by introducing a continuous truss alongside or below the deck, or by designing the deck as an aerofoil. In either case models of the design must be tested in a wind tunnel to ensure stability and to achieve the most economic design.

The supporting towers of many large span suspension bridges are constructed in a cellular design, but recent developments favour the use of box towers constructed from stiffened welded plates. This new concept was developed for the Severn Bridge between England and Wales. In addition to the new development for suspension towers, the Severn bridge has a 'torsion box' deck (Fig 7.18) which has been designed as an aerofoil. The box-deck or box-girder construction is now a very popular construction method used in all forms of bridge design.

(a) *Lattice beam below deck*   (b) *Torsion box as aerofoil*

Fig 7.18   *Methods of achieving stability of deck to suspension bridge*

Moveable bridges

These bridges are better known for their function, e.g. swing, bascule (or drawbridge) or vertical lift, than for their basic construction. They are in fact the same as, or variations of, the three basic forms of bridge. The need for moveable bridges arises from the demand for greater headroom than a normal fixed bridge can economically provide.

Swing bridges (Fig 7.19) are used for spanning wide openings. They pivot on a central pier, and so have the disadvantage of reducing the actual navigational channel by half. Their advantage is that the whole structure is balanced on the central pier when the bridge is open, thereby reducing the amount of support mechanism. The bridge is a cantilever type which acts as a continuous girder when in the closed position.

Bascule or pivoted cantilever bridges are basically drawbridges which are operated by means of a counter-weight behind the pivot point (Fig 7.20). The Tower Bridge, London, works on this principle.

Vertical lift (Fig 7.21) consists of simple beams or girders which are supported and raised by cables from high towers. The cables, counter-weighted to balance the dead load of the bridge, pass over sheaves at the top of the tower. Spans up to 167 metres have been achieved by this method, which has proved to be the simplest form of movable bridge, though not aesthetically the best.

Choice of bridge system

The first important factor is the clear span required. If it is a long span, i.e. over 300 metres, steel construction is the most likely solution; concrete arch bridges have so far been limited to 305 metres span. The steel construction may be cantilever girder, arch, or suspension. The cantilever form has great advantages in erection, since the cantilever arms can be built without centering and the centre sections of the span can be floated out and lifted into position. The arch form is very suitable for spans of up to 500 metres, but is more difficult to construct: the arch can be built out as a cantilever, but requires extensive back-anchoring which is very costly. Suspension bridges are the best known form for spans of over 600 metres. The high-tensile strength of cable wires produces a very economic design solution when compared with other forms of support.

In general, for a given span and given load the main girder weight decreases in the following order: cantilever, arch, suspension. However, foundation costs can be quite the opposite: foundations for cantilevers are simple by comparison with the other forms, owing to their vertical loading, and are therefore normally the cheapest. Foundations for suspension bridges are usually very extensive and costly. Small span bridges, up to 300 metres span, may be formed in steel, concrete or other material suitable for the span and load. In particular, steel box-girder construction and pre-stressed concrete box-girders have produced economic solutions in recent years. Many modern road bridges, especially 'overbridges' (carrying a minor road over a major road) have been formed as simple cantilevers carrying centre beams (Fig 7.22). The most economical solution, depending on span and aesthetics, has proved to be a combination of insitu concrete and pre-stressed units.

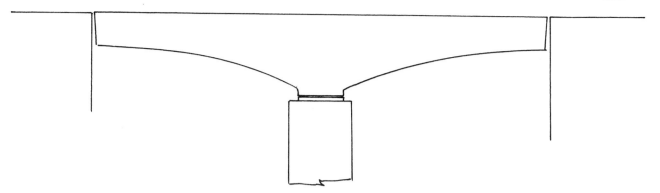

Fig 7.19   *Swing bridge*

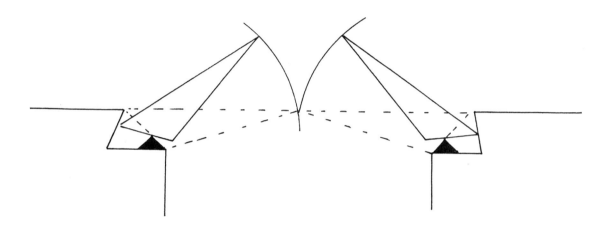

Fig 7.20   *Bascule bridge*

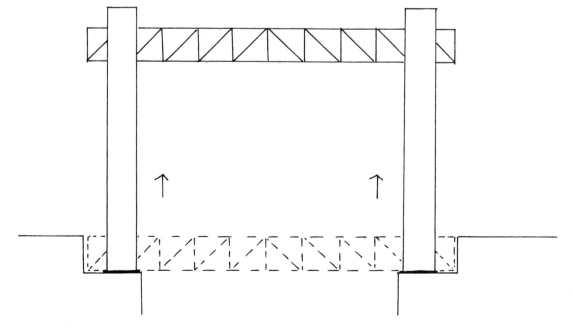

Fig 7.21   *Vertical lift bridge*

Fig 7.22   *Simple cantilever carrying centre beams* (Norwest Holst Group Limited)

7.2.2   Foundation techniques and bridge construction

The construction of bridge foundations on land presents little difficulty compared with those in water. If the ground is water-bearing there may be a need for a cofferdam or in some cases even a caisson, although the latter is a rare occurrence on land. The foundations are taken down to bedrock unless this is uneconomical, in which case a piled foundation will be necessary.

Foundations in water present various constructional problems which include protection of the men whilst working; transporting and placing concrete, and reduction in working time (if affected by tides). The technique of forming the foundation will normally involve the use of a cofferdam or caisson, although in some cases piled foundations may be used. Fig 7.23 shows pile driving in the River Ouse for the M62 crossing. Piles are capped off to receive a pier foundation; alternatively, they are prepared to receive cross-beams which support the main bridge construction.

Beam and girder bridges may be constructed in steel or concrete. The beam may take the form of a lattice a solid beam, or a hollow box-section; in addition a steel structure may have plate girders.

The piers are first constructed and the beams or girders are lifted on to them by cranes or hydraulic jacking. Cranes may be positioned on falsework cradled around the piers, or they may operate from ground level; when the bridge spans water a gantry may be built either on piles at just above water level or between the piers at high level. The beam sections are floated into position by pontoon prior to lifting. If the spans are not too great the beam sections can be 'rolled out' from the access point and lowered into position by crane: this method of construction is used for box-girder construction (Fig 7.24).

Fig 7.23   *Pile driving across River Ouse for M62 crossing* (Raymond Concrete Pile Company Limited)

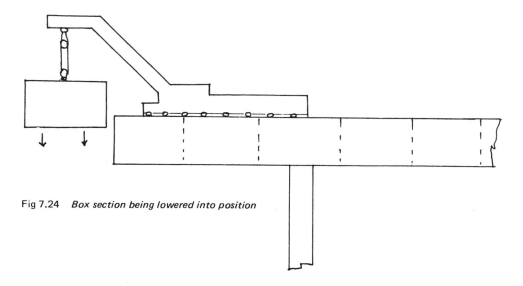

Fig 7.24   *Box section being lowered into position*

After placing the main girders, the bridge deck is positioned or cast insitu. Decking for steel bridges can take one of many forms: Fig 7.25 shows typical deck sections. Decking for concrete bridges may either be integral with the beam design or take the form of cross-beams and slab construction (Fig 7.26).

The design of an insitu bridge may vary, but for all forms the one common factor is falsework: this ranges from very heavy towers, supporting steel beams for high bridges, to a forest of heavy scaffolding for low bridges. Various systems of falsework are shown in Figs 7.27 to 7.29.

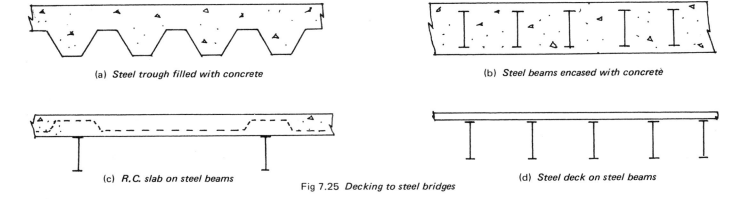

(a) *Steel trough filled with concrete*

(b) *Steel beams encased with concrete*

(c) *R.C. slab on steel beams*

(d) *Steel deck on steel beams*

Fig 7.25 *Decking to steel bridges*

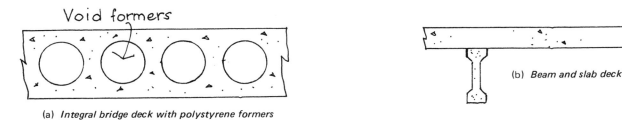

Void formers

(a) *Integral bridge deck with polystyrene formers*

(b) *Beam and slab deck*

Fig 7.26 *Decking to concrete bridges*

Fig 7.27 *Falsework to high level bridge* (John Laing & Son Limited)

Fig 7.28   *Formwork and falsework for bridge construction low level*
(R M Douglas Construction Limited)

Fig 7.29   *Special beam support to formwork over canal* (Norwest Holst Group Limited)

If the construction involves cantilever beams, the anchorage or anchor arm is completed first, to prevent movement of the pier when the cantilever arm is constructed. Alternatively, both arms may be constructed simultaneously (Fig 7.30).

Arch bridge construction

Steel arch bridges are usually erected by cantilevering the ribs out from the abutments (Fig 7.31) by means of cables which pass over an erection strut to an anchorage point. For very large spans the arch is cantilevered in the same manner but is built out in sections, from the basic cantilevered structure, by means of a creeping crane. The crane is mounted on top of the arch and lifts sections of rib from barges or pontoons below. The work proceeds from both abutments, and the final gap, which may range from 50 mm to 100 mm, may be closed by 'fleeting' (lowering both arch ribs until they meet). The bridge deck is then constructed from both ends, which consist of beams suitably decked, hung from the arch.

Concrete arch bridges, if pre-stressed, may be constructed in a similar manner to steel arches. Normal reinforced arches are unable to withstand cantilever stresses and are therefore lifted on to falsework which must be erected from the river bed. In situ arches may be cast in the same manner.

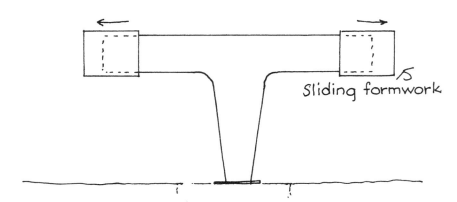

Fig 7.30   *Construction of insitu cantilever bridge*

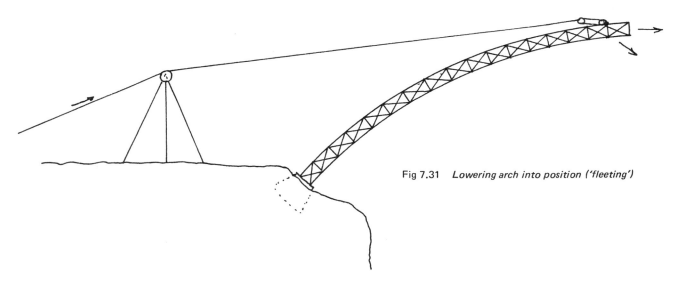

Fig 7.31   *Lowering arch into position ('fleeting')*

Suspension bridge construction

This involves four main operations: construction of the anchorage foundations; construction of the towers; spinning the main cables; and constructing the bridge deck. The anchorage foundations are usually taken deep into a hillside and tied back to rock by means of piles or rock-anchors. The towers may be of steel or insitu concrete (constructed by slip-form methods) founded on massive concrete bases. The bases are usually constructed within a cofferdam or caisson. Climbing cranes may be used for the handling of steel and concrete. The suspension cables are built up from multi-strands of high tensile wire. The wire is carried from one anchorage point to the other by means of a grooved wheel which is fixed to a continuous wire cable. The endless cable carrying the wheel is driven backwards and forwards, the wheel carrying the high tensile wire. On completion of one haul the wire is lifted off the wheel and fixed to the suspension shoe. The wheel then returns, carrying back another double strand of wire. Several wheels may be employed, laying as many as twelve wires on a double pass. The wires are all checked for sag and then bound together to form the main cable; anti-corrosion paint is applied to the cable during binding. The work of laying and binding the wires is carried out from a temporary catwalk (Fig 7.32) which is suspended just below the cable. The road deck may be erected by cantilevering the sections out from each end or by lifting the sections from pontoons on the water below; alternatively, if the sections are hollow they may be floated into position (as for the Severn Bridge) and lifted. (See also Chapter 8 Section 8.2.2).

Fig 7.32   *Laying the wires in the saddle at the top of the tower — temporary catwalk in background*
(William Tribe Limited — Raglan)

7.2.3   Bridge bearings and expansion joints

Bridge bearings are made of either metal or a flexible material such as rubber. Metal bearings should comply with the requirements of BS 153 and rubber bearings should comply with the requirements of the DoE Technical Memorandum (Bridges) No. BE 1/76.

The requirements of BS 153 include provision for changes of length in girders due to temperature and stress variations in spans over 9.14 metres. Where spans exceed 15 metres an allowance must be made for angular deflection at the supports: at one end the span should have a roller, rocker or other efficient expansion bearing. Some provision must be made to prevent uplift at the bearing point; this can be achieved by a sliding lug or key. Metal bearings for small-span bridges may consist of steel blocks resting directly on the concrete or steel bases. Expansion can be accommodated by setting the steel block on phosphor-bronze strips, which are fixed to the supporting base. Where bridges are supported entirely on elastomeric bearings it is often necessary to provide 'guide bearings' to prevent excessive lateral movement. Guide bearings do not carry load: they simply resist movement in one horizontal direction.

Metal bearings for large spans may be of the rocker or roller type (Fig 7.33); the lower saddle may be fixed or rest on phosphor-bronze strips or some other form of expansion base. Leaf bearings are used to suit applications where complete reversals of vertical loading can occur or where very large rotations are required about a single axis (Fig 7.33).

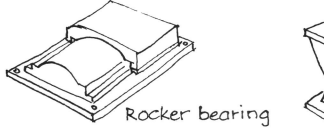 

Fig 7.33 *Bridge bearings*

Rubber and plastic bearings may be used as alternative means of allowing movement. Rubber bearings consist of alternate layers of steel and rubber, which allow movement in both vertical and horizontal directions. Plastic laminates, Polytetrafluorethylene (PTFE) by name, have been used in lieu of rubber: this plastic is highly resistant to weather and is ideal for situations where low resistance to sliding is all that is required. PTFE sliding bearings were used for the bridges in Milton Keynes, which cross the River Ouzel and the Grand Union Canal.

The bearings may be located on the piers engaging the bridge beams by means of projecting studs.

Where necessary, resilient pads may be placed between the bridge bearing and the concrete pier, thus equalising the pressure under the bearing and preventing damage to the concrete by excessive stress concentrations.

Expansion joints for bridges and elevated motorways can be formed in various materials and may function in different ways. The two most common ways to accommodate expansion are by an interlocking comb-joint and by compressible filler. The interlocking comb-joint (Fig 7.34) is bolted to the concrete or steel deck at intervals which will accommodate maximum expansion, nine such joints being used on the Greater London Council's Western Avenue Extension which is 4.4 km long. Similar expansion joints (Fig 7.35) have rubber-mounted running surfaces which ensure structural independence of the joint from one side to the other. With the latter type of joint the asphalt or bituminous road surfacing is carried across the joint without interrupting the laying operation. The black-top is cut either side of the joint, the studs of the joint being exposed and screwed up to the correct position to receive the joint. The joint is then bedded to the correct level in epoxy-mortar and, when set, the studs are tightened down.

Another popular type of expansion joint is the transflex joint (Fig 7.36); this consists of an integral neoprene-steel moulding which spans and seals the road or bridge deck. The steel plate reinforcement distributes the loads and the neoprene encasement gives high strength, flexibility and wearing qualities.

Fig 7.34 *Comb-type expansion joint*

(Client: Greater London Council
Consulting Engineers: G. Maunsell & Partners
Contractor: John Laing Construction Limited)

Compressible fillers range from bituminised foamed polyurethene and low density polyethylene to bitumen-impregnated wood-fibre board. The filler is usually sealed (Fig 7.37) with a suitable sealing compound to prevent entry of dirt or water: this operation should be carried out when the main bridge temperature is between 10 °C and 16 °C. Where the filler material is held between epoxy-resin mortar nosings, the nosing must be formed as specified in the DOT Specification for Roads and Bridges, Clause 2303.

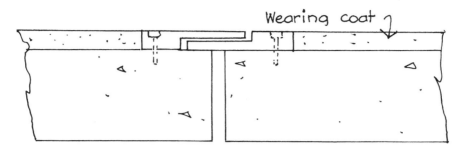

Fig 7.35   *Rubber surfaced expansion joint*

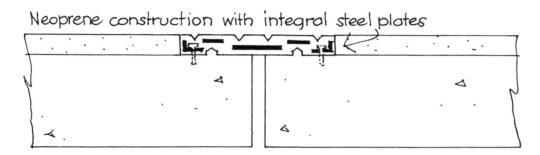

Fig 7.36   *Transflex expansion joint*

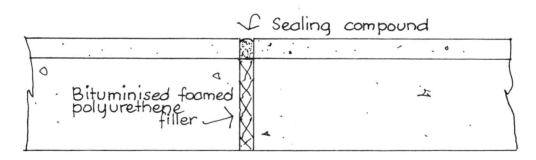

Fig 7.37   *Traditional expansion joint*

7.2.4   Waterproofing and surfacing of bridge decks

Concrete bridges and elevated roadways must be protected against the deleterious effects of water and de-icing chemicals, which may cause corrosion of the reinforcement. This may be achieved by applying a surface treatment, or a membrane under the road surface.

The former method of treatment may take the form of a very thin coat of epoxy-resin or of a built-up bituminised surface. The epoxy-resin is applied to the surface of the finished deck in two coats, the final coat being sprayed with fine aggregate to produce a non-skid surface. The built-up bituminised surface has been developed to replace the conventional sand asphalt topping: it withstands structural movement and stays flexible at very low temperatures.

Sandwich membranes may be applied as an alternative method of waterproofing. They may be epoxy-resin based or tough flexible bitumen-polymer sheeting. The bitumen-polymer sheeting is fixed by bonding with hot bitumen compound and is protected by a road surfacing material with or without a sand asphalt under-layer, depending on the thickness of the bitumen-polymer. (Reference may be made to DOE Technical Memorandum (Bridges) No BE 27 'Waterproofing and Surfacing of Bridge Decks').

7.3 SUBWAYS

7.3.1 Methods of construction

The constructional system for an underpass or subway may be one of three methods commonly used:

Precast concrete units

Thrust-bored units

Insitu concrete

Precast concrete units are available as standard units ready for supply at little or no notice; specially designed units may also be employed, but waiting time for supply may prove a disadvantage. Standard units may be supplied as complete box-like, open-ended sections; portal frame segments, which are located on a predetermined concrete slab; or separate units for the walls and roof. The box units (Fig 7.38) are assembled on a concrete bed and packed to the correct levels before winching together. The joints between the units are formed by means of a pre-formed sealant strip in a socket and spigot joint. The units are connected together by bolted connection plates in the floor and roof, or alternatively they may be pre-stressed by the Macalloy bar system (see Chapter 8 Section 8.1.5). With the pre-stressed units, the lower waterproofing membrane, which may be asphalt or neoprene sheeting, is placed on the concrete slab, and continuous granolithic concrete bearing pads, 300 mm wide and 25 mm deep, are laid. After the pads have reached the required strength, the units are placed in position, the pad being lubricated with a graphite paste to reduce friction during stressing. The portal frame units (Fig 7.39) are located over a flat bottom rail which is carefully positioned and levelled on the concrete base, a steel channel section having been cast into the legs of the portal. The units are winched together and sealed by a pre-formed sealant strip which is compressed during winching; final connections are made with external connecting plates. Care must be taken to ensure that the connecting plates and bolts are made watertight.

The wall and roof unit system (Fig 7.40) consists of precast units for the walls and roof of the subway. The wall units are placed in position and the insitu floor is cast, using the units as shuttering. This is followed by placing the roof units and pouring the insitu loading slab, the thickness of which depends on the loading requirements. The wall units have plain joints without seal, which gives the advantage of dimensional flexibility.

The method of construction in thrust boring (Fig 7.41) has been fully described in Chapter 5 (Tunnelling), and consideration of details of inserting the units can be limited here to aspects concerning location. Normal methods involve the formation of a driving pit and the construction of a thrust block, but if the subway is to be driven through an embankment, the driving pit will not be necessary. In the case of driving through embankments, a series of holes is first driven and cables are threaded through the holes to load a distribution base on the far side of the embankment. The reactions from the pushing rams are transferred to the embankment via the cables. If neither of the above methods is suitable, a thrust block can be cast above ground level. The units for jacking may be circular or rectangular, the latter being suitable for the majority of subways. Lubrication may be necessary during thrust-boring and this is usually achieved with a suspension of bentonite.

The jointing of units to prevent the ingress of water is an expensive item. The units must have direct edge contact to transmit the thrust load, which eliminates the normal pre-formed sealing strip. The jointing method used must allow edge contact for jacking, yet be designed to receive a sealing compound from the inner face. The latter can be accommodated by forming a rebated joint which can be filled with mortar prior to the application of sealant. Insitu concrete subways need no explanation in a book of this nature, the construction following the pattern for any underground concrete construction.

Fig 7.38   *Precast concrete subway unit being positioned* (Mono Concrete Limited)

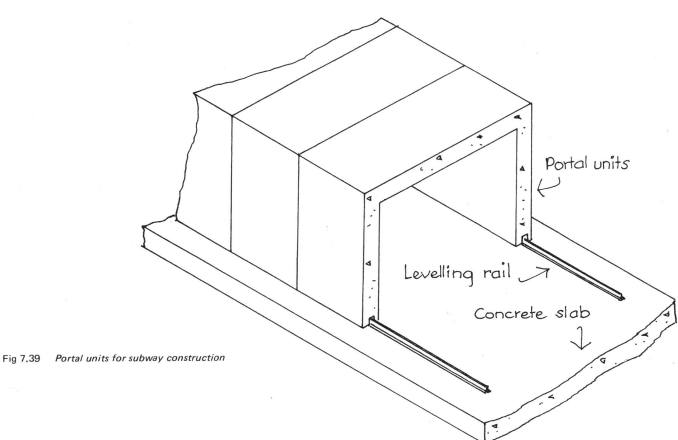

Portal units

Levelling rail

Concrete slab

Fig 7.39   *Portal units for subway construction*

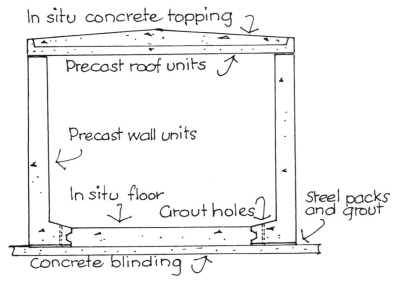

Fig 7.40   *Wall and roof units in subway construction*

Fig 7.41(a)   *Units being driven in thrust-bored subway*
(M & H Tunnelling Limited)

Fig 7.41(b)   *View inside thrust-bored subway*
(M & H Tunnelling Limited)

7.3.2   Methods of waterproofing

Waterproofing to subways may be achieved by applying mastic asphalt, bituminous or neoprene sheeting, or painted membrane.

Mastic asphalt should be laid in two coats and conform to the Code of Practice CP 144 Part 4. Joints in the layers should be staggered at least 150 mm and positioned as agreed with the resident engineer.

Bituminous sheeting may be applied in two or three layers, each layer being fully bedded in hot bitumen. The concrete surface must be carefully primed with cut-back bitumen or similar primer, allowed to dry before applying the first layer of sheeting. Joints between sheeting should be lapped with end laps of at least 150 mm and side laps of at least 100 mm.

Pre-formed sheeting membranes such as 'bituthene' — a self-adhesive bitumen polythene — have become increasingly popular in recent years. They require the same preliminary work as bituminous sheeting but are laid more quickly than other membranes and can be applied by unskilled labour (Fig 7.42). Other membranes may also be used for waterproofing. Tar or bituminous painting should consist of two coats of hot-applied tar (2 square metres per litre) or two coats of cut-back bitumen (3 square metres per litre). Painted membranes, used on pre-cast units, must be compatible with the sealants used for jointing. On completion, the waterproof membrane must be protected against puncture. This is normally achieved by constructing a concrete-block skin against the membrane prior to backfilling with granular material.

Fig 7.42   *Bitu-thene 1000 used for tanking subway*   (W.R. Grace Limited)

7.3.3   Lighting, finishes and drainage

Lighting for subways may be incorporated in the walls or roof units. These should be recessed to give maximum protection against vandals, and all light fittings should be of toughened glass. Finishes to subways may vary to suit criteria such as location and degree of use, level of vandalism anticipated, and types or quality of finish on adjacent buildings. For industrial and agricultural use a plain concrete finish may suffice, but subways and underpasses in urban areas should be bright and attractive, otherwise the subway may be ignored by a large proportion of potential users. Attractive surface finishes can be achieved by using mosaics, tiling and fine white aggregate rendering which can be applied by spray gun. Drainage to subways, which may be necessary in storm conditions, can be achieved by normal falls, screeded floor, gullies or continuous side channels. These channels or gullies will empty direct into the storm sewer, if it is low enough, or alternatively a sump and pump system can be operated.

7.4 AIRFIELD CONSTRUCTION

The term 'airfield' is used in the United Kingdom to refer only to military stations. The recognised international term for civil aviation is 'aerodrome', though the term 'airport' is preferred for aerodromes with port facilities, i.e. Customs, immigration and health control.

7.4.1   Introduction to pavement design

The construction of airfields is similar to road construction in that the type of pavement depends a great deal on the load it has to carry. While the strength of any pavement depends upon the nature of its construction and underlying subgrade, the stresses applied by aircraft can be exceptionally high and variable. By comparison, loads on aircraft pavements may be eight times greater than those on road pavements. The intensity of loads and stresses on aircraft pavements is such that aircraft are classified by a number and the pavements are designed to carry aircraft within certain classifications. This allows an economic design to be produced. The classification of aircraft by number, known as the LCN system (Load Classification Number) is determined by wheel load, undercarriage configuration, and tyre pressure. The pavement design and construction is determined by this number; and it will be appreciated that aircraft can only regularly use pavements that are designed to carry loads and stresses equal to or greater than their particular classification group. The Department of the Environment have published a paper giving the LCN of aircraft currently operating which equates LCN numbers with load classification groups (LCG). This allows the designer to select pavements for a particular airport to suit the type of aircraft most likely to use it. Load classification numbers range from LCN 10 for light aircraft to LNC 120 for very heavy aircraft. Concorde has an LCN of 85, the highest for a civil aircraft.

7.4.2   Foundation considerations

The subgrade for pavements is classed as 'good' or 'bad' with various intermediate conditions. The extreme conditions are based on typical gravel or chalk subgrade and clay subgrade respectively. The subgrade is tested by means of a loading plate and its deflection under load is measured. The pressure for a unit deflection is known as the 'k' value; a 'good' subgrade would have a 'k' value of 200 $MN/m^2/m$ and an indifferent subgrade would have a 'k' value of 50 $MN/m^2/m$ or less. The 'k' value of the subgrade is all-important when considering the type and thickness of pavement. Charts are available giving the relationship between flexural stress in concrete, the LCN of the aircraft, the actual subgrade characteristics and the theoretical thickness of concrete slab. Having determined the 'k' value of the subgrade and the LCG into which the LCN of the aircraft falls, the various options for the pavements in terms of type and thickness can be quickly established.

If the subgrade consists of unfragmented rock which is a metre or more in thickness, then flexible pavements can be formed with 100 mm lean concrete for levelling the surface, plus the bituminous surfacing.

7.4.3   Pavement construction

The function of any pavement is to reduce the maximum applied load for which it is designed, down to a figure which the subgrade can take.

Experience gained over many years has limited pavement construction to three types:

Rigid

Composite

Flexible.

A rigid pavement performs its function by virtue of the flexural strength in the concrete, thereby spreading the load to the subgrade. Flexible pavements reduce the load by the inter-granular friction of its base material. Composite pavements contain, as the name suggests, elements of both flexural strength and inter-granular friction.

Rigid pavements (Fig 7.43) may be either reinforced or unreinforced pavement quality concrete. Pavement quality concrete (PQC) is concrete which will give a minimum flexural strength of 3.5 MN/m^2 or more at the age when the pavement is brought into use. Rigid pavements of unreinforced concrete are normally used for runway and taxiway junctions, aprons and hardstandings, and similar areas subject to fuel spillage and on which aircraft will stand.

Composite pavements (Fig 7.44), similar to road pavements, consist of continuously reinforced concrete with bituminous topping. The bituminous surface must have high stability and smooth riding qualities; these qualities can be achieved by using Marshall asphalt. Marshall asphalt is the term used in the United Kingdom to indicate a high stability stone-filled hot rolled asphalt (the term 'asphaltic concrete' is used in the United States and elsewhere). The material is designed and controlled as the work proceeds by the 'Marshall' method which requires a specially equipped laboratory. The Marshall method, which ensures the careful grading of aggregate and optimum binder control, may also be applied to the equivalent dense tar surfacing which when available may be used in place of bitumen bound material. The bituminous surface spreads the load to the concrete surface and provides better riding qualities. The thickness of asphalt will normally vary from 75 mm to 125 mm depending on the risk of reflective or sympathetic cracking over the concrete pavement joints and cracks. The base course, having an aggregate size of 25 mm, is rolled to a thickness between 50 mm and 100 mm, and the wearing course may be up to 50 mm finished thickness.

Flexible pavements (Fig 7.45) consist of granular material, stabilised material, or both, for the load spreading element which is topped with bituminous surfacing. They are not generally economical in Britain for heavy duty pavements, but compare favourably in cost with composite pavements when used for light aircraft. The working stress for pavement concrete is based on its tested strength (generally at 28 days) increased to allow for a continuous though diminishing gain of strength throughout the 'life' of the concrete. The eventual apparent modulus of rupture is subject to a 'Factor of Safety' varying from 1.5 or less for lightly trafficked runways and other pavements to as much as 2.0 for heavily trafficked aprons, tracks and runway ends at busy airports. The higher factor of safety for aprons, taxiways and runway ends is due to the greater frequency of loading, which creates fatigue failure.

Joints in concrete pavements are similar in design to those shown for concrete roads (Section 7.1) but the positioning of joints is more complex. Expansion joints should be placed between the main runway and any contiguous concrete; they may also be placed in both directions in a large concrete surface. In a continuously reinforced slab there are no transverse joints of any kind. The reinforcement is lapped, or better still, welded, to give uniform continuity.

Drainage of runways is of great importance, since a thin film of water may cause aquaplaning of the aircraft. The cross falls on the runway should be in the region of 1 in 66 and runway shoulders may be increased to a fall of 1 in 40. Gullies should be placed so that no part of the pavement is more than 30 metres from a gully or drainage channel. A further means of reducing the risk of aquaplaning is to finish the asphalt with an open-graded macadam, which will serve as a friction course. This requires careful control, selected materials and good laying technique.

The drainage on areas subject to fuel spillage should be channelled to a fuel and oil interceptor to prevent pollution of water course and to reduce the risk of fire. As all aircraft pavements are subject to fuel spillage and as intermediate interceptors are potential danger areas, it is usual to provide a single open trap near the drainage outfall.

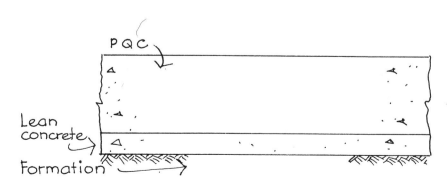

Fig 7.43 *Rigid pavement*

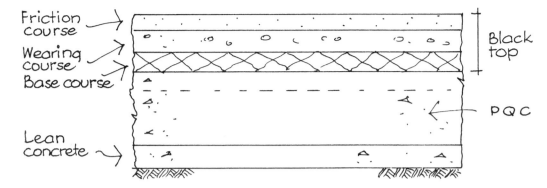

Friction course
Wearing course
Base course
Lean concrete
Black top
PQC

Fig 7.44   *Composite pavement*

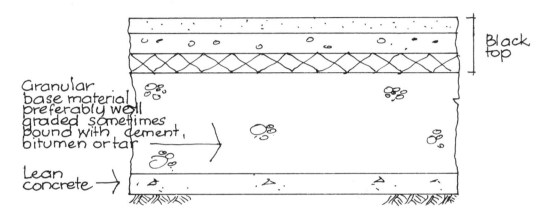

Granular base material preferably well graded sometimes bound with cement, bitumen or tar
Lean concrete
Black top

Fig 7.45   *Flexible pavement*

Chapter 8

Concrete and Steelwork

8.1 CONCRETE

8.1.1 Materials

The principal materials for making concrete are cement, fine aggregates, coarse aggregates and water.

Cement is the most expensive ingredient in concrete and although assumed to be the most reliable, since it is very carefully controlled during manufacture, should be sampled and tested. Important qualities of cement include its strength, durability, and defined setting and hardening characteristics. These qualities are determined by the chemical composition, the manufacturing process and the fineness of grinding, all of which have resulted in a British Standard which should be quoted when specifying the material. Cements are grouped according to their chemical composition and manufacturing processes, the characteristics of which determine the use of the material. It will be appreciated therefore that although Ordinary Portland Cement and Rapid-hardening Portland Cement represent the bulk of all types of cement used, there are many special cements, e.g. low heat cement, sulphate-resisting cement, which have been developed for special purposes. In civil engineering the amount of cement used on a project may justify the production of one of these special cements rather than the use of other technical solutions.

Fine aggregates may be obtained from various sources; they must be clean, hard and chemically inert. Pit sand nearly always requires washing — hence the name 'washed sand' for concrete. Crushed stone may also be used provided that it is free from excessive dust and not too flaky. Crushed limestone and granulated slag should be carefully checked before using in reinforced concrete because they are often of low strength. Sea sand, suitably graded, may be used for concreting if taken from below high-water level, but tests should be carried out for organic impurities and salt content.

The sand, whatever the source, must be checked for correct grading; the grading of fine aggregate is more important, when considering the strength of concrete, than the grading of coarse aggregate. Reference may be made to the current British Standard relating to the grading of concreting sands.

Coarse aggregates must also be clean, hard and chemically inert. They must be free of an undue quantity of elongated or flaky particles, organic matter, coatings of harmful chemicals or, if crushed, excessive dust. The material can be dug from pits, rivers and beaches, or formed from crushed rock from a quarry: large quantities of dredged marine aggregates are also used. Pit gravel requires more cleaning and screening than river gravel and may contain more large stones that require reducing by crusher. Beach gravel must be checked for organic impurities and salt content; again, materials taken below the high-water level tend to be acceptable.

Gravel aggregates are slightly superior to crushed stone, owing to their lower volume of voids, and are therefore suitable for impermeable concrete; they are also more resistant to sulphate attack. The relevant British Standard (BS 882) sets the limits for shape and strength of coarse aggregates.

Crushed stone aggregates or angular aggregates can be produced from granite, flint or hard limestone; sandstone should be avoided since it tends to be porous and therefore much weaker than the other stones. Whinstone chips make good coarse aggregate but the combination of whinstone chips and whinstone sand or fines may produce a concrete which fails to harden: siliceous sand should be used with whinstone aggregate.

Clinker and ashes must not be used as aggregates for structural concrete because of their low strength and possible high sulphate content; the exception to the rule is 'fly ash', which is produced by burning pulverised coal.

Crushed blast furnace slag produces a high quality aggregate which is comparable with gravel for strength: it can be used to provide complete protection of reinforcement against corrosion, this being achieved by the dense concrete it produces.

Size and grading of coarse aggregate

For normal reinforced concrete the maximum size of aggregates will be 19 mm but this will vary according to the thickness of the element being poured and the spacing of the reinforcement. The normal 19 mm coarse aggregate will be suitable for elements not less than 75 mm thick, providing the spacing of the reinforcement allows full compaction. Where the reinforcement is closely spaced a richer mix with 10 mm aggregate should be used to ensure full compaction. Large concrete bases, where the spacing of reinforcement is no problem to compaction, may be poured in concrete containing 38 mm aggregates. In all cases the best results are achieved by correct grading. Test cubes should be made with various gradings of aggregates to confirm the adequacy of the proposed mix design.

Storage of materials

Aggregates are clean when they arrive on site and must be stored in such a manner as will maintain their cleanness and their separate gradings. This usually involves the construction of aggregate bins, which consist of a concrete slab suitably divided into segments to allow ease of access for delivery. The divisions or partitions can be formed with vertical steel H beams into which horizontal boards are slotted. The coarse aggregates should be delivered to site in separate sizes.

Large contracts may also use steel bins in an elevated position for the storage of aggregates. These bins may be filled from elevated roadways, which could consist of an embankment or temporary staging, and they may be filled by crane, high-loader shovel or elevator. The last is probably the least expensive and suitable for all methods of delivery. The capacity of the storage bins and batching plant will depend on the size of the contract and on the amount of concrete required per day.

Cement will be normally stored in steel silos adjacent to the batching plant, although on small contracts it can be stored in sheds which have a raised timber floor. If the latter is used, each consignment of cement should be kept separate and used in the order of delivery.

The water used for mixing should be fresh, clean and free from acids, alkali or other harmful substances which may pollute the supply.

Sea water may be used for mixing if it contains no more than five per cent common salt and is otherwise clean. The effect of sea water in concrete is to retard the setting time by about ten per cent and produce efflorescence. The efflorescence may be acceptable but care must be exercised when calculating the times for striking the formwork. Where there is doubt concerning the quality of water it is necessary to make trial test cubes with both fresh clean water and the water supply in question, the test result being indicative of any detrimental effect.

Water supplied from the mains may be charged to the contract by one of two methods. The first is a rate dependent on the value of the contract, the second by metering the quantity used. The former method of assessment enables the contractor to establish a definite cost when estimating and eliminates the need to save water. However, to encourage saving of water, the metering method may be specified, in which case the appropriate charges should be mentioned in the contract documents.

8.1.2 Concrete mixing and placing

The methods of mixing, distributing and selection of plant is discussed in Chapter 3, Section 2.3 to which reference should be made. This section deals mainly with aspects which the Quantity Surveyor must consider when preparing a specification. In respect of mix designs for concrete the reader is referred to the DoE publication 'Design of Normal Concrete Mixes'.

Concrete mixing for a job normally falls under one of three heads, each with its own problems:

Site mixing with the smaller contractor

Such a contractor may lack both knowledge of and interest in concrete technology; it is therefore particularly important to give sufficient amplification in the contract documents to achieve adequate pricing and avoidance of difficulties during construction. As for all contracts it should be clearly stated how much routine testing is to be carried out and of what kind, e.g. number and size of cubes per test; site curing facilities and procedure; method of cube compaction (kango hammer or standard rod) etc. It should also be clearly stated how the concrete is to be judged for compliance, e.g. specified maximum statistical defective rate per cent with associated margin between specified characteristic strength and achieved mean strength.

There are several specification methods open to the client's engineer, the two most suitable being prescribed mix, and designed mix with quality control procedures.

Prescribed mix (CP 110 Tables): these tables are intended to replace the old Nominal and Standard type mixes and are suitable for small jobs with little concrete where full design and quality control may be considered inappropriate. Mix quantities are laid down for the various qualities of mix, and compliance control is simply a matter of checking the weigh batcher to ensure accuracy of weighing and consistency of batching by the batchman. Cube testing may be carried out as a check but cannot be contractual since the specification is based on batch quantities. These mixes are somewhat rich for most though not all parts of the country.

Designed mix with quality control procedures: if it is decided to use quality controlled concrete then trial mixes may be desirable and the contractor may need guidance on the initial mix design. To prevent a delay in the concreting programme a start can be made using the appropriate prescribed mix, provided that this is covered by the contract documents. The contractor will also need guidance as to the appropriate initial margin so that he can design on the appropriate mean strength.

Site mixing with a contractor of national repute

Most, though not all such firms are well acquainted with the more sophisticated procedures for mix design and production control and will respond efficiently to a specification of quality controlled concrete, i.e. designed mixes. However, they will lack the positive background information (i.e. of working on the same site with the same batchman, aggregates, cement, etc.) to justify initial acceptance of a mix design. It is advisable therefore to specify that initially the mix design shall be based on a standard deviation of not lower than 7 N/mm^2 but that this will be reviewed after (say) 40 No 28-day test cubes.

The compliance control chart, available in earlier publications of the Cement and Concrete Association, which combines a histogram with Arithmetic Probability Paper (APP), is an excellent means of ensuring overall control by simple graphical means. The Property Service Agency of the Department of the Environment has used control charts of this kind as their national procedure for compliance control of concrete.

Ready-mixed concrete

Owing to the rapid development of the ready-mixed concrete industry during the last decade there can be few sites for which ready-mixed concrete is not available. The industry offers both expertise and convenience, and therefore an increasing number of contractors are using this means of supply. The central association of members of the supply industry, the BRMCA (British Ready Mixed Concrete Association), has done much in recent years to improve the efficiency of the industry by the introduction of their Authorisation Scheme. The scheme includes training of staff, investigation of complaints, inspection and certification of depots (i.e. ready-mixed concrete production plants) to ensure conformity to laid-down standards. Those depots complying to the BRMCA standards are well able to produce good concrete consistently and will do so providing the requirements are clearly specified. However, the client's engineer must exercise effective overall compliance control as a necessary safeguard against the occasional accident.

The expertise and experience of the industry are readily available to prospective clients and it is wise to discuss with them any special needs such as pumped concrete, watertight mixes or special mixes for particular finishes. The actual production process and control of ready-mixed concrete is, for all practical purposes, outside the control of the client's engineer apart from spot checks on materials, although he may inspect depots if he so wishes. Nevertheless, the client's engineer can exercise very effective compliance control, even at long range, by the use of a method such as the histogram/APP chart already mentioned or some other method described in CP 110: 1972.

Where concrete is ready-mixed it is the contractors' responsibility to check the details of characteristic strength, batch weight, slump and batching time on every delivery ticket immediately on delivery to ensure that a wrong mix is not incorporated accidently.

Ready-mixed concrete suppliers should be able to produce past and current records of their standard of production control (in terms of Standard Deviation), and should always be required to produce details of the Standard Deviation, Margin and batch quantities for every grade of concrete supplied. This information should be supplied before quotations are accepted.

Water/cement ratio

The reader should be aware of this factor in mixing and therefore only a passing reference is made to it. The water/cement ratio of a concrete mix depends upon the strength specified and will remain constant whatever the workability required. The amount of water/cement paste will vary with the workability required and with the use of any additive having a lubricating effect. The W/C ratio will normally be decided by the concrete mix designer who will translate it first into total water per batch and then to added water per batch, depending upon the amount of water in the aggregates. Allowance will have been made for required slump when deciding upon the cement content of the batch. Added water will vary with the varying moisture content of the aggregates, especially the fine aggregates. In practice the W/C ratio is of little value to the client's engineer for control purposes because it is not easily and quickly determinable. It can be reasonably assumed that if the mix design is correct and the batching of solid materials is also correct then a batch having the right slump will contain the correct amount of water. A constant eye on the workability will therefore help to obtain low variability of strength and generally good consistency.

Testing and compliance control of concrete

Sampling, curing and testing of concrete are usually required to be carried out by the contractor in accordance with the relevant BS and Codes of Practice. This should be made clear when specifying, so that the tenderers are given the opportunity to price for it: in so doing the onus, for correct procedures and valid results, is placed on the contractor — an important point in the event of unacceptable results occurring. However, sampling and curing should be observed or supervised by the client's engineer or his staff, to ensure that he is satisfied as to the adequacy of the procedures. Testing of cubes is normally carried out by a mutually-approved independent test house which may be a commercial firm, a cement manufacturer's laboratory or a technical college. Whichever is used, care should be taken to ensure that crushing machines are currently tested and certified, and that curing facilities, staff competence and procedures generally are above reproach. Slump testing will normally be carried out by the contractor under observation by the client engineer's site staff.

It may be necessary to include a provisional sum in the contract documents to cover special testing such as coring, wet analysis, dry analysis, ultra sonic testing etc, which might be required should trouble arise. Such testing would also be carried out by an independent testing house, mutually agreed but normally nominated by the client engineer.

Compliance testing

Compliance testing of concrete calls for a clear understanding by all concerned of the proper basis for mix design. Owing to the inherent variability of concrete, it is necessary for any designed mix to be based on a mean strength requirement substantially higher than the specified characteristic strength.

The margin between the specified characteristic strength and the mean strength on which the mix is designed will depend upon two factors: the maximum permitted defective rate, which must be specified (normally 5%), and the supplier's standard of production control (usually thought of as the Standard Deviation). Standards of control achieved in practice range from about 3.5 N/mm² or less, which is good, through 5.25 N/mm² which is average, to 7 N/mm² or more, which is poor.

The margin would be twice the Standard Deviation for a specified maximum defective rate of 2½% (i.e.

maximum permitted rate of cubes of less than the specified characteristic strength) and 1.64 SD for a 5% defective rate. Other values of margin can be obtained readily for other specified defective rates.

Distribution and placing

This should be executed so that contamination, segregation or loss of constituent materials do not occur; the concrete must be placed within 30 minutes of discharge from the mixer. Deposited concrete should have a temperature of not less than 5°C and not more than 25°C. The height from which the concrete is poured should not exceed 1.8 metres unless agreed by the engineer. Methods of distribution are discussed in Chapter 2, Section 2.3.3, to which reference should be made. Ready-mixed concrete is delivered to site in one of the forms described in 2.3.3, but it may be also distributed in open trucks. This involves the use of either a mixing plant close to the site, or a batching plant set up by an independent supplier on the site itself. This would apply only to large construction works such as dams and motorways. Where trucks are used the truck body must be leak-proof to prevent loss of grout, and the concrete should be covered during transit to protect it from wind, rain and sun.

The choice of distribution plant will depend on the accessibility of the work (Fig 8.1), the rate of placing necessary for completion of concreting (Fig 8.2), the amount of concrete to be placed, the distance and height of the mixing plant from the point of placing, and the availability of plant. The access to the point of placing — particularly in deep basements, dams, deep foundations and the like — usually results in the choice of pumps, chutes, cableways and other forms of distributing plant which can move the concrete from the mixer to the placing point without disturbance of reinforcement, at the same time maintaining high delivery rates. Distribution by conveyor is shown in Fig 8.3; this method of distribution is easy to control and keep clean, and easily modifiable to site requirements. Conveyors are particularly useful for distributing concrete in precasting yards.

The rate of placing will depend on the type of structure: high, relatively thin structures such as silos require a low rate of placing and therefore do not justify the use of pumps or other rapid distribution methods. Even with moving formwork the rate of pour can be easily maintained by craneage on such structures. Reference should also be made to Section 6.3. — Underwater Foundation Construction.

Fig 8.1   *Heavy duty platforms constructed to give high level access to Ready-mixed concrete trucks*

(British Ready Mixed Concrete Association)

Fig 8.2   *Placing concrete on M56 Sharston*
By-pass by mobile pumps
(British Ready Mixed Concrete Association)

Fig 8.3   *Distribution of concrete by conveyor*
to deep excavation placing by tremie
pipe (Wickham Engineering Limited)

8.1.3 Formwork and reinforcement

The term 'formwork' is commonly used to denote the process by which wet concrete is constrained and supported until it is sufficiently strong to carry its own weight and additional loads that are necessary at the time of construction. The forms are the parts of the temporary work which will be in contact with the concrete, and the actual supports for the forms, whether patent props, scaffolding, or other material, are referred to as 'falsework'. The formwork must, in addition to supporting the live and dead loads involved, prevent the loss of material from the concrete. In the main the most serious loss, which may be detrimental to the structure, is one of grout; this can be overcome by sealing the joints with a compressible filler or by masking the joint.

Since the cost of formwork may account for 60% of the total cost of the reinforced concrete structure, any economies in design will affect the overall costs appreciably. Factors which will affect the final cost include:

Rationalisation of dimensions

Simple formwork design

Design for multiple re-use

Protection of the formwork face

Time involved in the 'turn-round' of forms.

Rationalisation of dimensions for concrete structures can have the greatest effect on formwork costs; some authorities have suggested a 40% reduction in formwork costs by this factor alone. Simple formwork design, which allows easy fixing and stripping, will prevent damage to forms and increase their utilisation factor. Designing for re-use involves two factors: first, the strength and construction of the form, and second, the size of the forms. Forms for re-use in other shapes and sizes must be designed to allow dismantling and cutting. Protection of the face of a form by oil or other substances will greatly increase the life of the form. Some treatments also improve the quality of the concrete finish.

Fig 8.4   *Adjustable form for a rectangular tapered column* (Stelmo Limited)

Fig 8.5   *Caisson form with centre cores* (Stelmo Limited)

The time for 'turn-round' of formwork — namely the complete time taken up by erecting, placing, curing and stripping — depends a great deal on the specification, height of pour, striking time, and lifting equipment. Specifications tend to become out-of-date and current practice is the force that changes them, so with formwork the specification should be as up-to-date as current practice; otherwise cost may be greatly increased. A typical example is the height from which concrete may be poured in one lift; some specifications limit this to 1.2 or 2 metres, whereas in fact pours up to 10 metres have been achieved without adverse effect. Thermal control, by insulated formwork and ponding, has allowed very large pours to be made in one single day; bases and rafts of 1200 m^3 to 2000 m^3 have been poured without detriment to the strength of the structure. This form of control results in formwork being released much earlier. Striking times in specifications often reflect other outdated specifications from which they have been copied. Striking time must be reduced to the minimum if economies are to be gained with large forms, particularly if the forms are mechanised or hydraulically operated. The protection and curing of the concrete can be achieved by other covering materials. Lifting equipment and careful programming of formwork lifts also affect the cost; this is the contractor's responsibility and is by no means the least of the factors considered in formwork 'turn-round'. Linked with lifting and moving is the actual formwork carpenter who is becoming increasingly hard to find; as a result high fixing costs may be incurred. Proprietary forms and purpose-made steel forms play an important role in economic formwork; they are suitable for repetitive work, such as blocks of flats, when table forms are used, or for special projects which require heavy duty forms for large pours (Figs 8.4 to 8.9). These types of form require heavy lifting equipment but are nevertheless very economical if a sufficient number of uses is obtained.

The fixing of formwork is not covered in this book since numerous building text-books cover the operation in detail. However, it should be stated that proprietary bolts, ties and clamps are used rather than the outmoded methods indicated in some publications.

Fig 8.6   *Adjustable crosshead form* (Stelmo Limited)

Fig 8.7   *Column forms for a full height pour*
(Stelmo Limited)

Falsework

As mentioned earlier, falsework is that part of formwork which supports the forms. In civil engineering the heights and weights encountered are normally in excess of standard propping facilities and some form of scaffolding is used. There are three basic types of scaffold which can be employed in falsework: scaffold tubes and fittings, prefabricated systems, and specially designed falsework in the form of prefabricated units. The first two types were initially designed for the access scaffolding market but have been used increasingly for falsework. The third type, prefabricated tubular units, is available from any of the formwork and scaffolding specialists. The units vary in type and have advantages and disadvantages depending on the type of falsework required. Tube and fittings used as falsework provide the most versatile material available, although unlikely to be the most economic; the labour in erecting and dismantling is very high compared with unit systems. Prefabricated systems, initially designed for simple access scaffolding, have made a great impact on the falsework market. The systems usually consist of vertical frames which are linked together by a patent bracing system; this form of linking can be visually inspected to ensure stability, whereas normal tube fittings cannot be checked by the same method. Proprietary systems of decking, including telescopic beams or prefabricated beams, are often linked with falsework systems. The prefabricated systems therefore offer simplicity of erection coupled with a built-in grid which give high control of component spacing. Prefabricated falsework systems are made from larger diameter tube and are capable of carrying heavier loads than the normal scaffold units. These systems are used extensively for supporting bridges and other heavy structures which require variable height falsework. Fig 8.10 and Fig 8.11 show typical falsework structures.

Fig 8.8 *Purpose-made travelling form used in the construction of a culvert* (Stelmo Limited)

Fig 8.9
Construction of six reinforced concrete towers, each 64.6 m high, by the slipform method — Heysham nuclear power station (British Lift Slab Limited)

Surface finishes

The majority of forms are constructed of Douglas fir ply which gives a satisfactory finish for most structures. If very smooth finishes are required, the ply face may be treated with epoxy-resin, sheet metal, or any other material which will produce the required finish. Featured surfaces are also very popular: these can be produced by fixing the desired pattern to the face of the ply form. Often the feature may be designed to hide the joining marks made by the forms; this can be achieved by nailing variable thicknesses of sawn boarding to the panels, and produces a random depth and spacing of joints as well as a pleasing textured finish. Fibreglass or plastic moulds may also be used to produce specific details. Some surface finishes, e.g. exposed aggregate, can be produced by coating the ply face with a solution which will retard the setting of the contact surface. When the forms are removed the cement face can then be removed easily by wire brush in order to reveal the aggregate. Tooled finishes can be produced by pneumatic tools, but these tend to be expensive labour items.

The contact face of the form, unless retarding liquids are used, should be coated with mould-oil to enable easy removal and to minimise cleaning.

Fig 8.10   *Super-slim soldiers, supplied by Rapid Metal Developments Limited, supporting formwork in the construction of an abutment wall*
(R.M. Douglas Construction Limited)

Fig 8.11   *Erection of scaffolding falsework in bridge construction* (Sir Alfred McAlpine & Son Limited Kwikform Limited)

Reinforcement

The main aspects of reinforcement for consideration include:

Types of reinforcement

Methods of supply

Labours involved in preparation

Fixing.

The main types of reinforcement are hot-rolled mild steel bars, hot-rolled high yield bars, cold-worked bars, cold-drawn wire for fabric, and expanded metal. All manufacturers or suppliers are in a position to supply mild steel bars to BS 4449, but few manufacturers are currently producing high yield bars to the same BS. The mild steel bars are produced to a specified tensile strength of 250 N/mm^2; they are mainly plain round bars but deformed bars are available. Hot-rolled high yield bars to BS 4449 have a specified tensile strength of 425 and 460 N/mm^2 depending on diameter and have trade names e.g. 'Barbond' (produced by BRC). For the purpose of identifying the grade of steel of any rolled bar other than mild steel, the bars have special markings. These marks, usually consisting of small ribs, are rolled on the surface of the bar during manufacture. A number of suppliers import high yield bars, mainly from Scandinavia, which have the stress characteristics of cold-worked bars (BS 4461); the tensile stresses of imported bars are 425 and 460 N/mm^2. Bars that are imported should have an Agrément Certificate before they are accepted for reinforced concrete work. Cold-worked steel bars (BS 4461) are available currently in two forms, deformed, type 1 (twisted square or twisted chamfered square) and deformed, type 2 (twisted ribbed bars): the latter being the one most commonly used. Twisted rib bar has a higher bond strength than type 1 (see CP 114). The tensile strength specification varies with normal size: up to and including 16 mm the specified strength is 460 N/mm^2; over 16 mm it is 425 N/mm^2.

Generally, suppliers stock a normal range of 6 mm to 40 mm diameter but some manufacturers will produce this range together with 50 mm diameter bars if requested. The maximum stock length of bar is 12 metres, but certain bars are available in 18 metre lengths.

All cold-worked bars and mild steel bars are produced from steel with a carbon content of below 0.25% the specification maximum (see Chapter 1: Materials). The specification for hot-rolled high yield bars does not include a maximum carbon content. The manufacturers use niobium or vanadium to precipitate hardening; this is also true of Scandinavian steel, but the latter is not so reliable for constant carbon content. The carbon content has the greatest effect on ductility and weldability, and high carbon content, as found in some imported bars, therefore creates problems in welding. Zinc-coated reinforcement is used extensively in thin precast concrete units, which may be subject to water penetration and so result in corrosion of the steel. It is also suitable for concrete used in marine and river works, or in works subject to pollution. The steel may be treated by one of five possible processes[*] but the most common method is hot-dip galvanising, which is undertaken by most manufacturers. Bars are supplied to site in several forms, including straight stock lengths, lengths cut to suit requirements, and reinforcement cut and bent ready for assembly. The first method is suitable if a large amount of steel is being used and if a bar bending area can be installed on site. Cut and bent steel is suitable for use on congested sites or where the amount of steel used would not produce great economies if bent on site. The latter method necessitates careful storage and organisation so that bars can be found when required without too much double handling. Cutting and bending on site is normally achieved by power-operated machines, although if small amounts are involved the cutting may be carried out by bolt croppers. Bending is facilitated by means of a bar-bending bench with the necessary pins and jigs for forming the shapes. Power-operated benches are also provided with hand bending tools for small diameter bars which are used in stirrups.

Steel fabric is the other main form of reinforcement and should comply with BS 4483: 1969. There are four different types of fabric with preferred sizes in each type. They are square-mesh fabric, structural fabric, long-mesh fabric, and wrapping fabric. The fabric is made up of hard-drawn steel wire complying with BS 4482, or from

*Ref: Building Research Station Digest No. 109 (HMSO) September 1969

cold-worked steel bars complying with BS 4461. It is formed by interweaving or electrically welding the wires so that the fabric will withstand normal handling.

Square-mesh fabric has a mesh size of 200 mm x 200 mm and a weight range of between 1.54 kg and 6.16 kg per square metre. Structural fabric has a mesh size of 100 mm x 200 mm and a weight of between 3.05 kg to 10.9 kg per square metre. Long-mesh fabric, which is used mainly in road slabs, has a mesh size of 100 mm x 400 mm and a weight ranging from 2.61 kg to 6.72 kg per square metre. A special fabric is produced for carriage-ways, having a mesh size between 80 and 130 mm x 400 mm and weighing 5.55 kg per square metre (BS 4483).

Bar fixing has to be very accurate and strong enough to withstand the placing of concrete. Vertical bars can be positioned in two different ways. The first method is to fix an accurately bent spacer bar between the two vertical layers, thus keeping the bars apart; the second method is to use a timber spacer above the proposed concrete line. In both cases the bars will have plastic or concrete bar-spacers clipped on to the bar to maintain the minimum distance between the steel and the form. Reinforcement cages may be suspended from the forms if spacers are not desirable. Reinforcement in slabs normally requires chairs or spacers to provide the correct clearance between steel and deck.

Steel fixing usually precedes the erection of formwork in foundations, columns and walls, although one side of the wall form may be in position prior to fixing of the steel. Fixing of reinforcement in slabs follows the erection of formwork and the same applies to beams with the exception that one side panel is usually left off. Reinforcing bars for columns and beams should be carefully wired together with links, helical binding, or beam binders (stirrups): this will normally allow prefabrication and lifting to take place without undue distortion. Where reinforcement cages for long beams are subject to distortion during lifting, a special lifting beam should be used.

8.1.4   Jointing in concrete structures

There are two types of joint which may be used in reinforced concrete structures, namely construction joints and movement joints.

Construction joints are introduced for convenience in the construction of the element and, as a guide, should be placed where shear stress is at a minimum. This would be the centre or within the middle third of the span in slabs and beams, as near as possible to beam haunching in columns, and at the top or bottom of openings in walls. Vertical joints in walls should be kept to a minimum and, where possible, the day's concreting should terminate at a permanent joint. The joint is formed by a stop in the formwork, which is carefully fitted around the projecting reinforcement and often incorporates a tapered piece of timber (Fig 8.12) to form a key or 'joggle' joint in the element being cast. After stripping, the joint should be cleaned down to remove any laitance or loose material; this is essential on horizontal construction joints, which, by the very nature of their position, are very susceptible to laitance. Horizontal joints, which are not sealed off with a stop or key, may have the cement-sand matrix brushed away from the aggregate shortly after stripping. Before the next section of concrete is poured the formwork should be checked for tightness at the construction joint, to prevent the escape of grout. The joint should be thoroughly cleaned off, best achieved by a combined water-compressed air jet.

In walls and slabs which retain liquids, either as storage vessels or in retaining ground water, the joint should include a water-bar. The water-bar may be of non-ferrous metal, rubber or plastic (Fig 8.13). Alternatively, a system of waterproofing such as those discussed in Section 6.7.3 may be employed.

Movement joints

These include contraction joints, expansion joints and sliding joints.

A contraction joint is a deliberate discontinuity of structure with no initial gap between the two pours of concrete. It allows the sections of structure to contract or shrink, thus eliminating high stress in, and in some cases failure of, the structure. There is a distinction between partial and complete contraction joints: the former has continuity of steel, while in the latter both steel and concrete are interrupted. The formation of the joint is similar to the construction joint.

Expansion joints usually have complete discontinuity in both steel and concrete, but may have continuity of steel to restrain warping of the panels in the case of slabs. Both types are shown in Section 7.1.3. In the case of the latter type, the bars are coated with bitumen to prevent bond between bars and concrete, and the bars are capped to allow movement. Sliding joints (see below) may also be used for expansion in walls. The filler material usually consists of impregnated fibre board, cork or other bituminous impregnated material. This type of joint depends on the ability of the concrete elements to move independently and equally; if walls and slabs are restrained or partially restrained by ground friction, the total expansion of any two elements may impinge on one joint and in so doing cause failure.

Sliding joints are movement joints with complete discontinuity in both reinforcement and concrete, at which special provision is made to facilitate movement in the plane of the joint. They are used, in the main, for liquid-retaining tanks and reference should be made to Section 6.7 in which this type of joint is illustrated.

Temporary open joints may be used in the construction of long slabs or walls, so that they may shrink fully before the joint is filled. The joint is formed by leaving a gap (Fig 8.14) of suitable size in the wall, permitting joint preparation prior to filling, after the long element of walling has shrunk. The joints may incorporate water-bars if the shrinkage of the concrete filling the gap would cause leaks in water-retaining structures. The function of the joint is to accommodate drying shrinkage of the concrete already placed.

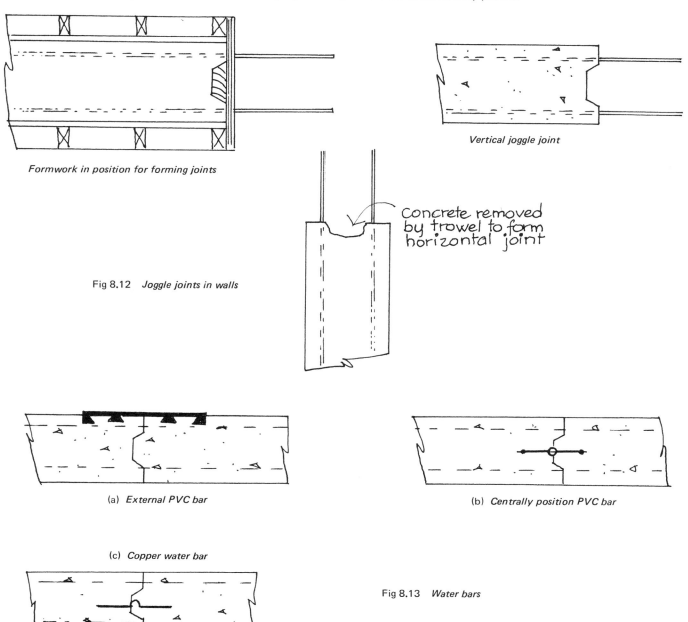

Vertical joggle joint

Formwork in position for forming joints

Concrete removed by trowel to form horizontal joint

Fig 8.12   Joggle joints in walls

(a) External PVC bar

(b) Centrally position PVC bar

(c) Copper water bar

Fig 8.13   Water bars

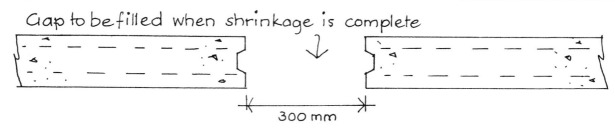

Gap to be filled when shrinkage is complete

|← 300 mm →|

Fig 8.14   *Temporary open joint to counteract contraction in wall construction*

8.1.5 Pre-stressed concrete

Pre-stressing, by definition, is a technique of construction whereby initial compressive stresses are set up in a member to resist or annul the tensile stresses produced by the load. Pre-stressed concrete is concrete in which effective internal stresses are induced artificially, usually by means of tensioned steel prior to loading the structure. Concrete is a material of high compressive strength and relatively low tensile strength. The technique of pre-stressing has therefore had far-reaching developments in reinforced concrete structures. Unlike ordinary reinforced concrete in which stresses are carried by normal reinforcement, pre-stressed concrete supports the load by induced stresses throughout the complete structural element. The pre-stressing wires, cables or bars are only a means, up to the limit of the working load, of producing the stress required in the concrete to withstand the load. In addition, where overloading may occur and cracks appear in the concrete member, the pre-stressing cable will prevent failure, providing the stress incurred is not above the elastic limit and the cracks will close without any deterioration in the structural element. Pre-stressed concrete has the advantage of being more resistant to shock and vibration, and as it is suitable for thin long structures and can have much smaller sectional areas than normal reinforced concrete to support an equal load, savings in steel, concrete, and hoisting are effected.

The development of pre-stressed concrete began as early as 1885 - 1890 when several attempts were made to tension concrete to increase its bearing capacity. No great advantage was gained in these early attempts because the steel used for tensioning was mild steel, which lost its tension very quickly owing to creep. In the early 1900s a French engineer, Eugene Freyssinet, carried out pre-stressing on the tie of a large concrete arch bridge. He succeeded in lifting the two halves of the arch, to remove the falsework, by stressing the tie. This success led to the development of the technique for other bridges in the 1920s. By 1928 Faber and Glanville in England had published their findings on the phenomenon of creep in steel which confirmed Freyssinet's deduction and enabled him to establish his theory of pre-stressing. About the same period similar work on pre-stressing was being developed in America and Germany, the main aim then being to develop a suitable steel. By 1935 high-tensile steel wires were being used as the pre-stressing medium on a moderate scale. Applications of pre-stressing are numerous, but it has been used successfully for making railway sleepers, floor beams, piles and other long-line elements, and also for many individual projects such as bridges, water tanks, roof structures and runways.

All the developments in pre-stressing can be placed in one of two groups: pre-tensioning and post-tensioning.

Pre-tensioning consists of stressing the wires or cables prior to the placing of concrete. When the concrete has hardened and gripped the steel by shrinkage the tension is released from the jacks and transferred to the concrete. The steel is then cut off at the ends of the member; dividing plates can be placed at any point along the member which, when removed, permits the cutting of the wires and thus produces shorter members. This method of pre-stressing is particularly useful for the 'long-line' method of casting that is employed in precast works (Fig 8.15). The wires are anchored at the end of a metal form, which may be 120 metres long, and connected to a jacking block at the other end of the line. The jacks stress the wire to the desired stress, plus 10 per cent or other calculated amount to allow for creep and other losses of pre-stress. The side moulds are then fixed and the concrete placed around the tensioned wires. When the concrete has reached the desired strength, usually 28 N/mm^2 in 24 hours by steam curing, the wires are released to transfer the load to the concrete. The bond between the concrete and wire is improved by crimped or indented wire, and grips may be used on single strand pre-stressing.

Post-tensioning takes the reverse procedure to the above, the concrete member is cast and the pre-stressing occurs after the concrete has hardened. The wires, cables or bars may be positioned in the unit before concreting commences, but they are prevented from bonding to the concrete by means of a flexible duct or sheath.

Alternatively, a duct can be formed or cast in the member through which the wires or cables can be subsequently threaded. If a duct is to be formed the concrete is cast around long, thin, inflated rubber tubes which are deflated and removed when the concrete has hardened. Pre-formed ducting (Fig 8.16) in the form of corrugated sheathing is fixed between the normal reinforcement, (which is used for handling purposes and anchorage reinforcement), and shaped to carry the wires or cable from the upper level at the ends of the units down through the lower level in the centre of the unit. The wires or cables are anchored by means of a special end block and grips at one end, and stressed from the other end. When the required stress has been reached the wire or cables are anchored, the ends of the unit are sealed with cement mortar and the ducting is pressure-grouted. Various forms of post-tensioning are discussed below.

Fig 8.15   *Pre-stressing by long-line method*   (Pierhead Limited – Liverpool)

Fig 8.16(a)   *Sheathing in position for deep beam*
(PSC Freyssinet Limited)

Fig 8.16(b)   *Sheathing and cables in position for floor slab*
(PSC Freyssinet Limited)

Materials for pre-stressed concrete

The concrete for pre-stressed work should contain between 300 kg and 540 kg of cement per cubic metre of finished concrete and have a works cube strength at 28 days of not less than 40 N/mm^2 for pre-tensioned work or 30 N/mm^2 for post-tensioned work.

Where the bond between the concrete and the steel is relied on for the transfer of the pre-stress the cube strength of the concrete at transfer should preferably be not less than 35 N/mm^2. A lower strength may be accepted in certain members cast under factory conditions, but in no case should the lower strength be less than 27 N/mm^2. Concrete used for post-tensioning systems should have reached a minimum strength of 27 N/mm^2 before transfer of load.

Steel for pre-stressed work may be in the form of wire or bars. Steel wire is manufactured to BS 5891: 1980, and is cold-drawn from plain carbon steel. The wire may be plain round, or deformed by indenting or crimping. The diameters available range from 3 mm to 7 mm. The strength of the wire is specified as follows:

a The BS number

b The material

c Strength N/mm^2

d Diameter

e Process ie D = drawn; P = straightened

f Treatment: E = smooth; I = indented; C = crimped

g Class of relaxation (Class 1 or 2)

A typical specification would be BS 5896/2 — wire — 1670 — 7 — PI — Relax 1.

Indentation or crimping gives better bond strength; the diameters used for normal pre-stressing are 4 mm, 5 mm, and 7 mm. Strands of up to 18 mm diameter, formed from cold drawn wire (to BS 3617:1971), are used for stressing large components by the post-tension method. Seven wires form a strand comprising a straight core wire around which are spun six helical wires in one layer.

Round carbon chrome steel bars are also used as pre-stressing tendons. They are prepared from hot-rolled bars by cold working to give the required properties. The diameters range from 20 mm to 50 mm and the bars can be threaded for standard post-tensioning anchorages (BS 4486:1980). Normal lengths range up to 18 m, lengths over 18 m are obtained by joining bars with special couplers.

Loss of pre-stress

This is due to the following causes:

Elastic deformation of the member

Shrinkage of the concrete

Creep of the concrete

Relaxation of the pre-stressing steel

Steam curing.

The first three causes can be reduced to an acceptable minimum by using high strength concrete with a low workability. Relaxation of the pre-stressing steel can be counteracted by increasing the initial stress on the steel, but losses may occur in post-tensioned work due to slip. The slip occurs as the mechanical anchorage takes the strain: the tapered wedges move slightly as they take the load and the anchorage may also deform slightly. Steam curing causes loss of pre-stress by reducing the force in the tendon, by thermal expansion of the steel, before it becomes bonded to the concrete.

Post-tensioning systems

There are numerous post-tensioning systems but the main principles of them all are exemplified in the following: PSC Freyssinet system, CCL Multiforce system and the Macalloy system.

The PSC Freyssinet system is known as the 'K' Range system and has been developed from the well-known MonoGroup system used by the Freyssinet organisation. The system has an extremely reliable and well

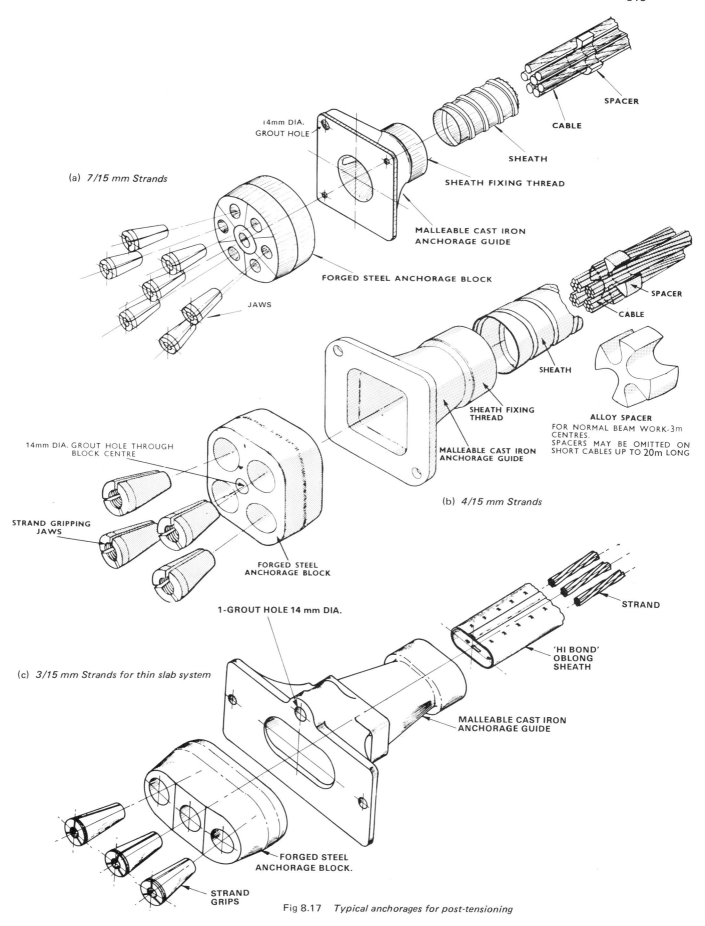

(a) *7/15 mm Strands*

14mm DIA. GROUT HOLE

SPACER

CABLE

SHEATH

SHEATH FIXING THREAD

MALLEABLE CAST IRON ANCHORAGE GUIDE

FORGED STEEL ANCHORAGE BLOCK

JAWS

SPACER

CABLE

SHEATH

SHEATH FIXING THREAD

MALLEABLE CAST IRON ANCHORAGE GUIDE

ALLOY SPACER
FOR NORMAL BEAM WORK-3m CENTRES.
SPACERS MAY BE OMITTED ON SHORT CABLES UP TO 20m LONG

14mm DIA. GROUT HOLE THROUGH BLOCK CENTRE

STRAND GRIPPING JAWS

FORGED STEEL ANCHORAGE BLOCK

(b) *4/15 mm Strands*

1-GROUT HOLE 14 mm DIA.

STRAND

'HI BOND' OBLONG SHEATH

MALLEABLE CAST IRON ANCHORAGE GUIDE

(c) *3/15 mm Strands for thin slab system*

FORGED STEEL ANCHORAGE BLOCK.

STRAND GRIPS

Fig 8.17   *Typical anchorages for post-tensioning*

proven method of anchoring and the traditional tensioning technique used in all Freyssinet systems. The 'K' Range system has been developed to enable the stressing strands to be tensioned simultaneously using centre hole tensioning jacks. The cables in the 'K' Range system form two principal groups: the 13 mm range and the 15 mm range (Fig 8.17). A further range, one to four strands, is available for thin slab construction. The strands in the 'K' Range and thin slab range can be 12.5 or 12.9 mm diameter or 15.2 and 15.7 mm diameter. The strands are threaded through the cable sheath, which has been previously cast in the concrete elements (Fig 8.16), having been first formed into a cable and fixed by binding tape. In order to prevent inter-strand friction it is normally necessary to provide 'spacers' at 3 metre centres; these may be omitted on cables under 20 metres in length provided that this is only slightly curved in one plane. The strands are tensioned simultaneously and anchored by tapered jaws, as in Fig 8.18. The 'K' Range system is ideal for pre-stressing elements up to 50 metres in length and has been specially designed for the 'medium range' field of pre-stressing. The 'K' Range system uses a combination of either normal or drawn pre-stressing strands. All cables consist of parallel-laid strands cut to approximate length and requiring no special treatment at the ends of spacers along their length. All cables are stressed in a single pull with the appropriate model of jack (Fig 8.19). The anchorages accommodate cables of between 1 and 55 strands. The transverse forces set up by the anchorages are resisted by reinforcement spirals (Fig 8.16(b)) or by conventional reinforcement. All systems are pressure-grouted on completion through a grout hole in the anchorage.

Fig 8.18 *High tensile strands individually anchored by tapered jaws*
(PSC Equipment Limited)

Fig 8.19 *Stressing jack*
(PSC Freyssinet Limited

In the CCL Multiforce system each strand is anchored by an individual wedge or compression grip. The tendons or cables are normally made up on site and placed in the formwork before concreting; this method eliminates the problems that can arise when threading tendons through a completed structure. The tendon is made up of a number of high tensile steel strands, as in the 'K' Range system, and fitted with steel strip sheathing to allow movement during stressing. Each tendon is positioned and fixed in the formwork, usually between specially prepared reinforcement supports which prevent undue sagging of the tendon. If tendons have to be threaded, e.g. in segmental construction, a cable sock with a swivel eye is used to draw the tendon through the duct, the swivel eye preventing the tendon from rotating. Very long tendons or vertical tendons which cannot be threaded efficiently with a cable sock can be welded at the end and a steel loop welded to the centre strand for the draw-rope; after threading, the tendon is cut back 150 mm from the weld. The anchorage system is similar in principle to the 'K' Range system (Fig 8.18) in that individual wedges grip each strand against a bearing plate, which in turn transmits the load to the concrete.

In the Macalloy system, stress is applied to the concrete by means of a solid bar. The type of bar used has been described in the paragraph on materials used in pre-stressed concrete. The bar is anchored at each end by a special nut which screws on to it and which bears against an end plate to distribute the load. It may appear that anchorage by means of a thread on a bar may lead to difficulties because the thread reduces the diameter of the section, but this problem is overcome by rolling the thread instead of cutting it; the strength of the bar is increased locally by work-hardening and this offsets the loss in diameter. The advantage of this system is its simplicity and complete elimination of slip during anchorage; a further advantage is that re-tensioning is also made much simpler. The main disadvantage is that the bars must be produced to exact lengths at the works. In addition to the use in post-tensioning concrete units the system is suitable for ground and rock anchoring.

Fig 8.20   *Wire winding machine suspended from trolley*

(Preload Limited)

Circular tanks

Pre-stressing of water tanks or other liquid-retaining tanks can be achieved by applying external pressure by means of high tensile wire winding. The tanks are built of precast blocks or insitu concrete, and when the concrete has cured sufficiently the spirally bound wire is applied by a power driven trolley suspended from the periphery of the tank. (This is known as the pre-load method.) The trolley pulls itself around the tank (Fig 8.20) on an endless chain drawing the high tensile wire through a tapered die. The tapered die creates the tension in the wire as the trolley moves forward; the wire is anchored by clips at frequent intervals and, on completion, is protected by sprayed concrete. An alternative method of pre-stressing can be produced by looping individual wires, or several wires in parallel, around the tank and tensioning them from both ends simultaneously. The ends are fixed to anchor blocks which are cast into the structure. Protection is achieved in the same manner as before.

Pipes can be pre-stressed in a similar manner to tanks, the pipe being first spun centrifugally with a wall thickness of 63 mm and, on hardening, wound with high-tensile steel wire under constant tension. The pre-stressing wire is anchored and covered with cement mortar (see Section 9.1).

8.1.6   Special concreting systems

Gunite, otherwise known as Shotcrete, is a fine aggregate concrete conveyed through a hose and pneumatically projected at high velocity on to a surface. The force of the jet impacting on the surface compacts the material, the water-cement ratio being very low (in the region of 0.34). The dry mixture is capable of supporting itself without sagging and can be built up to a thickness of 150 mm in one operation.

This system of concreting produces an excellent bond with a number of materials and has consistent waterproofing qualities. It is particularly useful for curved or folded structures, e.g. roofs, walls, tanks, reservoir linings, canal linings, tunnel, sewer and shaft linings. It has been used extensively for retaining the rock faces of tunnels and as a weight coating for submarine pipelines. It also has a very valuable use in the renovation of bridges, marine structures, cooling towers and other highly exposed structures.

The aggregates used in gunite consist mainly of sharp sand with a 4 mm down to fines grading, although coarser aggregate can be used. The aggregate is mixed dry with Portland cement, 1 part of cement to 3 parts sand (by volume). After mixing, the dry mixture is fed into a 'cement gun' which consists of a feed hopper, a compressed air chamber and an outlet pipe. The material falls into the compressed-air chamber which is sealed off and pressurised. The opening of a release valve sends the material through a 63 mm diameter reinforced hose to a special nozzle. The nozzle is fitted with a manifold through which water is sprayed, under pressure, on to the dry mix, and the mixed material is then jetted by the compressed air on to the work surface. During the operation a proportion of large aggregate is blown to waste, so protective screens should be used to protect nearby windows and workmen. Lightweight aggregate to BS 3797 may be incorporated in the mix if thermal insulation is required, or heavyweight aggregates (not covered by a British Standard) may be used for concrete weighing between 2850 kg and 3200 kg per metre cube. Reinforcement for gunite usually takes the form of electrically-welded steel mesh fabric, of a weight and type dependent on the circumstances of use. Work in progress is seen in Figs 8.21 and 8.22.

Wirand concrete

Wirand concrete is a new composite material consisting of concrete and chopped mild steel wire of very small diameter; the name Wirand is a trade mark of the Battelle Development Corporation, USA.

The chopped steel fibres which are included in the mix assume random distribution throughout the mix and act as crack arrestors, thereby improving the physical properties of the material. Wirand concrete is not a substitute for reinforced concrete; it has different properties and should be treated as a different material. The ultimate flexural strength of the material is between 6 N/mm^2 and 17.5 N/mm^2, more than three times higher than plain concrete; its compressive stress lies between 35 N/mm^2 and 84 N/mm^2. In addition to improving the strength of plain concrete the fibres impart improved resistance to impact and greater resistance to abrasion. The special properties of Wirand concrete are perhaps best exploited in thin sections, e.g. airport runways, concrete pavements, (Fig 8.23) and roof decking. Other applications include factory floors and bridge decks where high abrasion may be encountered. It is also suitable for thin-wall concrete pipes, water-retaining structures and cladding panels. Refractory concrete can be produced by using stainless steel wire with high-alumina cement.

Fig 8.21   *Guniting a rock face in dam construction — Llyn Brianne Dam*

(The Cement-Gun Company Limited)

The materials used in Wirand concrete include aggregate which does not usually exceed 12 mm in size, sand as used in conventional mixes, and wire. A typical proportion of mix, by weight, would be: Ordinary Portland cement, 1.00: concrete sand 2.50: crushed gravel (10 mm) 2.50: chopped steel fibre (25 mm long x 0.4 mm diameter) 0.30; water/cement ratio 0.52.

The mixing of Wirand concrete is dependent, to a great extent, on the mixer. With some types of mixer it is possible to add the wire with the other constituents, but with other types of mixer the wire is added either after the sand and gravel has dry-blended or after all the other materials have been thoroughly mixed. The addition of wire fibres to a concrete mix reduces its workability, and therefore a plasticising agent may be required. Once mixed, the concrete is transported and placed in the same way as any other concrete, except that it is best spread with forks rather than with shovels. The rusting of the wire strands, where it occurs at the surface, is only local and in no way affects the structural performance of the material.

Steelcrete

Steelcrete is a sprayed concrete which contains wire strands as a reinforcement (see Wirand concrete). It has the same applications as gunite and has been used extensively for the lining of tunnels and other underground structures.

Fig 8.22
Close-up of guniting operation

(National-Standard Company Limited)

Fig 8.23

Steel fibre reinforced concrete 80 mm thick as an overlay to an existing concrete road slab on the M10

(The Cement-Gun Company Limited)

8.1.7   Cutting and demolition of concrete

The methods used in cutting and breaking concrete depends on the type of concrete, its position in the structure and the purpose for which the cutting or breaking is being undertaken. (See BS 6187:1982.)

If the concrete is ordinary reinforced concrete it may be demolished by explosives, cutting, or some form of expansion device. Normally explosives are only used for complete demolition of structures, where space and vibration presents little or no problem, therefore more passive systems of demolition are generally employed. Such methods include cutting by means of thermic lances, or forcing the concrete structure apart by expansion devices. The most successful method of demolition, which eliminates noise, dust and vibration, is the use of 'thermic lance'. Thermic lancing is the process of drilling or cutting of silica or part-silica materials by thermo-chemical action. The process is based on molten oxydised mild steel which fuses with the silica or other material to form a slag. The speed at which the reaction takes place minimises damage to the surrounding steel and concrete. To obtain a cut in any material a series of holes is bored to form a continuous slot. The technique is very suitable for cutting out structural members during demolition operations (Fig 8.24): the member is supported by crane and lifted out of position when the cutting is complete. The absence of noise and vibration means that massive structural alteration can be carried out during working hours without disturbing other staff working on the premises. The lance burns oxygen at a temperature of 3500 °C, and causes lava to flow from the surface of the concrete member. This hot lava must be contained in a bed of sand or asbestos sheeting to prevent damage to adjacent surfaces. Ventilation and extraction of smoke may be necessary during the cutting process, but further problems are not normally encountered. The high temperatures used in cutting the concrete do not damage the concrete further than 75 mm from the cutting edge; this is due to the extremely poor thermal conductivity of concrete.

Thermal reaction is used in conjunction with wire pulling. The member to be severed is surrounded by a mixture of metal oxide and reducing agent which produces great heat when ignited. The member loses strength due to the heat and wire pulling completes the operation.

Gas expansion and hydraulic expansion devices can be used for 'bursting out' concrete, but the reinforcement requires cutting to free the ruptured member. Walls may be jacked over, having first been freed from connections at their top and sides. Gas expansion operates with explosive force in a prepared cavity whereas hydraulic expansion is achieved by means of wedges and pistons.

Demolition of pre-stressed concrete must be executed with great care. Fully bonded or pre-tensioned members may be cut and lifted out in a similar manner to other forms of reinforced concrete, but post-tensioned structures should never be cut or burst. The demolition of post-tensioned units may be undertaken in the reversed procedure to that of erection. Temporary supports should be placed under floors and beams while the end anchorages are re-stressed and the tension slowly released. The units may then, and only then, be cut and lifted out of position. Failure to follow this procedure may result in a post-tensioned unit exploding, especially if the stress is suddenly released by cutting. The procedure for this work is given in detail in BS 6187:1982.

The breaking up of slabs in roads and runways may be economically achieved by means of a concrete breaker called the 'Nibbler' (Fig 8.25). The Nibbler* is an attachment for use with a hydraulic excavator. Instead of striking the concrete, which many other forms of attachment do, it breaks the concrete slab by bending — a process that produces a negligible amount of noise. The main component of the experimental Nibbler, which was made in Building Research Station's workshops, are two J-shaped side frames with teeth or shoes at their lower ends, a large hydraulic ram mounted at the top of the frames, and a smaller ram to adjust the angular position of the large ram. In action the driver manoeuvres the Nibbler so that the shoes are forced under a concrete slab at a free edge. When the shoes are engaged, the driver uses the small ram to rotate the larger ram so that it will act on the top of the slab at a point ahead of the shoes. After operating the large ram to clamp the device to the slab, he uses the digging controls so that the concrete is subjected to an upward force at the shoes and a downward force at the ram. This action subjects the concrete to bending and results in a tensile fracture. Slabs of 125 to 175 mm in thickness can be broken at a rate of 53 m² per hour: this includes reinforced slabs. The machine breaks the slab without damaging underground services and clears the debris without the use of additional plant. The attachment can also be used for demolishing floors at first floor level.

*Extract from 'BRE News 27'. Reproduced by permission of the Director, Building Research Establishment.

(a) *Cutting or drilling* (b) *Lifting out the cut members* (c) *Close-up of cut*

Fig 8.24 *Demolition of reinforced concrete structure by Thermic lance*

(The Kaybore Thermic Lancing Company Limited)

Fig 8.25 *The Nibbler breaking a test slab*

Reproduced by permission of the Director Building Research Establishment

Fig 8.26   *Concrete wall sawing*   *(The Kaybore Thermic Lancing Company Limited)*

Concrete wall sawing is an advanced technique carried out by The Kaybore Thermic Lancing Company Limited and other specialist contractors. The technique is used for cutting openings in reinforced concrete up to 375 mm thick. The concrete is cut from one side of the wall by means of a diamond-edged wall saw, the saw being mounted on a pre-determined wall track. This process gives a very accurate clean cut for the installation of doors (Fig 8.26), windows and other forms of opening.

8.2   STEELWORK

8.2.1   Types of structure

The types of structure most commonly used in civil engineering are the skeleton frame, used in buildings such as power houses; the trussed frame, normally used for bridges and other complex structures; and stressed-skin panel structures.

The skeleton frame is constructed with hot-rolled 'I' section columns and beams which are riveted, bolted or welded together; the frame is designed to transfer all loads to the columns and thence to mass foundations. The column sections may be selected from a range of universal beams (UB) or universal columns (UC), depending on the magnitude of the loading. Low-rise factory blocks with wide-span roof frames may be constructed using universal beams as column members, with greater economy than the purpose-made column. Heavily-loaded structures, however, are more economically supported using columns selected from the UC series; each serial size, e.g. 305 x 305 mm has a range of sizes and weights. The serial size 305 x 305 mm has a weight range of between 97 and 283 kg per metre of column. In addition to the normal beam construction, the frame may incorporate girders, lattice beams or castellated beams. Girders and lattice beams are normally designed so that their depth occupies a storey height, thereby maintaining normal overall height of building. Girders include stiffened plate girders and vierendeel girders (Fig 8.27), whilst the lattice girder takes the form of a braced structure (Fig 8.28). Castellated beams (Fig 8.29) are particularly valuable in the construction of low-rise, large span, factory construction.

Trussed frames, or plane frames, may be used in building work; but in civil engineering such forms are associated with more complex structures, e.g. bridges, working platforms and temporary structures. Bridges may be constructed in one of many steelwork forms, including trusses, plate girders, arch bridges and portal frames. For spans of up to 50 metres the constructional plate girder may be used, but above that span the plate girder will require stiffening with a concrete deck to form a composite structure. Deep plate girders may be stiffened by horizontal webb stiffeners. Trusses are commonly used on bridge structures over 50 metres, the most common form being of the Warren type (Fig 8.30). Spans of over 50 and up to 150 metres can be bridged with Warren type girders which have inclined upper chords (Fig 8.31). Cross-bracing is normally provided between vertical members in deck-type bridges, whereas through-type bridges are braced with sway bracing (Fig 8.32) between verticals, and portal bracing between the end supports.

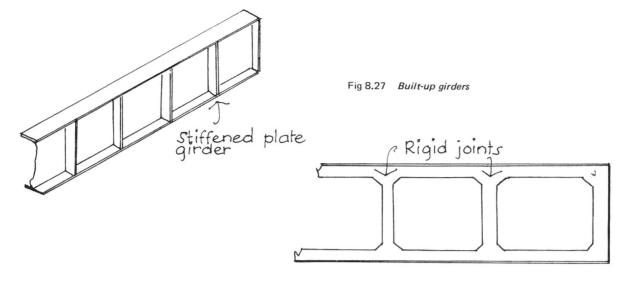

Fig 8.27   *Built-up girders*

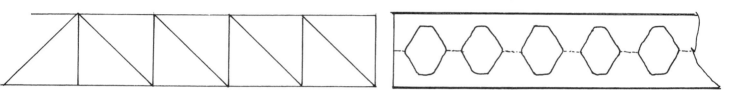

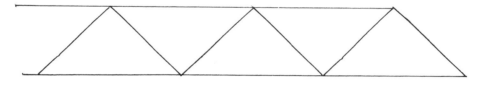

Fig 8.28   *Lattice girder*

Fig 8.29   *Castellated beam*

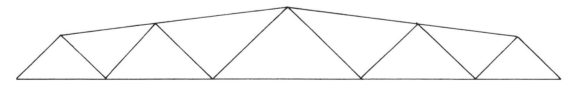

Fig 8.30   *Warren girder*

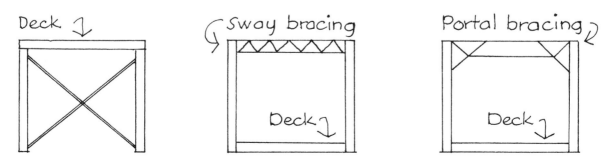

Fig 8.31   *Warren girder with inclined upper cord*

Fig 8.32   *Sections through girder bridges showing bracing methods*

Stressed-skin panels: perhaps the most common form of stressed-skin panel construction is the box-girder construction as used in bridges. The box section is better known as a 'torsion box' and consists of plate welded to a pre-determined streamlined section. The Severn bridge-deck is a fine example of this type of structure, the box sections being designed to form a continuous aerofoil.

The same principle of design can be used for the construction of steel framed buildings, the sections being much thinner and consisting of steel members sheeted on one face with pre-formed steel sheeting. The sheeting is fixed in such a manner as to prevent slip at the fastenings and so produces a diaphragm which stiffens the frame and significantly increases the load-bearing capacity of the structure.

8.2.2   Erection of buildings and bridges

Buildings to be erected can be divided into two broad categories: those which are low-rise or single storey, sometimes referred to as 'shed-type' buildings; and those which are multi-storey. Some buildings, however, may incorporate structures which can be placed in both categories, and such buildings require special consideration when selecting the erection procedure. In each case there are certain factors that have to be considered, including method of erection, height of building, weight of members being lifted, maximum reach required, and time allowed for erection.

The amount of space available will influence the method of erection, a congested site being best served with a tower crane or similar appliance, whereas open sites may use mobile cranes to greater economy. If the building is multi-storey the height of lift will be of a major importance; mobile cranes are normally limited by their jib lengths. However, mobile cranes with jib lengths of up to 60 metres are available; alternatively a Scotch derrick may be used (see Chapter 2). The mobile crane is ideally suited to erection work, subject to the comments made above, and providing the crane can place the members without a long reach. This would be suitable for compact tasks which occur with the erection of gantries, temporary platforms, or tall but narrow-based buildings. Mobile cranes are also suitable for erecting 'shed-type' buildings, provided that the crane can operate within the structure to lift wide-span trusses. When the structure is too high for a normal mobile, the frame can be erected to the limit of the mobile and completed by means of a Scotch derrick or guy derrick mounted on the partially completed structure. Mobiles used for steel erection should have crawler tracks to distribute their load while lifting.

Shed-type buildings vary greatly in span and size but the erection procedure varies little in principle. The first two or three bays of steelwork should be erected and temporarily braced to prevent movement. This initial erection should be checked for alignment and verticality prior to final bracing and tightening-down. If this procedure is carried out carefully the first few bays of steelwork will act as an anchorage for the remainder of the steel erection, care being exercised to include further bracing as the work proceeds. Failure to brace and secure the initial erection can result in the whole mass of steelwork moving and causing irreparable damage to connections. For simple roof-truss structures, the columns and connecting eaves members are erected and lined to within ± 10 mm This is followed by the erection of the roof trusses and purlins, with bracing to the first bay. Shed buildings with wide span roofs may incorporate lattice girders to support the trusses. This will involve the erection of columns and lattice girders before lifting the trusses. Since the latter will have to be lifted from a position outside the completed bay, a longer jib or 'luffing' jib may have to be employed. A small mobile crane has the advantage of being able to lower its jib and travel under the lattice girders. If the lattice girder cannot be lifted by one crane and is difficult to handle using two cranes, one at each end, then it may be lifted by guyed derrick and temporarily supported until the interconnecting trusses are lifted. Wide-span buildings with space-frame roofing present some difficulty in erection. The space-frame should be fully erected on the ground and then lifted at the points of support. Some roof frames have been lifted with lattice erection masts; alternatively, if the span is not too great the whole unit can be lifted with four mobile units.

Arched roof structures and space frames which are too large to be lifted in one lift should be erected with the aid of trestles. The trestles are erected to give the correct camber, and sections of the arch or frame are lifted into position for final adjustment by jacking methods.

Multi-storey buildings are often erected by tower crane, especially if the crane can also be employed for lifting the claddings and other materials. If, however, the frame is to be erected as a separate contract, the type of lifting appliance may vary. One of the most basic and economic methods of lifting steelwork on high-rise structures is the guyed derrick. The derrick (see Chapter 2, Fig 2.38) consists of a latticed steel mast, tall enough to erect two storeys of steelwork without having to be lifted. When being moved the slewing jib is lifted by the mast to the new high level, and the jib, which is a similar lattice mast, is used to lift the mast. This method of moving the derrick is known as 'jumping' the crane. As with 'shed-type' buildings the frame requires bracing during erection which may involve both permanent and temporary braces. The temporary bracing often takes the form of wire cables to reduce distortion during lifting operations: these movements are caused by the slewing and lifting of the derrick which transmits the load to the frame. An alternative type of crane used in erection is the Scotch derrick — see Chapter 2 (Fig 2.37). This has two major advantages over the guy derrick: firstly it has no guys, and secondly it can be track-mounted and moved around or within the building. The disadvantage of the Scotch derrick is its limitation to a sweep of 270°, which may involve extra craneage to cover the complete erection area. It must be stated, however, that for most purposes either mobile cranes or tower cranes are used for both low and high-rise structures.

Erection of bridges varies a great deal from the erection of buildings in that temporary structures and braces are more widely used. If, however, the bridge is to be constructed on land there may be no need for temporary support such as trestles, although temporary bracing may be required. If the bridge is to be erected over water there is the problem of positioning the crane and materials prior to lifting. Materials are normally floated out to the lifting position, either on barges or on pontoons; in some instances, e.g. box-girder construction, the unit may be towed into position by barge.

Where the space between bridge supports can be effectively utilised, a system of trestles may be used. This will be suitable as a means of temporary support for girder and truss construction.

The method of construction for bridges will vary with the type of structure and length of span. Members in plate-girder and trussed-girder bridges of up to 50 metres span can be lifted by mobile cranes without much difficulty. The main girders are first positioned, followed by the lifting and placing of the cross beams which support the deck. The main girders may be of a length and weight that require two cranes, one at either end, to lift the member on to the prepared seating. Truss-constructions can be supported on trestles or on a rigid platform which is designed to carry both bridges and craneage. Long plate-girders or trussed-girders may be hauled across an opening with the aid of rollers and temporary trestles. The crane, situated on temporary trestles possibly at mid-span, hauls the member on to rollers on the trestle and completes the operation from a new position on the opposite bank. The operation is termed 'launching a girder' and it is very suitable for erection over deep ravines and gullies. An alternative method of positioning long beam-girders is cantilever launching. The beam is launched from one bank, having sufficient ballast to counteract any overturning force. If the span is excessive for a complete cantilever operation, a temporary trestle can be constructed, approximately one-third of the distance across the span; the trestle is capped with rollers to reduce friction.

In both methods of cantilevering, the beam is hauled across the span by means of a winch (Fig 8.33). Where more than one span is necessary for the bridge construction the first span can be constructed by launching methods and the remainder by true cantilever construction. The first span acts as a counterbalance and working platform while the other spans are being erected.

Erection by means of barges is a suitable method for small bridges, which have to be constructed over waterways which cannot be closed. The barges or pontoons are equipped with suitably braced trestles on to

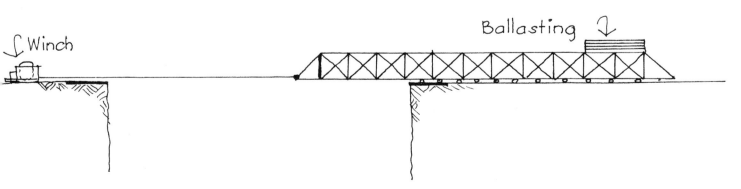

Fig 8.33 *Launching a girder bridge*

which the bridge structure, usually a trussed-girder, is placed. They float the bridge into position, where it is lowered on to the bridge bearings by means of jacks; alternatively the barges may be slowly sunk by flooding the ballast tanks.

In all of these methods the actual girder or truss has to be lowered into position because the rollers or trestles are positioned so as to deliver the girder over its bearing. The operation of finally positioning the girder or truss is known as 'jacking down': the girder is fitted with jacking cleats to facilitate this operation.

Steel arch bridges are erected by one of two methods; either by cantilevering the ribs out from the sides of the span, or by supporting the arch by means of trestles until it has been constructed. The second method is suitable for low arch bridges, where trestles can be constructed economically. The first method is suitable for bridges over deep ravines or rivers which cannot be spanned with trestles. The construction is achieved by means of a crane on a 'creeper' frame; a 'creeper' frame is a special unit on which the crane is situated, which is hauled along the arch as it is constructed. The arches are held by guy ropes until the bridge is complete (Fig 8.34).

One further method of erecting arch bridges, which may be classed as a modification to the method described above, is cableway erection. Arches are formed from each bank and cantilevered by guy ropes as before, but the bridge sections are placed by cableway. This method relieves the guy ropes of the stress created by the 'creeping' crane. The cableway has the extra advantage of being able to pick up bridge sections from the bank, thus eliminating the cost of floating craft.

The towers of suspension bridges are erected on specially formed foundations, usually caisson foundations. They may be erected by any form of climbing crane, but both tower cranes and Scotch derricks are commonly used. The cable housings are constructed at the same time; these may take the form of massive concrete blocks positioned in the water near each bank or they may consist of heavy anchor blocks cast deep into the hillside or river bank.

When the towers and cable housings are complete, the main suspension cables are 'spun'. This involves a large number of high tensile wire strands being carried over the span by a cable laying trolley (see Section 7.2). The trolley is suspended from a pilot cable which passes from the cable housing over the towers to the other cable housing. The cables are carefully laid in position in saddles before being hydraulically clamped together and bound into one main cable (Fig 8.35). The work is carried out from a temporary hanging walkway which is suspended from the pilot cable. Once the main cables have been constructed a series of hangers is fastened to them by means of special brackets, commencing at the centre of the span and working back to both towers. The bridge deck is then commenced from both towers to maintain equilibrium during erection (Fig 8.36 and 8.37). If the cable housings are constructed 'off-shore', approach spans will have to be constructed at both ends: these can be constructed by traditional pier and beam construction.

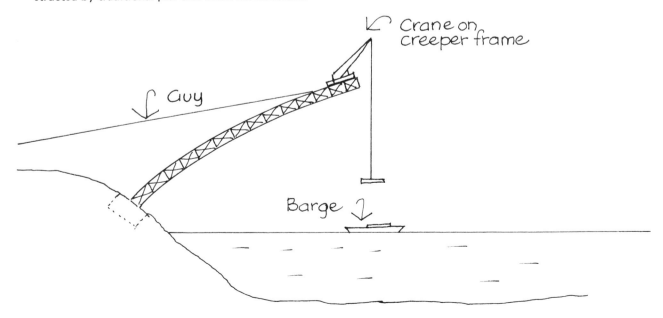

Fig 8.34   Erection of steel arch by 'creeper' frame

Fig 8.35 *Wires hydraulically clamped together to form main suspension cable* (William Tribe Limited)

Fig 8.36 *Construction of bridge deck — Severn Bridge*
(William Tribe Limited)

Fig 8.37 *Hoisting bridge deck section — Severn Bridge* (William Tribe Limited)

8.2.3   Bolting, riveting and welding

Bolting

Bolting offers many advantages over riveting: for example, riveting requires specialist plant and equipment, whereas bolting can be achieved by spanners or torque wrench. Bolting can be carried out in adverse weather conditions, whereas this is almost impossible in the case of riveting. Bolted structures can be dismantled easily, either for demolition or for alteration. Bolting, as an operation, is much quieter than riveting, and is therefore suitable for cases in areas where the noise level created by riveting would be prohibitive. Bolting can be carried out by men working on the frame wearing a safety harness, whereas riveting requires some form of temporary staging.

Site connections are now commonly achieved by the use of bolts, which simplifies erection and reduces the erection cost. The most common type of bolt used in site connections is the 'black' bolt. These bolts, made from mild steel, must have a hole clearance so that they can be placed without damage and without over-stressing other bolts already placed; the hole clearance for such bolts is 2 mm greater than the diameter of the bolt shank. Since this type of bolt requires a clearance for assembly the joint is subject to slight movement and calculations assume a reduced strength factor.

Turned and fitted bolts may be used in lieu of black bolts on connections which are highly stressed. The extra strength is obtained by preventing movement of the joint. The bolt shank is accurately turned and fitted to the diameter of the holes in the connection, and the bolt is driven into the hole and secured by a nut. The disadvantage of this method is that the joint alignment necessary for the bolt to be driven home must be precise, which is very difficult to achieve on site, especially when erecting steelwork at great heights and in adverse weather conditions. For these reasons the method is largely superseded by the use of high-strength bolts.

High-strength friction grip bolts are bolts made from high-strength steel which enables them to be highly stressed when gripping together the plates being joined. Such bolts are tightened by a torque wrench which controls the stress being applied. This method of tightening is necessary to prevent the bolt from being over-stressed and to ensure that each bolt has equal loading. The bolt applies a pressure to the clamped faces of the plates, inducing very high friction between the plates. The strength of the bolt and the increased friction between the plates combine to make a joint which can carry much higher loads than the normal bolted or riveted joint.

There are various forms of high-strength bolts, ranging from bolts that shear near the end when the required strength is reached, to bolts which have specially recessed heads into which feeler gauges may be placed during loading to indicate the amount of applied load by the size of a gap between the head of the bolt and the washer. The first type of bolt, known as the 'torshear' bolt (Fig 8.38(a)), has a 'waisted' end which shears off at a pre-determined torque. A special torque wrench, pneumatically operated, grips the end of the bolt while the nut is being tightened, and when the required torque has been reached, the end of the bolt is sheared off by the anticlockwise movement of the tool. No further tightening of the nut is necessary.

The second type referred to is the 'load-indicating' bolt (Fig 8.38(b)). The four corners of the bolt head bear against the washer and are compressed as pressure is applied; the amount of pressure applied can be ascertained by measuring the gap between the bolt head and the washer.

All high-strength bolts have one thing in common, apart from the fact that they are made of high tensile steel: the underside of the head and nut are semi-finished, to provide a flat surface against the washers. The washers are hardened to prevent the head and nut of the bolt from becoming embedded during the tightening process and they also distribute the load to the softer steel of the structural member.

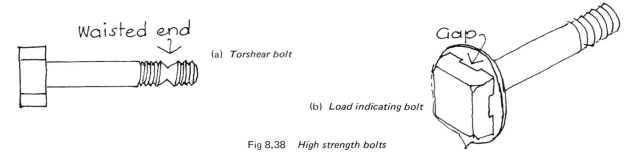

(a) *Torshear bolt*

(b) *Load indicating bolt*

Fig 8.38   *High strength bolts*

Riveting

The riveting of structural members, as a site operation, has been superseded by the use of bolts and welding. It is, however, still employed in the manufacture of large composite beams and columns as an alternative to welding.

The ordinary rivet is known as a 'snap-head' or 'dome-head' (Fig 8.39(a)). It is inserted into the hole in a red-hot condition and is then 'closed' to give the finished shape. The riveting or closing is achieved by pneumatic tools or hydraulic clamps, horse-shoe in shape. On cooling, the rivet shrinks and grips the plates by producing a great deal of friction between them. Where a connection has to bear against another surface, e.g. a truss base plate against the head plate of a column, countersunk rivets are used (Fig 8.39(b)).

Rivets 19 mm in diameter are normally used for general structural work but on heavily loaded girders or stanchions, where the number of 19 mm rivets required may weaken the connection plate, rivets up to 25 mm diameter may be used. This extra rivet strength will also result in a saving of gusset plate size, which would need to be larger to receive the standard rivet pitch of small rivets.

Riveting is particularly useful for cleat connections, which are normally made in the workshop.

The spacing of rivets (known as the pitch) must be such as to prevent the metal between them from rupturing. The metal will rupture or tear when there is insufficient metal between the rivets to carry the transferred load. This can be prevented by spacing the rivets at a minimum of two-and-a-half times their diameter (measured centre to centre). The end rivet should be one and a half times its own diameter from the edge of the plate.

Fig 8.39   *Rivets*

(a) *Dome-head or snap-head rivet*   (b) *Countersunk rivet*

Welding

Welding is being increasingly used as an alternative to shop riveting and bolting. It is not popular in the UK for site connections on structural frames for several reasons. Site-welded joints produce a rigid structure which, under load, can cause deflection of the columns and result in adverse stresses being applied to claddings and structural members. Other problems of site welding include: access and difficult working conditions at high levels; the difficulty of assessing the quality of the welded joints; the permanency of the joint, which does not facilitate alterations or demolition; and the high degree of skill required compared with other methods of jointing. Basically, welding is the running of molten weld metal into the heated junctions of steel plates to form a continuous member. Certain types of weld require the plates being welded to be shaped to receive the weld metal (Fig 8.40). Welds are made in two basic forms; butt welds and fillet welds.

Butt welds (Fig 8.40) are used to join plates end-to-end and are classified according to the shape of the ends of the plates prior to welding. The thickness of the weld is determined by the thickness of the plates being welded; if plates of varying thickness are to be welded the weld will assume the thickness of the thinnest plate. Single-welded joints, e.g. the single-V joint, are more easily accessible for welding, but involve a greater amount of heat, which may result in distortion of the plates. Thick plates are best jointed by the double-U section weld, which gives good accessibility and uses less weld metal than V-joints of the same thickness.

Fig 8.40   *Butt welding*

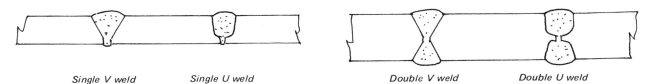

Single V weld   Single U weld   Double V weld   Double U weld

Fillet welds (Fig 8.41) are used for jointing plates at right-angles to each other or plates which overlap each other. The weld metal is deposited as a fillet at the junction of the two members. The strength of a fillet weld is calculated on the throat thickness and the length of weld. If the direction of the load is parallel to the length of a fillet weld, it is known as a side fillet weld; if the load is at right angles to the weld it is known as an end fillet weld. Fillet welds up to 10 mm are formed by one run of weld metal; larger welds are formed by further runs.

Structural work is normally welded by the arc welding process in which heat generated by an electric arc melts the two surfaces of the metal plates and additional metal (called filler) is added to the joint. The joint is completed when the metal has cooled. Oxy-acteylene welding equipment may also be used, in which case a flame from a blow pipe heats the surface of the plates to melting point and at the same time melts a filler rod into the joint. The filler metal fuses with the parent metal. Arc welding has superseded oxy-acetylene welding for most site work.

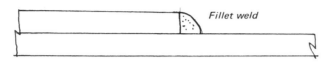

Fig 8.41   *Fillet welding*

Chapter 9

Services

9.1 PIPELINES FOR WATER, GAS AND SEWAGE

9.1.1 Introduction

Pipelines for water, gas and sewage vary in size depending on the service requirements. This book deals only with those pipelines which would be found in a national grid or other large supply line. The excavation is not dealt with in this section, although specialist plant, e.g. trenching machines, have been developed for this work. The backfilling, bedding or other treatment of pipes is discussed because of the specialised nature of the work.

Pipeline developments affect large numbers of people who own or occupy land, and they therefore involve an encroachment on the rights of the individual. This has led to the development of legislation to control the construction of pipelines. In Britain there are a number of Acts of Parliament which enable various authorities or bodies to construct pipelines: these include the Pipelines Act 1962; the Public Health Acts 1936 and 1961; the Gas Acts 1948 and 1965; the Water Acts 1945 and 1948; the Requisitioned Land and War Works Acts 1945 and 1948; and the Land Powers Act 1958 — the last dealing with Government oil pipelines. These and other Acts must be considered before pipelines can be planned and constructed.

When all negotiations have been completed, a working width for land pipelines is established. This is the width of the land, an average of 12 metres wide, required for executing the work, which is fenced off to protect the public, the owner of the land, or his animals. The pipes are distributed end-to-end along the route, leaving gaps between them to permit movement of livestock. Trenching is carried out by special trenching machines or hydraulic backacters (see Chapter 2, Plant). For further references on installation, see CP 2010 Part 1: 1966.

9.1.2 Pipe materials

Materials for pipes can vary from cast iron to glass-fibre concrete. The material will vary with the type and purpose of the pipeline.

Water pipelines use the largest range of materials; these include cast iron, asbestos-cement, steel, concrete and plastic. The spun cast-iron pipe and spun concrete pipe have been used for many years and their advantages and disadvantages are well known. Two important pipe materials which are being used increasingly in water engineering are ductile spun iron and pre-stressed concrete.

Ductile spun pipes are manufactured by the centrifugal casting process normally used for spun iron pipes. The addition of magnesium alloy to molten iron causes the flake graphite structure to become spheroidal or nodular, which gives high ductility and tensile strength; this improved metal structure produces a stronger, tougher pipe. The material, pipes and fittings should comply with British Standard 4772: 1980. The impact resistance and inherent toughness of ductile spun iron ensure that accidental damage which may arise in rigorous working conditions is no longer a problem. Tests have shown that ductile spun iron will withstand impact blows without sustaining damage. The exceptional strength of the material has resulted in a reduction of the pipe wall thickness compared with grey iron pipes, which makes the pipes lighter and easier to handle.

Pre-stressed concrete pipes are produced in two forms: pre-stressed concrete cylinder pipes and pre-stressed concrete non-cylinder pipes. Concrete cylinder pipes differ from other types of concrete pipe in that they have an integral steel cylinder. The cylinder is made of welded sheet steel and has spigot and socket rings welded on to each end to provide jointing surfaces; the complete unit is subjected to a hydrostatic test to check the welds. After testing, the steel cylinder is centrifugally lined with concrete, followed by a winding of high tensile wire. The pre-stressing wires are covered with a dense cement mortar coating not less than 20 mm thick. The pipes are jointed by means of a simple push-in joint (Fig 9.1) known as the lock joint. Extra-strong duty pipes are produced by double winding of the wire, the first winding being coated and further stressed, on reaching the required strength, by a second winding. The second winding is then coated with cement mortar for protection (Fig 9.2). The advantages of this type of pipe construction include a high factor of safety, a continuous water-tight membrane, simple jointing and the elimination of normal protective finishes.

Pre-stressed non-cylinder pipes are concrete pipes which are longitudinally and circumferentially pre-stressed. The core of the pipe is formed around longitudinal pre-stressing wires which provide the stress when released; on completion of the longitudinal stressing the core is circumferentially pre-stressed to withstand pressure and design loads. The pre-stressing wires are covered with a cement mortar to protect them. As with cylinder pipes the jointing of pre-stressed non-cylinder pipes is achieved by push-in joints.

Pipes for general use over long distances include plastic and steel. Plastic pipes are used extensively and have the advantages of light weight, ease of handling, low frictional loss in flow, good abrasion resistance and good chemical resistance. Disadvantages are lower tensile strength than metal pipes and non-resistance to temperature change. They are supplied in diameters ranging from 100 mm to 600 mm and in standard lengths of 6 metres, although 9 metre lengths are available to order. The chemical resistance of the plastic, coupled with the increased flow, due to the smooth bore, makes the pipe suitable for sewage and water pipelines.

Steel pipes are particularly suited to large diameter pipelines extending over great distances. The pipes are produced by spiral welding methods which produce diameters ranging from 150 mm to 3 metres. High-tensile steel pipes are available in diameters up to 1.06 metres and lengths up to 24 metres.

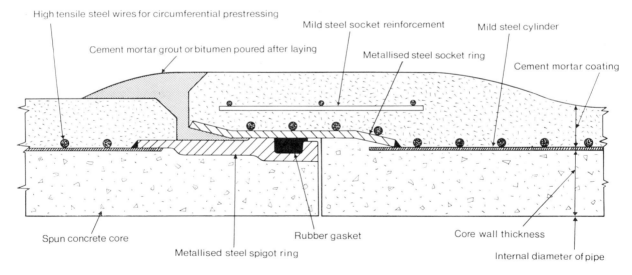

Fig 9.1   *'Lock joint' for prestressed concrete cylinder pipes*   (Stanton and Staveley Group)

Choice of pipeline material

The choice of pipeline material will depend on the following factors: design of basic pipeline; ability of the material to withstand internal and external forces, simplicity of jointing and laying; durability; impermeability and frequency of maintenance.

Pipelines in sewage work (Ref CP 2005: 1968) are classed as rigid or flexible; the former will fracture before any significant deformation of the pipe has taken place, while the latter will deform significantly and trans-mit the loads to the surrounding fill. The advantages of flexible pipes for sewage work are also applicable to water lines, the incidence of failure in pipes in both cases being much higher than in other types of pipeline. The type of pipe used will affect trench preparation: some pipes require a specially prepared bed and careful backfilling, while others can be placed without special preparation or careful backfilling. Flexible pipes are subject to change in cross-sectional shape due to ground movement, and this may affect the flow. In the main, pipes are tested before back-filling, but certain pipes, e.g. ductile iron with its very efficient push-in joint, can be laid and backfilled with confidence before testing. Materials for general pipeline application are shown in Table 9.1

Fig 9.2   *Automatic spray coating of prestressed concrete pipes*   Stanton and Staveley Group

TABLE 9.1

APPENDIX A
PRESENT GENERAL PIPELINE APPLICATIONS

Type of pipeline	Part No. of CP 2010*	Fluid									
		Crude oil and petroleum products	Liquefied petroleum gases	Natural gas	Town gas	Industrial gases	Water	Slurries and sludges	Chemicals	Trade waste and sewage†	Brine
Steel with butt-welded joints	2	A	A	A	A	A	A‡	A	A‡	A ‡	A‡
Steel with other than butt-welded joints	2			Aˢ	Aˢ		A‡	A	A‡	A‡	A‡
Grey iron and ductile iron	3			Aˢ	Aˢ		A‡	A	A	A	A
Asbestos cement	4						A	A		A	A
Concrete (prestressed and reinforced)	5						A	A		A	A
Non-ferrous metals		A		A					A	A	A
Plastics				A	A		A	A	A	A	A

A = the general application.
*   Part 1, 'Installation of pipelines in land' is applicable to all subsequent Parts of the Code.
†   See also CP 2005, 'Sewerage'.
‡   These applications may require the pipeline to be lined to prevent internal corrosion.
Aˢ· This type of pipeline is used for the conveyance of town and natural gases at lower operating pressures.

9.1.3 Jointing of pipes

Asbestos-cement pressure pipes are normally jointed by means of sleeves and rubber rings (Fig 9.3). The sleeves may be either of asbestos-cement, with two grooves to hold the rubber rings, known as the 'push-on' joint; or they may be metallic sleeves with rubber rings compressed between the sleeve and the pipe by loose flanges and bolts, known as a 'detachable' joint. Both types of joint give joint flexibility as specified in BS 486. Cast iron pipes, whether grey iron or ductile, are supplied with spigot and socket or flanged ends. The spigot and socket joint may be caulked with lead, or it may have push-on joints or bolted gland joints (Fig 9.4). Ductile pipes are normally jointed with push-in joints or bolted gland joints, the latter either having a plain spigot or incorporating a self-anchoring device, achieved by means of a circlip located in a specially formed groove in the socket and spigot. The anchored joint is used primarily for gas pipelines at pressures of up to 8 bar. Steel pipelines may be jointed by welding or more conventional methods. Welding is used on pipelines where 100 per cent line-tightness is essential for reasons of safety. The field welding of pipelines should comply with BS 4515 or with a specification of equivalent or higher standard than the British Standard. Butt welding is normally employed for gas and oil pipelines, but it is not an acceptable method for water line-work because of the risk of corrosion on the internal face of the welded joints. Steel pipelines for water may be constructed by welding spigot-and-socket pipes; the welding is usually applied to both the inside and outside of the pipe at the joint, although the internal weld may be omitted on small diameter pipes. Welding may be carried out by automatic welding machines which operate either externally or both internally and externally on any one joint. Other methods of jointing steel pipes include flanged joints, screwed joints and proprietary joints with sealing rings of rubber (Fig 9.5).

Plastic pipelines may be solvent-welded, connected by coupler and rubber rings, or they may have spigot and Z-socket ends (Fig 9.6). The coupler and rubber ring joint is suitable for pipes of up to 300 mm diameter; the other jointing systems are suitable for all diameters. Concrete pipes subject to movement are usually jointed by some form of flexible pipe joint which employs a gasket of rubber or synthetic material, depending on the use of the pipeline. Pipes may, however, be jointed by socket and spigot joints, and ogee joints, both of which are self-centring and thereby eliminate the use of spun yarn. When the pipes are winched together they are automatically held in position for the jointing operation to be carried out with ease. Self-centred joints are normally grouted or filled with cement mortar, grouting being achieved through grout holes in the pipe collar. Pre-stressed concrete cylinder pipes are jointed by means of a rubber gasket, known as the 'lock joint'. The joint has a circular-section rubber gasket (Fig 9.1) located in a groove specially formed on the pipe spigot: as the spigot is pushed into the socket the gasket is compressed to form a watertight seal.

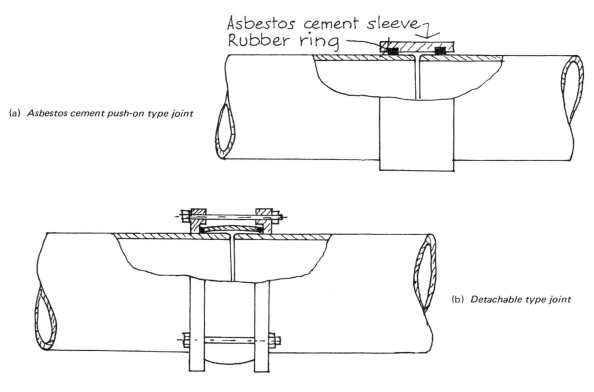

(a) *Asbestos cement push-on type joint*

(b) *Detachable type joint*

Fig 9.3   *Joints for asbestos pipes*

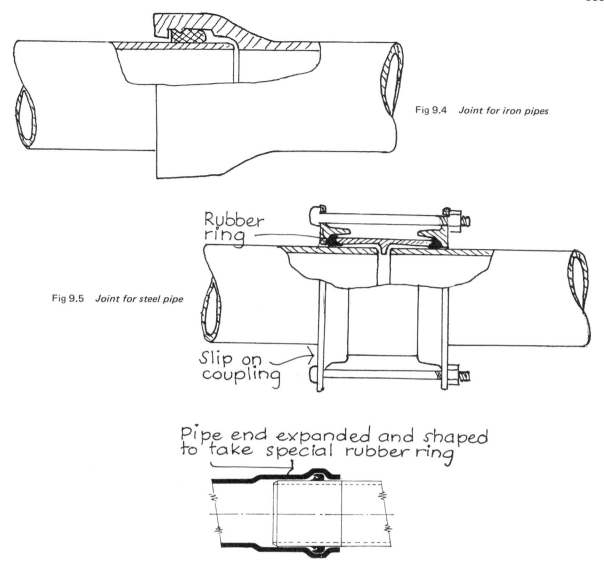

Fig 9.4   *Joint for iron pipes*

Fig 9.5   *Joint for steel pipe*

Fig 9.6   *Joint for plastic pipe*

Anchors

All pressure mains fitted with flexible joints should be provided with anchorages or 'thrust-blocks' at bends, tees and capped-ends. These anchorages resist the thrust arising from the effects of internal pressure. Flexible joints offer no appreciable resistance to 'blow-out', and joint failure will result unless restraints are provided.

Anchorages, usually of concrete construction, should be designed to take into account the maximum pressure the main has to carry on test and the stress which the surrounding ground will support.

9.1.4   Construction methods

There are two distinct areas of operation in pipeline construction; the first covers pipelines which are constructed on land, and the second deals with pipelines laid under water. Pipes for the construction of pipelines on land are first laid out — an operation called 'stringing' — along the route. The pipes should be handled with slings of canvas or other non-abrasive material to prevent damage to the pipes, which should not be dropped, dragged or rolled. Pipes requiring welding or other forms of jointing before being lifted into the trench are placed on timber skids. Steel pipes used for a change in direction may be bent on site by a pipe-bending machine. Long pipes should be cleaned out prior to alignment and jointing.

When the pipeline has been jointed it is lowered into the trench by side-boom tractors or similar plant. Concrete pipelines are jointed in position in the trench (Fig 9.7). All pipelines should be sealed with night caps at the end of a day's work to prevent ingress of small animals and other objects. The preparation of the trench for pipes will depend on the type of material used for the pipeline and will range from a bed of granular material to carefully shaped sand beds (Fig 9.8). On no account should hard packing materials used to lift or pack up the pipes be left in position. Heavy pipes may be lifted by pneumatic elevators to remove the initial packing (Fig 9.9) before being bedded on sand bags or granular material.

Trenching for pipelines may be undertaken by backacters or trenching machine (see Chapter 2 – Plant). The trench should be 300 mm wider than the outside diameter of the pipe, additional room being necessary at each joint to provide sufficient room for joints to be made and inspected. In hard or rocky ground the trench should be taken deeper than the required depth and brought to levels or gradient with granular material. Backfilling should be completed as soon as the section of pipe has been tested; testing should be preceded by cleaning. This is achieved by means of a 'foam-pig' (a cylinder of material, such as expanded polystyrene, driven through the pipe). Pipelines crossing roads, railway lines or rivers should be sleeved, the sleeve being placed by the open-trench method, power-driven auger or thrust-boring. The diameter of the sleeve should be 100 mm greater than the outer diameter of the pipeline. (See Chapter 5 – Auger-boring)

Fig 9.7   *Hoisting and laying of pre-stressed concrete pipes*
(Stanton and Staveley Group)

Fig 9.8(a)   *Preparing the sand base for a 1.83 m dia steel pipeline*
(Ground Engineering)

Pipelines under water may be constructed or positioned by one of three methods: the pulling method, the lay barge method, or floating and sinking. The pulling method (Fig 9.10) consists of jointing long lengths of pipe on the shore and pulling the completed line into the water by winches carried on anchored barges. The lay barge method consists of a special barge on which the pipeline is constructed and lowered to the river or sea bed. The barge is winched along the pipeline route leaving the completed line in position. The floating and sinking method involves the construction of the pipeline on shore, fitting it with buoyancy tanks on completion, and floating it out to position (Fig 9.11). The buoyancy tanks are flooded or deflated as the pipeline is lowered into position by winches on pontoons. A weight coating is used to prevent natural buoyancy of the pipe (see Section 9.1.5).

Fig 9.8(b)   *Lowering a 1.83 m diameter steel pipe on to the prepared base*   (Ground Engineering)

Fig 9.9   *Pneumatic elevators used to lift gas pipeline for removal of timber packings and for lowering on to sand bag support*   (RFD-GQ Limited)

Fig 9.10 *Pulling a 900 mm diameter gas pipe across the River Humber* (The Dredging and Construction Company Limi

Fig 9.11 *Hunstanton PVC outfall floated into position*
(The Dredging and Construction Company Limited)

9.1.5   Coatings and linings

Protection of steel pipes

When iron or steel is exposed to moisture, corrosion reactions are inevitable, particularly if the moisture is acidic or contains dissolved salts and oxygen. The reactions are electro-chemical and involve the passage of electricity between the moisture and steel. Thus the most obvious — and indeed cheapest — way to prevent corrosive attack is by coating the steel surface with an inert substance which effectively separates the steel surface from the corrosive environment and at the same time resists the passage of electricity which is so essential to corrosion reactions. Provided that the coating is complete, corrosion is prevented, but in practice breaks or 'holidays' in the coating may arise, for example from rough handling or severe abuse. At such places where the metal is exposed directly to the corrosive environment, corrosion can occur unless cathodic protection is applied.

External protections

Bitumen coating (sizes 17 mm to 2134 mm outside diameter): bituminous coatings, which are applied to tubes by dipping in a bath of molten bitumen or painting with a bituminous solution, are relatively thin. They are suitable for mildly corrosive conditions only, and for above ground where periodic inspection and maintenance painting is possible. They do not afford lasting protection to the external surfaces of pipes laid underground. For such conditions one of the other protections should be adopted.

'Security'* bitumen enamel wrapping (sizes 89 mm to 2032 mm o.d.): the pipe is primed to BS 4147 and is then given a flood coating of hot bitumen enamel, a mixture of blown bitumen and slate flour, supplemented by an inner spiral wrap of glass tissue fully immersed in and impregnated by the enamel. A further spiral wrap of pre-impregnated, reinforced glass tissue is applied to the outer surface. The surface is given a final heat-reflecting coating of limewash. 'Security' bitumen enamel wrapping is used on pipes which are to be laid underground, e.g. water, gas, oil mains and sewers. It affords protection against all types of corrosive soil and also against stray-current electrolytic corrosion.

'Security' reinforced bitumen enamel wrapping (sizes 89 mm to 2032 mm o.d.): this protection is similar to 'Security' bitumen enamel wrapping except that the outer wrap has incorporated in it additional reinforcement in the form of a woven glass cloth. The reinforced protection provides increased resistance to mechanical damage during transit, storage, handling and laying.

'Security' tar enamel wrapping (sizes 89 mm to 1118 mm o.d.): the pipe is first primed with a type of of primer defined in BS 4164 and is then flood-coated with hot coal-tar enamel conforming to the requirements of BS 4164. An inner spiral wrapping of glass tissue and an outer wrap of coal-tar impregnated glass tissue are applied. (Bituminous and coal-tar wrappings are not normally recommended for use at operating temperatures exceeding 38 °C. They can, however, be used for operating temperatures over 38 °C and up to 66 °C if the pipe is embedded in sand containing no sharp stones.)

'Security' plastic cladding (Securiclad) (sizes 14 mm to 324 mm o.d.): steel pipe is flood-coated with an even layer of hot-melt adhesive undercoat. Immediately following this, a seamless plastic sheath of high-density polythene is continuously applied. In the event of minor damage to the plastic cladding, the adhesive has the ability to flow and seal the areas of damage. Standard colours are yellow for gas mains and services, black for water and light brown for oil service distribution pipes. Plastic-clad pipes are supplied screwed and socketed in sizes up to 114 mm o.d. and with plain ends or ends bevelled for welding in sizes up to 324 mm o.d. The pipes may be bent cold, provided suitable precautions are observed.

'Security' plastic cladding is suitable for operating at temperatures ranging from minus 40° C, to a maximum, of 79° C, providing that at the high temperatures the pipe system is adequately engineered to accommodate the slight softening of the polythene which occurs. The main use of these pipes is for underground services. The high-density polythene cladding affords excellent protection for steel pipes against all types of corrosive soil and also against stray-current electrolytic corrosion. It is unaffected by most alkalis, salts and acids, has negligible water absorption, is highly resistant to fungi and bacteria, and in addition, as site experience has shown, possesses excellent resistance to damage by abrasion and impact.

---

* 'Security' is a heavy duty protection which may be of 6.4 mm thickness on the larger pipe sizes. 'Security' as applied to bitumen and coal tar protections is a registered trade mark and 'Securiclad' is the registered trade mark for security plastic cladding.

Testing of applied protections

Strict quality control of the materials used and care with each operation in the application is practised to ensure that the wrappings and claddings are uniform in thickness and tight on to the pipe wall. A high voltage test is applied to the protected pipe to ensure that no pinholes, thin places or 'holidays' occur.

Cathodic protection (See BS Code of Practice 1021: 1973)

With pipelines and other buried structures corrosion may be induced by the heterogeneous nature of the soil around the structure. Variations in salt content, oxygen levels and water content result in differing electrical potentials being set up at the soil/metal interface, and the formation of galvanic cells.

At areas of lower potential, positively charged metal ions leave the metal and electrons flow to areas of higher potential. Areas of low potential which lose metal ions and where corrosion occurs are termed 'anodic' and the areas of higher potential where corrosion does not occur are termed 'cathodic'. The distance between cathodic and anodic areas can be very small or many miles in length, e.g. 'long-line' corrosion.

The object of cathodic protection is to make the whole of the pipework cathodic, with no anodic areas, so that corrosion does not take place. In practice the required electric current may be obtained in one of two ways. The pipework may be connected to anodes composed of a more readily corrodible metal such as magnesium or zinc. These corrode preferentially and the flow of electrons to the pipe will render the pipe cathodic. Such an arrangement is known as a 'sacrificial anode system'. Alternatively the flow of electrons to the pipe may be obtained from direct current generators or rectified mains current. These are connected to the pipework and also to electrodes of graphite or silicon iron which are held anodic to the pipework. Such an arrangement is termed an 'impressed current system'.

The question often arises whether it would be feasible to lay a pipeline without any protective coating and to rely entirely on cathodic protection to prevent corrosion. While this is technically possible it would be uneconomical. It is now accepted that cathodic protection obtained either by impressed current or sacrificial anodes is most economically employed in conjunction with high quality applied protections. The reason for this is that current consumption is in proportion to the areas of metal exposed by accidental damage or other cause and this is least with good quality coatings.

Because of problems of installation and maintenance, cathodic protection as applied to steel pipes is almost always concerned with the external surface.

Internal protections

Bitumen lining (sizes 60 mm to 2134 mm o.d.): this is a heavy-duty protection and can be 6.4 mm thick for large pipes. The surface preparation consists of the thorough removal of mill-scale by shot blasting or by pickling and phosphate coating by dilute phosphoric acid. The treated pipe is coated with a primer of the type defined by BS 4147. The requisite quantity of bitumen to provide a lining of the required thickness is introduced to the pipe and applied centrifugally; cooling by water-spray then occurs until the lining has set. Steel pipes protected internally with bitumen lining are suitable for the conveyance of raw and potable waters, sea water, sewage and highly contaminated effluents. Apart from its protective efficiency, a bitumen lining provides a very smooth surface having minimum resistance to flow. Maximum throughput is maintained throughout the service life of the pipeline since pipes are immune from deterioration by nodular incrustation which is the chief cause of diminished carrying capacity in old, unprotected pipes. Bitumen-lined pipes are not normally recommended for use at operating temperatures exceeding 38°C. Neither should they be used where oil or hydrocarbon solvent contamination is likely.

Plastic lining (sizes 17 mm to 2134 mm o.d.): this form of lining can be produced from thermosetting epoxy-phenolic paint, by applying the paint in successive coats to build up the required thickness. Plastic-lined pipes with a coating thickness of 0.254 mm are suitable for a wide variety of highly corrosive media including acidulated brines, sea waters, mine waters and acid solutions with a pH range of about 2 to 5. For less corrosive media such as certain brine solutions, alkalis and slightly acid solutions, a coating thickness of 0.127 mm is normally adequate. At this thickness the lining is also suitable for all aliphatic and aromatic hydrocarbons, oil, petrol, etc. In addition it is suitable for the lining of oil-well tubing to diminish maintenance time due to wax deposition, and of large diameter pipes conveying material which must not be contaminated. Operating temperatures for plastic-lined pipes range from sub-zero to a maximum of 82°C for aqueous media and 204°C for dry heat or oils.

Red lead paint: this paint, complying with BS 2523, is used for the internal protection of pipes conveying gas. In the case of service pipes it is the only form of internal protection supplied at present.

Epoxy-based paints: for gas mains, as distinct from service pipes, approved epoxy red lead or epoxy red oxide paints are standard alternatives to red lead paint.

Cement lining (pipes from 75 mm to over 3 metres diameter (o.d.): steel pipes may also be protected internally with a cement lining. This type of lining is suitable for:

Pipes carrying potable water

Oil refinery cooling water

Salt water and fire water mains.

The lining can be applied at factory, stockyard or on site and is useful for reconditioning the interior of existing pipes. The thickness of cement varies from 5 mm to 11 mm. Sulphate-resisting cement is specified for salt water and other sulphate-bearing waters.

Thermal Insulation

Thermal insulation may be required for certain pipelines, e.g. those transporting liquids such as crude oil which can be pumped more easily by raising the temperatures of the liquid and reducing its viscosity. The insulation used may be polyurethene or expanded polystyrene of a minimum thickness of 50 mm.

Weight Coatings

Weight coatings (Fig 9.12) are applied to the outer surfaces of pipelines to counteract buoyancy when immersed in water. The coating is usually concrete, and may be sprayed on to the pipes by the gunite method or cast around the pipes using special formwork. The thickness of the coating depends on the weight required to sink and stabilise the pipe, and it should be applied over any anti-corrosive coating.

An alternative method of stabilising pipes has been achieved by concrete weights attached to the pipes or wire ropes anchored to concrete blocks at the river or sea bed. Attachment to piles may also be used as a means of anti-buoyancy.

Fig 9.12(a)   *External wrapping — River Humber gas pipeline crossing — weight coating applied in factory*

(The Dredging and Construction Company Limited)

Fig 9.12(b)   *Weight coating being cast prior to pipe launching*

(The Dredging and Construction Company Limited)

Laying of protected pipes

In laying and backfilling every care should be taken to avoid damage to the external protection. Blemishes should be examined by a 'holiday' detector, and all damage repaired. The soil on which pipes are bedded and that used for backfilling the sides and top should be free from stones and rock fragments and carefully tamped round the pipes. Care should be taken to ensure that rock fragments etc do not come into direct contact with the pipe during backfilling, otherwise damage may occur to the protective coating during subsequent tamping operations.

In rocky terrain, where the provision of suitable backfilling material would be difficult and probably costly, the use of armour-wrap or rock shield is sometimes introduced. Various forms of armour are available, but generally they are of thick bituminised felt incorporating either asbestos or glass tissue.

9.2   SEWAGE TREATMENT

9.2.1   General considerations

Sewage is of two kinds: surface-water sewage, which is the run-off from rainfall, and foul sewage, which is formed of domestic wastes and trade effluents. Sewage is conveyed to points of direct disposal or treatment plant; the conveyance system consists of gravity sewers, which may be pipes or open channels in which the flow is not under pressure. Manholes are provided at regular intervals for access and cleaning, and also at any change of direction. Gravity sewers are always laid in straight lines between manholes. If excessive flow develops in a gravity sewer, so that the level of the sewage rises in the manholes or perhaps overflows, the sewer is said to be 'surcharged' — a most undesirable state.

Where sewage has to be conveyed uphill, pumping stations are necessary. The sewage is pumped up a pressure pipe, known as a rising main, either into a gravity sewer or direct to a disposal point. Modern practice, in rural areas in particular, is to limit the number of small treatment plants in favour of a central treatment point, with an extensive sewerage system which may have more than twenty pumping stations.

Sewerage systems may be separate, combined or partially-separate. In a separate system the surface water is completely excluded. The design of these systems is based on the Dry Weather Flow (DWF), which is made up of the domestic flow, trade flow and infiltration, i.e. leakage into the sewer from the surrounding soil.

The domestic flow, the flow per day per head of population, is usually taken as 180 litres/day; in rural areas a figure of 150 litres/day may be used while in modern residential areas the figure may rise to 270. The trade flow from factories, food processing etc might be of any volume and from many different sources. In some cases the discharge may take place throughout the full day, i.e. 24 hours, while in others it may be concentrated into short periods of time.

Infiltration from the surrounding soil should be very small in new sewers, but in old systems it could be appreciable. It is then a question of economics whether to re-lay the sewer or accept the extra flow. As the flow varies during the day, the system should be designed for a maximum likely rate of flow; depending on circumstances, a separate system is designed for a maximum flow of four to six times the DWF, and pumping stations are designed accordingly.

In a combined system the surface water falling on the drainage area is accommodated. Sometimes only part of the surface water is taken into the system, e.g. a partially separate system whereby road drainage and roof drainage from the front of the houses only is taken into a storm sewer, but the foul drainage and the rear roof drainage is taken into the combined foul sewer. This economises on the amount of drainage pipework needed to be provided to the rear of property.

In the combined system the flow due to surface water is generally far greater than the DWF and is a very complex matter to determine; the main point to decide is what intensity of rainfall has to be accommodated. The greater the storm, the more seldom it is likely to happen, and it is a question of economics what intensity is to be adopted. If excessive rainfall is unlikely to cause any serious damage, the system is designed for a one-year storm, i.e. a storm likely to occur only once a year. If, on the other hand, flooding could have serious consequences, the system might be designed for a five-year or even a fifty-year storm, i.e. the heaviest storm likely in that period of time.

To design a sewerage system to convey water all the way to the disposal point would be exceedingly wasteful, and therefore in combined systems, where excess surface water can be safely discharged, overflows are provided at convenient points adjacent to rivers. The design of these overflows is based on a formula incorporating the three factors making up the DWF, which works out at about six times the DWF. Flows in excess of this usually pass out through screens which trap any floating debris. Similarly, when the flow has to be pumped the pumps are designed on the same basis, with overflows to accommodate any excess.

A refinement in storm overflows, particularly where there is a high percentage of road drainage, is the provision of storage tanks. When a storm occurs, particularly after a long dry spell, the first run-off from roads is very noxious and could pollute the stream into which it discharges. Tanks can be provided to retain the first flush, overflowing into the stream only when they are full and the discharge has become innocuous. After the storm the tanks empty back into the sewer.

9.2.2 Methods of treatment

Sewage can either be treated before discharge to a suitable river, or discharged without treatment direct to the sea or large river. Direct discharge has been extensively used in the past and still exists in some seaside towns where short outfalls, i.e. those outfalls which are constructed on the beach but do not reach low tides, have caused extensive and offensive pollution. Such outfalls are being replaced as quickly as possible.

Direct discharge to the sea is contemplated only if hydrographic conditions are favourable and there is no possibility of constructing inland treatment plant. Any proposed outfall should be subject to the most rigorous investigation to ensure that the point of discharge will not cause nuisance or allow sewage to drift back on to the beach. Such outfalls might be several miles long, formed either in tunnels or by pulling pipes in long lines from an assembly area (Fig 9.10) and laying them in a trench excavated in the sea bed. In sheltered waters the pipeline may be buried under a sand or gravel foreshore; alternatively, it is placed on concrete pads or stub columns and held in position by metal clamps. If the foreshore is rocky the concrete pads are anchored to the rock by reinforcement, which is fixed to the rocky base during low water (see Fig 9.13). The sewage would at least be screened and macerated to remove visible evidence before passing through to the outfall; settlement tanks, as described later, might also be incorporated into the system. In certain circumstances storage tanks are provided so that sewage is retained for discharge only on the ebb tide. In some cases existing outfalls may be retained but this should be in conjunction with new treatment plant so that only fully-treated effluent is discharged into the sea. It should be emphasised that sea outfalls are very unlikely to be used in the future if there is any possibility of alternative treatment.

The object of sewage treatment is to render sewage fit to be discharged to a watercourse. When sewage is discharged to a watercourse there is a reduction in the concentration of dissolved oxygen in the water, owing to its absorption by bacteria living on and breaking down the organic matter of the sewage. If the organic load is too great all the dissolved oxygen may be lost and the stream will then putrify. The amount of organic matter is measured by the Biochemical Oxygen Demand (BOD), which expresses the amount of oxygen, expressed as parts per million or Mg/litre, used by a sample of the sewage when incubated for five days at a temperature of 20^0 C, Another criterion is the amount of suspended solids in the sewage, again expressed in parts per million.

These criteria were originally devised by the Royal Commission on Sewage Disposal early in this century; for normal conditions the standard of effluent is known as the Royal Commission Standard and is 20 ppm BOD and 30 ppm Suspended Solids (SS), commonly known as the 20/30 standard. This standard implies a minimum dilution in the stream to which the effluent discharges of at least 8.1; if the dilution is less, or if there are special circumstances, a more stringent standard may be imposed, e.g. 10/10 or even 5/5, which would necessitate more intensive treatment.

The standards discussed so far apply to domestic sewage. Where trade effluents are concerned the situation may be far more complicated, as special standards are imposed to regulate the discharge of dangerous or noxious chemicals. Before certain trade effluents are accepted into a public system the manufacturers concerned may have to provide some form of pre-treatment to an agreed standard; alternatively, they may be required to contribute towards the cost of the extra treatment necessary at the treatment works.

Fig 9.13 *Sewer outfall held in position by concrete anchorage bases*

(The Dredging and Construction Company Limited)

Stages of treatment

In conventional plant the treatment is in two stages: primary and secondary.

The primary stage consists in passing the sewage through screens to remove large debris. Such screens may be of many different forms, usually incorporating some form of mechanical raking which removes the material, perhaps washes it, and dumps it ready for incineration or burying. An alternative to screening is comminution. This is a process whereby the solids are cut into small particles by comminutors, which are revolving vertical drums with cutting edges; after passing through these the shredded solids continue in the sewage flow. In combined systems grit may be present in the flow, washed off the roads or land, and this is removed by constant-velocity channels: these channels allow the sewage to flow with such low velocity that the grit settles out; the grit is then mechanically removed. There are also various patent forms of grit remover. The sewage then flows into settlement tanks where the solid matter can settle out to form a sludge at the bottom. These tanks may be rectangular with sloping bottoms, mechanical scrapers slowly moving the accumulated sludge towards one end from where it is removed; or they may be circular tanks with conical bottoms. In the latter type the sludge is moved towards the centre with scrapers revolving on radial arms; the sewage enters at the centre and flows outwards (radial flow). Other tanks may be square in section, with the sewage entering at the base and rising, to overflow at the perimeter into a peripheral trough (vertical flow). In either case the sludge is drawn off at the bottom, usually by a hydrostatic head, and pumped away for further treatment.

The object of the secondary stage of treatment is to bring the sewage, in the presence of air (oxygen), into close contact with a large mass of purifying bacteria which will break down/oxidise the polluting matter present.

There are two main methods of achieving this: percolating filters or activated sludge plants.

Filters

Filters consist of 1800 mm deep beds filled with 16 mm sized media, generally of slag or similar inert material. On this media the bacterial slime, which effects treatment, is allowed to grow whilst at the same time the interstices between the pieces of media allow the free passage of air.

Filters are built in either a circular or a rectangular shape. In either case the settled sewage is fed at a controlled and even rate on to the surface of the medium, through which it trickles slowly to be collected at the bottom by under-drains. On rectangular beds the sewage is fed through travelling distributors which are rope-hauled backwards and forwards along the top of the beds by means of a mechanical winch. On the more usual circular filters revolving distributors are used (Fig 9.14). These can be electrically driven but more usually rotate by the force of the sewage issuing from small jets on the distributor arms.

It should be noted that the term 'filter' is a misnomer as the process does not filter anything.

Fig 9.14
Carlton revolving distributor on percolating filter

(Tuke and Bell Limited)

The effluent from these beds contains fine particles of the biological film which forms in the bed, as well as other solid matter; this is known as 'humus' and is removed by passing the flow through a 'humus' tank. Humus tanks are very similar to settlement tanks and are often the same size; the effluent, having passed through these tanks, normally passes to the watercourse. If a higher than normal standard of effluent is required a tertiary treatment stage may be employed, the effluent from the humus tanks being given further treatment by passing it over grass plots or micro-straining through very fine filters. Sludge from the humus tanks is removed as in the primary tanks and may be kept separate for treatment but more usually is returned to the head of the works to be settled again with the primary sludge forming a mixed sludge of primary and humus to go forward for treatment by whatever sludge process is available on the works.

Percolating filters take up large areas of space and where this is limited other means of oxidation have been developed. One such development is a range of Rotating Biological Contractors currently marketed under the names of Bio-Surf, Aero-Surf and Surfact. All three bio-systems use the same basic bio-media which consists of specially moulded high density polyethylene discs having diameters up to 3.6 m (Fig 9.15). The discs are mounted on a horizontal square shaft, the latter being an epoxy-resin coated carbon steel. The Bio-Surf process differs from the other two in that the media is rotated by a motor drive unit and each assembly is driven individually (Fig 9.15(b)). The Aero-Surf and Surfact systems are driven by rising air bubbles; to achieve rotation a system of air cups is fixed to the perimeter of the media (Fig 9.15(c)). In the Aero-Surf system a low-pressure air pipe is fixed below the media to generate coarse air bubbles; these bubbles exert a rotational force on the air cups. The speed of rotation is controlled by the air flow but is normally 1—2 rpm.

The Surfact system has been developed to upgrade existing activated sludge works and therefore the media is rotated by existing air supplies.

Rotating Biological Contactors are mounted over concrete or steel tanks and 40% immersed in the liquid. A layer (1 to 4 mm thick) of micro-organisms forms on the surface of the rotating discs, ensuring rapid oxidation of the organic pollutants.

Fig 9.15(a)
Rotating Disc filters (made of polystyrene) being installed
(CJB Developments Limited)

Fig 9.15(b)
Close-up of Rotating Disc filter
(CJB Developments Limited)

Fig 9.15(c)
Aero-Surf system — showing air cups fixed to perimeter of discs
(CJB Developments Limited)

Activated sludge process

The activated sludge process is often used where there is a shortage of land to site the treatment works on, as it is more economical than filters on land needed per unit of sewage treated.

In this process the sewage passes through the same primary treatment as before, ie into primary settlement tanks. It is then mixed with an equal volume of 'Activated sludge' and aerated in tanks for a number of hours. The mixture of sludge and sewage is kept mixed and aerated either by injection of compressed air through jets in the bottom of the tank, or by mechanically driven agitators.

The 'Activated Sludge' consists of a floc which contains a mass of micro-organisms multiplying and living on the organic matter in the sewage. The sludge is separated from the purified sewage in the final settlement tanks, from where it is withdrawn and pumped back to the head of the aeration tanks in order to 'seed' the fresh sewage coming into the plant.

As the treatment continues and the micro-organisms multiply, the amount of 'Activated Sludge' available within the plant obviously increases. It therefore becomes necessary from time to time to withdraw the excess quantity and mix it in with the primary sludge for treatment and disposal.

In general 'Activated Sludge' plants consume more electrical power than conventional plants and it is often prudent to guard against power failure by providing standby generation on site.

Oxidation ditch method

A simple system, especially suitable for rural areas, is the oxidation ditch, commonly called the 'Pasveer ditch'. This consists of a shallow oval ditch into which the crude sewage is directly fed and circulated by means of one or more horizontal rotors; these are usually of a brush form, mounted above the surface, and they continuously rotate, thereby promoting oxidation. The sewage then passes to settlement tanks where the sludge settles and is continuously drawn off and returned to the head of the works to 'seed' the incoming raw sewage. There are several variations of this patented method.

Package plant

For small plants particularly where they are only temporary, there are various forms of 'package' plant which work on extended aeration or contact stabilisation. One such plant is complete in one circular steel tank with air compressors and all control gear. Its great virtue is the speed of installation; only a firm base is required on to which the plant can be off-loaded and connected up. When the plant is no longer required it can easily be moved elsewhere.

High-rate filters

For preliminary treatment of some trade effluents before they are discharged to a treatment plant, separate 'high-rate' filters are often used. These consist of plastic media packed in various patented shapes, often in high towers, which can accept a very high rate of flow and organic loading without 'choking' of the media by producing excessive growth of bacterial slime.

Sludge disposal

Whatever the process used, there is always a problem in disposing of the sludge. In small rural plants it can be spread on to open sludge beds to be dried, and then possibly disposed of to local farmers. In some cases the liquid sludge can be taken directly by tanker to the land without treatment. Larger quantities require artificial drying by pressing, vacuum filtration or other patented methods. The liquor produced by the drying process is returned to the head of the head of the works for treatment.

In large plants the sludge is treated by an aerobic digestion, i.e. heating in closed tanks; this converts the sludge into an inoffensive humus-like material which is suitable for agricultural use. The process also produces methane which can be used to generate power, often insufficient for all the power requirements of the whole plant. The sludge from very large plants, in coastal areas, may be shipped out to sea and dumped as an alternative to land disposal.

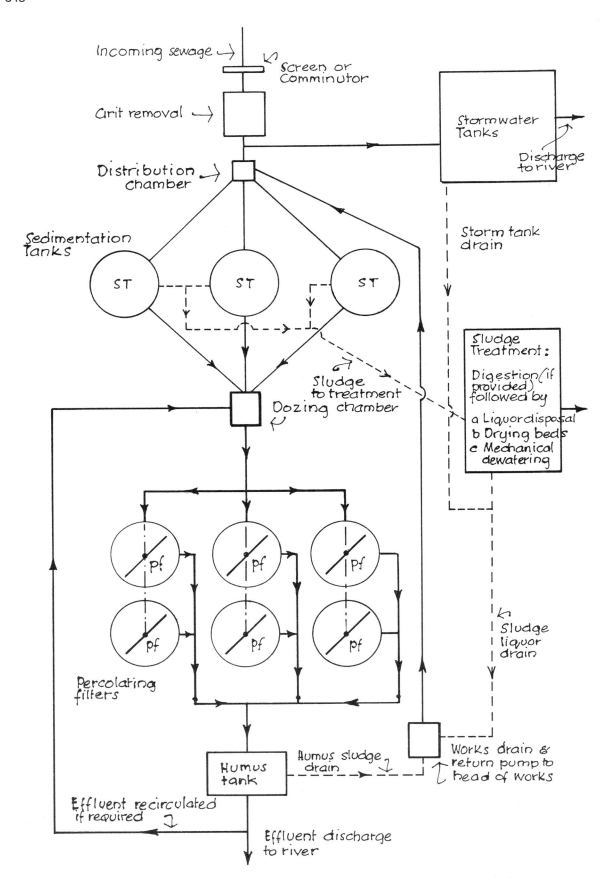

Fig 9.16   *Traditional filtration sewage system*

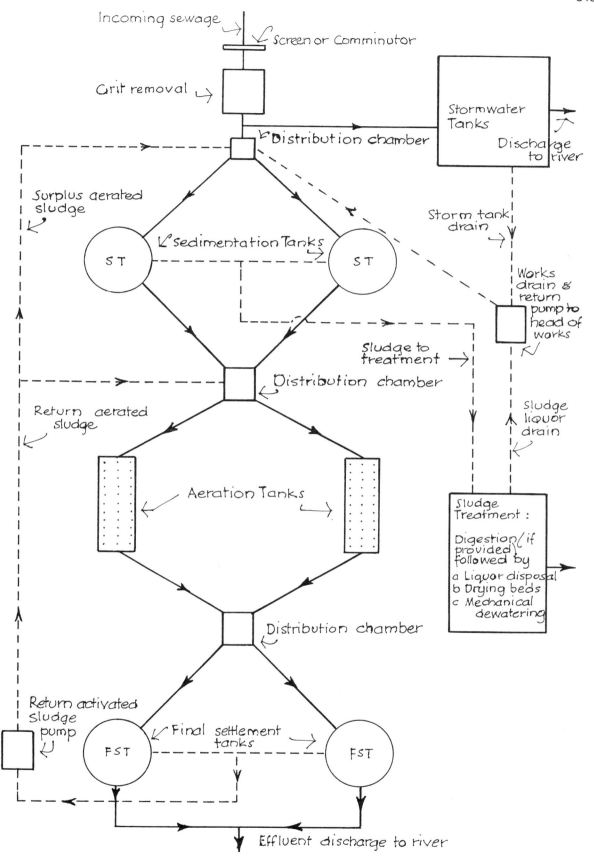

Fig 9.17   *Layout of Aerated Sludge Plant*

A point to remember is that while some domestic sludge is generally suitable as a fertiliser, trade effluents may contain elements which render the sludge unfit for use on the land.

Design of large plants

For large plants it would be uneconomic to design the plant to receive the maximum flow, which might be six times DWF. The usual practice is to design for a flow of three times DWF. Flows in excess of this pass to storm tanks, which are usually rectangular tanks, large enough to hold one hour's flow at six times DWF. If a storm fills these tanks, further flow overflows from them, usually direct into a watercourse; in either case the effluent is first screened and given some settlement treatment. After the storm the contents of the tanks are fed back for full treatment.

Typical layouts of conventional plant and activated sludge plant are shown in Figs 9.16 and 9.17.

Sewage treatment is the responsibility of Regional Water Authorities, who are also responsible for the management of rivers. It is they who set the standards of effluent discharged from treatment works and who ensure that these are maintained. There are still too many direct discharges of trade effluent to rivers, but these are gradually being reduced.

Chapter 10

Railway Trackwork, Chimneys and Cooling Towers

10.1 RAILWAY TRACKWORK

10.1.1 Introduction

Major future construction of railways in this country will arise as part of co-ordinated transport projects such as 'Underground' extensions or Channel Tunnel projects. They will continue to be an effective means of transport for many years to come, and the amount of work involved in the near future in the modernisation, conversion and electrification of British Rail will be extensive. In addition, docks, power stations, industrial premises, collieries and the like all have independent networks which, taken together, amount to an appreciable volume of engineering work.

This section deals with those aspects of railway construction with which the quantity surveyor may need to be familiar.

10.1.2 The Permanent Way

Types of rail

In this country the two principal types of rail used are Bullhead and Flat-bottom (Fig 10.1), weighing 47 kg/m and 56 kg/m* respectively; Flat-bottom rail section weight 54 kg/m is also available. The Flat-bottom rail has, to a great extent, superseded the Bullhead rail because it is better suited to heavier and faster traffic. Weight for weight, the Flat-bottom rail is considerably stiffer both vertically and laterally than the Bullhead section; this has resulted in longer track-life, greater stability and reduced maintenance. However, Bullhead rails are easy to fix and unfix to the sleeper, and these are therefore still used in situations where heavy traffic intensity necessitates frequent replacement.

The rails are supported by sleepers of timber, pre-stressed concrete or in some cases steel, which in turn are supported by a ballast foundation. The standard gauge for main lines has been 1.435 metres but is now 1.432 metres for main lines with continuous welded rails on concrete sleepers. The gauge is the distance between the inner faces of the heads of the rails, measured at a distance of 14 mm below the top of the rail (Fig 10.3). The unusual dimension of the gauge possibly resulted from the transfer of the flange from rails to wheels during the 18th century, the 'plateways' of earlier centuries being approximately 1.5 metres between wheels. The acceptable tolerance in standard gauge for safe operation is +8 mm and −5 mm, but railway engineering authorities may insist on closer tolerances than this, depending upon the importance of the track, e.g. main line and high speed routes. A large gauge, up to 1.454 metres, may be allowed on very sharp curves.

Rails are fixed to the sleepers in various ways; the Bullhead rail is fixed in a 'chair' by a hardwood or high-tensile spring key (Fig 10.1); the Flat-bottom rail is fixed with or without a baseplate, depending on the type of sleeper (Fig 10.4). Chairs for Bullhead rails are made to give the rail an inward tilt of 1 in 20, this bringing the upper surface of the rail into line with the coned tread of the wheels; the same facility is achieved with Flat-bottom rail by incorporating tapered baseplates or by forming a bevel on the sleeper. Both chairs and baseplates are now fixed to the sleepers by bolts, coach screws, or lockspikes, the spring-spike falling into disuse with the development of concrete sleepers.

Rail sections are still being described in imperial weights.

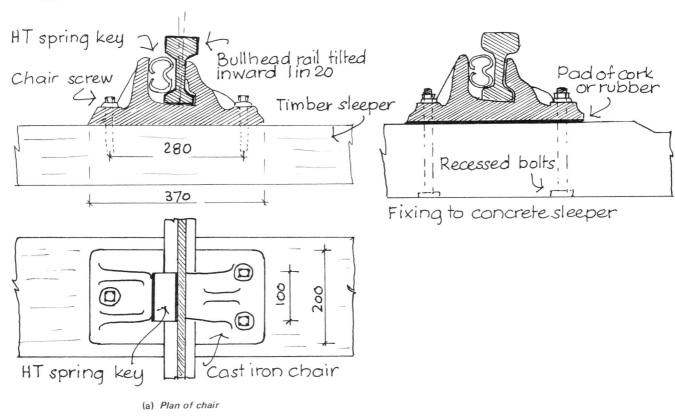

(a) *Plan of chair*

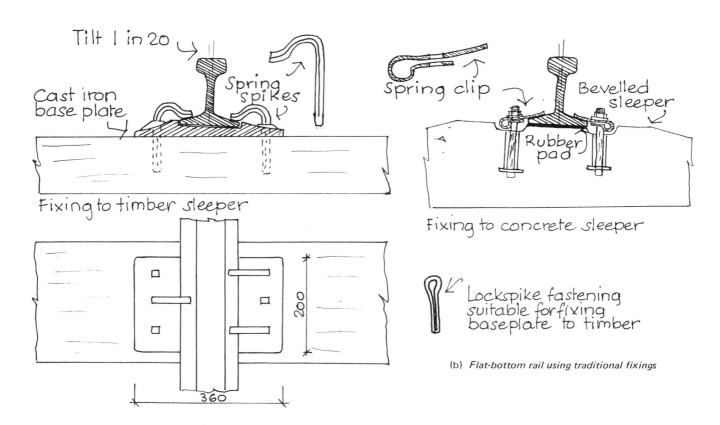

(b) *Flat-bottom rail using traditional fixings*

Fig 10.1 *Types of rail with traditional fixings to timber and concrete*

Pandrol rail clips

Pandrol rail clips are manufactured from high quality silicon-manganese steel. Since 1965 they have been adopted at the standard fixing for Flat-bottom rail on British Railways (Fig 10.2). In the case of timber sleepers the base plate is fixed to the sleeper with 'Lockspike' Baseplate Fastenings or with screws, depending on the type of base plate, whereas concrete sleepers are fitted with malleable iron shoulders, the latter being cast in during the manufacturing process.

When insulation is necessary for track circuiting purposes, an insulator of hard nylon or other similar material is placed between the shoulders and the edge of the rail foot (Fig 10.2c). An extention of the insulator rests on top of the foot rail beneath the 'Pandrol' Rail Clip. For severe conditions, e.g. very sharp curves, a composite insulator is available, consisting of a nylon insulating piece protected by a cover of malleable iron.

Rails are jointed either by fish-plates or by welding. The fish-plates, 450 mm long and 25 mm thick, are bolted to each rail with two bolts; this type of connection permits expansion. The joint for expansion is 0.33 mm/m at a temperature of between 10 and 24 °C. Welded rail is being increasingly used on main lines, the expansion and contraction being confined to relatively short lengths at each end of the track, where a special 'adjustment switch' is used to allow the welded rails to expand and contract. (Fig 10.2(d).)

Fig 10.2 *Standard flat-bottom rail fastenings for timber, steel and concrete sleepers using 'Pandrol' Rail Clips*

(British Rail and Pandrol Limited)

(a) *Fixing to timber using 'Lockspike' Baseplate Fastenings*

(b) *Fixing to steel sleeper*

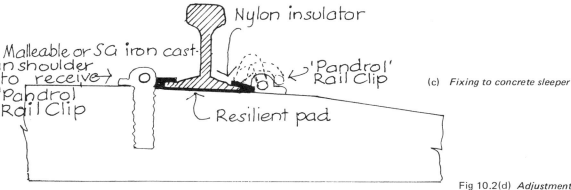

Nylon insulator

Malleable or SG iron cast-in shoulder to receive 'Pandrol' Rail Clip

'Pandrol' Rail Clip

Resilient pad

(c) *Fixing to concrete sleeper*

Fig 10.2(d) *Adjustment switch for welded rail*

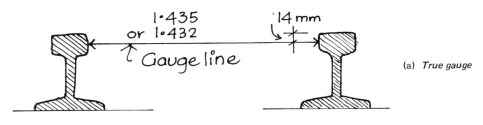

(a) *True gauge*

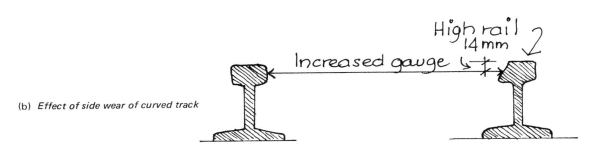

(b) *Effect of side wear of curved track*

Fig 10.3   *Measurement of gauge and effect of side wear*

Sleepers

It is normal practice to lay twenty-four sleepers per 18.3 metres of track, although this may be increased to twenty-eight per 18.3 metres for weak formations, curves and continuous welded rail.

Timber sleepers of Douglas fir, Baltic redwood and Jarrah have been used in the past but are being replaced by concrete on all permanent lines. Timber sleepers have a life of approximately twenty years on secondary lines, and are suitable for temporary trackwork.

Concrete sleepers are made to BS 986* which provides for five classes, A to E, for general use, and a special (class F) sleeper for use on heavily trafficked main lines; these are used only by British Rail. The other classes are used for private sidings by the National Coal Board, Gas Boards and the Central Electricity Generating Board. These sleepers are pre-stressed and, apart from being more durable, their extra weight increases the stability of the track. These advantages, together with the fact that concrete sleepers can be readily formed to receive the various types of track fixings, have proved that this material is superior to others being used.

Steel sleepers have been used for some time but are unsuitable on electrified lines, due to increased leakage of the return current, and they cannot be used where track circuits exist. They are used by the British Steel Corporation for tracks on which hot metal is being transported, but otherwise they have had a restricted use. They are made of steel plate, formed into an inverted trough with flanged ends; this shape is suitable for strength but creates difficulty if re-alignment of the track is necessary.

Sleepers are 2.5 to 2.75 metres long. Timber sleepers have an average cross-section of 125 mm by 255 mm; concrete sleepers have an average cross-section of 140 mm by 275 mm. However, due to increased thicknesses under the rail seating it is usual to specify sleepers by type and weight.

Formation and drainage

New works are designed by adopting appropriate alignments and gradients so that the amount of excavation (cut) will balance the amount of 'fill' in embankments — see Chapter 3, Earthworks. This system, however, can be employed economically only when the excavated material is suitable for use as fill.

If the soil is suitable, side slopes (batter) of 1.5 to 1 are commonly used; however, the side slope must be designed to suit the material. The top surface of the formation should be sloped outwards from a centre crown, to provide drainage to the track. The water is channelled away by ditch or other type of drain (Fig 10.5). Where the formation consists of a clay fill or formation it should be protected against ingress of surface water: clay becomes plastic when wet and the rolling stock may then force the ballast into the clay. The protection may consist of a layer of sand, stone-dust or ashes 150 mm to 350 mm thick, laid directly on the formation and covered with polythene sheeting prior to the placing of ballast.

Currently being reviewed.

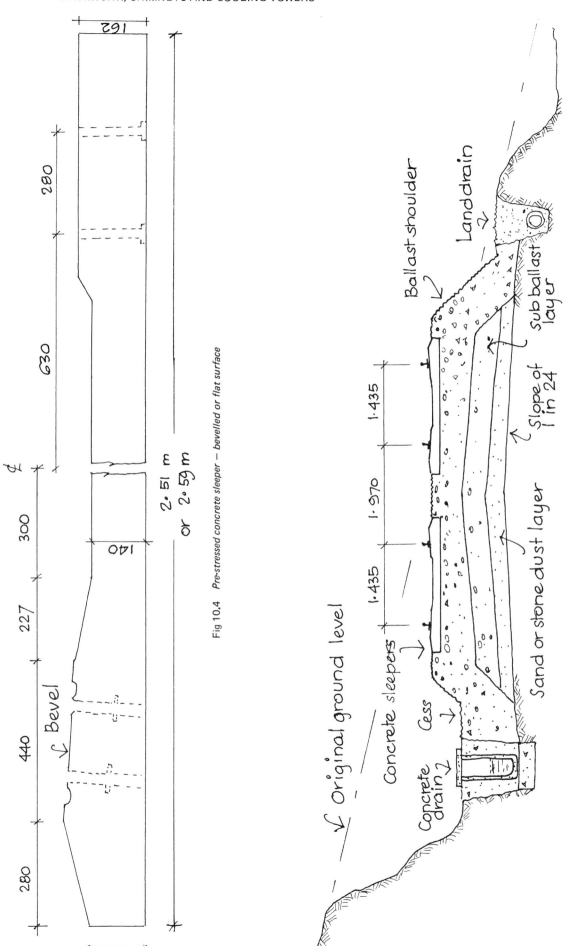

Fig 10.4 Pre-stressed concrete sleeper – bevelled or flat surface

Fig 10.5 Cross-section through rail track cut in sloping ground

Ballast

Ballast consists of crushed stone, e.g. granite or limestone graded from 12 mm to 40 mm, and is used as a base for the sleepers. The main function of ballast is to distribute the loads, applied by the sleepers, uniformly to the formation; it also absorbs vibration, provides track drainage and prevents the movement of sleepers. It is laid to a depth of between 225 mm and 300 mm, depending on the traffic load; the ballast is filled to the top of the sleepers and out to a distance of between 250 mm and 500 mm, the latter forming a shoulder to the outer edge of the track to restrain lateral movement.

10.1.3 Switches and crossings

Switches vary in complexity from a simple 'turnout' to complicated intersections seen in the approaches to a large terminal. A turnout is a junction formed by one track converging on another either from the right or the left (Fig 10.6). Switches with interlaced left- and right-hand turnouts are termed 'tandem turnouts' (Fig 10.7) or threeways.

A crossover is a connection between two adjacent tracks and comprises two turnouts connected by a section of straight track (Fig 10.8); the turnouts may be curved or straight.

A crossing results from one track crossing another and the plan shape gives it the name of 'diamond-crossing' (Fig 10.9). In these intersections certain terms are used for the various parts and these are indicated on the sketches by letters.

Frog (F), usually referred to as the common crossing, allows the flange of the wheel to pass where two rails cross. It consists of a 'V' made up of a point rail and splice rail which terminate the intersection of two converging rails (Fig 10.10).

Wing Rails (WR) form an integral part of the frog and terminate the ends of the rails diverging from the crossing.

Check Rails (CR), sometimes referred to as guard-rails (GR), are short rails with either bent or flared ends set securely on the rail opposite the frog. They prevent the flange of the wheel on the frog side bearing heavily on the frog while at the same time providing a guide to the correct rail.

Switch rails are movable and are used in connection with turnouts; by changing their position the train is directed to the desired track. The type of switch now in general use is the flexible switch (Fig 10.6); the short lengths of rail A–B and C–D are the switch rails and are connected by a tie-rod to provide simultaneous movement. Work to switches and crossings involve the use of timber sleepers, cut to suitable lengths; such work also incorporates special chairs or base plates and fastenings.

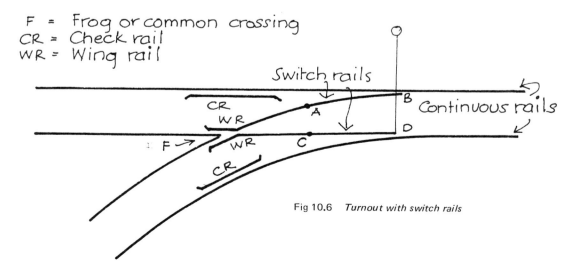

Fig 10.6   *Turnout with switch rails*

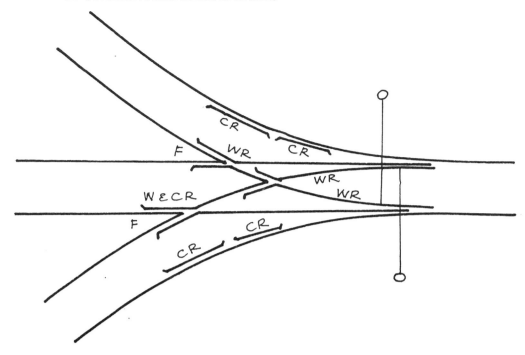

Fig 10.7   *Tandem turnout or threeway*

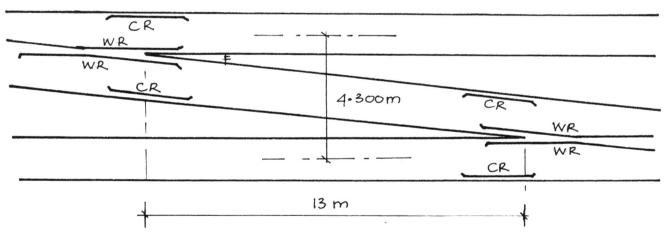

Fig 10.8   *Crossover*

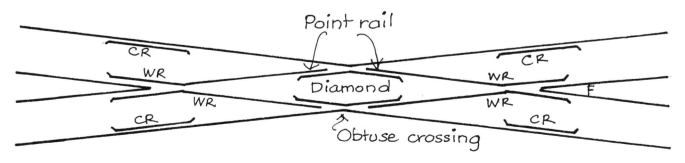

Fig 10.9   *Diamond crossing*

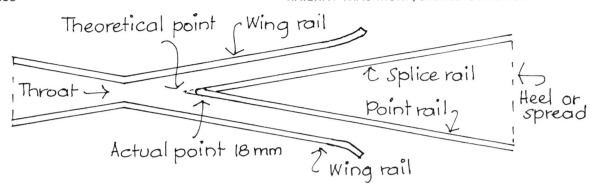

Fig 10.10   *Frog or common crossing*

10.2   CHIMNEYS AND COOLING TOWERS

10.2.1 Chimney construction

Design factors

Chimneys are constructed in differing forms and materials to suit the particular conditions for which they are to be used. A chimney is essentially part of the boiler plant, and as such, its design and construction will affect the efficiency of the plant and the amount of pollution which it passes into the atmosphere. Basically, the design of a chimney depends upon the amount of flue gases it has to handle and the sulphur content of the fuel. A chimney serving plant which burns fuel of low sulphur content is not required to be as high as those serving plant which burns fuel of high sulphur content. A simple method of calculating the approximate height of a chimney is given in a Clean Air Act Memorandum*. The internal diameter of a chimney should be determined by the volume, velocity, and temperature of gas emitted. The volume of the gas increases in direct proportion to the absolute temperature of the gas, assuming a constant flue diameter; an increase in temperature also increases the velocity of the gas through the chimney. The shape of the chimney flue e.g. circular, rectangular or elliptical, and the material used for the inner lining, will also affect its efficiency; this is due to the surface resistance of the material to the gases and the ratio of surface area to cross-sectional area. A circular flue gives the least surface area and steel or plastic liners give the least resistance.

Materials and construction

Chimneys can be constructed in such materials as brick, concrete, steel and reinforced plastic. Brick chimneys have been constructed for many years and have proved extremely successful. In the UK they have been built to heights of 135 metres and in South America up to 170 metres. In the last twenty years, brick construction for tall chimneys has been superseded by concrete and steel. Concrete chimneys, both precast and insitu, have been built since the 1920s. They were introduced as an alternative to brick construction, but were not very popular, the main problem being the lack of design knowledge under working conditions; as a result not many concrete chimneys, compared with chimneys in other materials, were built between 1930 and 1960. The 1960s saw a growing interest in this material and many small chimneys, i.e. up to 20 metres high, were built. Now that design knowledge is well advanced this form of construction is quite common.

Clean Air Act Memorandum – 'Chimney Heights' HMSO 1981.
Note: The CEGB refineries, smelters and cement works come under requirements of the Alkali Inspectorate; the Clean Air Act Memorandum covers only boilers on small installations.

Cast-in-situ chimneys are now used on large boiler-plant installations, such as electricity generating stations. The tallest concrete chimney in the UK is at the Drax Power Station in Yorkshire (Fig 10.11); it is 260 metres high and has three internal flues; the flues are elliptical in section, having axes of 13.7 x 9.15 metres (Fig 10.12). A typical 2000 MW station has a 198 metre chimney containing four circular flues.

Fig 10.11
*Concrete chimney 260 m high
at Drax Power Station — Yorkshire*
(Norwest Holst Group Administration Limited)

Fig 10.12
*Multiflue construction within
concrete shield at Drax Power Station*
(Norwest Holst Group Administration Limited)

Steel chimneys came into industrial use at the end of the nineteenth century and have been developed to reduce the cost of plant, as steel chimneys are generally far less expensive than chimneys of other materials. These chimneys can be designed and built to great heights: the Americans have a 305 metres chimney in steel as part of the Tennessee Valley scheme; Japan has steel chimneys up to 230 metres high; and the UK has steel chimneys up to 170 metres high. Steel chimneys of great heights can be built in a complex of three together in a triangular pattern and are braced for stability.

Industrial steel chimneys basically fall into the following categories:

Single-flue — self-supporting

Multiflue — self-supporting

Guyed chimneys

Bracketted chimneys

Single-flue self-supporting chimneys (Fig 10.13) are the most common; they range from 7 up to 60 metres in height and have diameters ranging from 150 mm to 2200 mm. The design criterion in most cases is deflection; tall stacks are usually of stepped taper design, although stabilisers in the form of helical strakes are usually fitted to the top third of tall stacks to reduce wind-excited oscillations. The anchorage of these chimneys is usually by a number of holding-down bolts cast into a mass concrete foundation.

Multiflue self-supporting stacks consist of a number of steel flues within a structural steel wind-shield. The number of flues depends on the boiler plant and can vary from two to as many as twelve. The internal flues are designed so that each can expand independently through a terminal weathering plate at the top of the stack. These chimneys are usually parallel throughout their height and can be built to heights of 120 metres and diameters up to 4250 mm. Anchorage and wind problems are similar to those of single-flue stacks. However, their design makes them less subject to wind-excited oscillations.

Fig 10.13(a)   *Single bore self supporting chimney with helical strakes to minimise wind oscillations*

(E.G. Reeve & Sons Limited)

Fig 10.13(b)   *Self-supporting steel chimneys 52 m high in extremely congested conditions*

(F E. Beaumont Limited)

Guyed chimneys can be directly mounted on a boiler, or supported at ground level. Three or four guys are usually taken from two-thirds of the total height of the stack, and should preferably be inclined at no more than 60° to the horizontal; very tall stacks can have guys at two or more levels. Guyed stacks are usually parallel, since their deflection stresses are small.

Bracketted chimneys are the same as guyed chimneys in design but are fixed to a restraining wall or tower (Fig 10.14) by means of steel brackets.

Groups of steel chimneys can be used as an architectural feature (Fig 10.15). Glass Reinforced Plastic (GRP) chimneys were first used in the UK in the 1950s. They have both advantages and disadvantages over the more traditional materials, e.g. they are ideal for carrying acid fumes but they have temperature limitations. This type of chimney is not built to be self-supporting but is normally supported by wire guys or brackets within a frame.

Treatment of chimney top

The chimney top may require some form of treatment against discolouration: this is normally provided by paint treatment. The concrete chimney at Drax Power Station (Fig 10.11) is painted at the top with a grey bitumastic paint, although it is now CEGB's practice to use chlorinated rubber paint; ceramic tiles may also be used. Another form of protection is a skin of dark-coloured facing bricks; these are built around the concrete chimney, recesses having been formed to carry the brickwork.

A further method of top treatment is the 'architectural' feature (Fig 10.16). This type of finish produces an aesthetically pleasing appearance as well as reducing the staining problem.

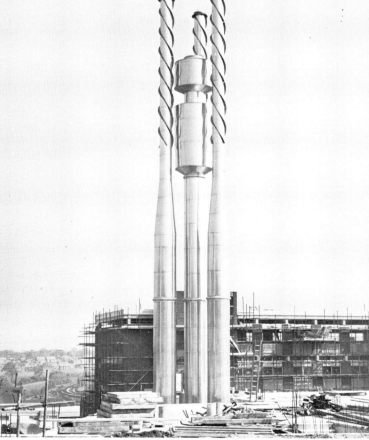

Fig 10.14   *Chimney supported by tower*
(F.E. Beaumont Limited)

Fig 10.15   *Three steel chimneys surrounding a water tower*
(F.E. Beaumont Limited)

Chimney foundations

Lightweight chimneys, such as steel and GRP, present no problem in the design of foundations, but concrete chimneys require special foundation design. Power station chimneys with a height of 200 metres can weigh up to 20 000 tonnes; such structures are normally founded on piles or cylinders the latter being up to 5 metres in diameter. The piles or cylinders are sunk down to a rock formation and capped with a ring beam on which the chimney is built. An alternative method of construction for heavy chimneys is a cellular foundation or buoyancy raft which may be 10 metres deep.

Fig 10.16   *Architectural feature as top treatment to chimney* (Norwest Holst Group Administration Limited)

10.2.2 Liners and insulation

Whatever the material and construction used, chimneys are subject to three basic types of attack: mechanical, thermal and chemical.

Mechanical attack can occur by natural weathering, i.e. atmospheric erosion; by wind loading, i.e. cracks caused by wind stresses; and by abrasion. In the last form of attack the surface of the chimney is worn away by the flow of grit particles from solid-fuel boilers.

Thermal attack is caused by overheating of a structure in which the lining cannot expand sufficiently and where expansion induces stress in the chimney structure. In special cases, e.g. high temperature flues, a composite lining of fire-resisting material and insulation is necessary.

Chemical attack, in the form of acid condensate, can cause serious damage to chimneys (Fig 10.17), and therefore insulation should be used to reduce condensation of the fumes.

Fig 10.17 *Uninsulated steel chimney corroded to a very dangerous condition* (F.E. Beaumont Limited)

Multiflue chimneys (Fig 10.12) have advantages over other types, not only in their stability and efficiency but also in their insulation: the space between the flue liners can be insulated either with loose mineral fill or with mineral wool mattresses. This efficient insulation of multiflue chimneys has led to their widespread use, the main types being:

Steel wind-shield with steel liners

Reinforced concrete wind-shield with steel liners

Reinforced concrete wind-shield with moler liners.

Mild steel liners are suitable for temperatures of up to 480°C beyond which they are subject to distortion; they are supported on a base or sub-base of the wind-shield, depending on the inlet position; the liner is insulated from its base support. The top of the liner can be fitted with a truncated cone (Fig 10.18), part of which can be manufactured in stainless steel to prevent excessive weathering. If steel liners are to be subjected to temperatures higher than 480°C, they should be lined with a cast-able refractory lining which will accept temperatures up to 1 000°C.

Steel liners may be insulated with Perlite or mineral wool. Perlite is an exfoliated aluminium silicate which is chemically inert, non-hygroscopic and free-flowing. Perlite insulation should be 150 mm thick; the material is subject to compaction and must therefore be topped up 12 months after installation. Mineral wool is used in the form of mattresses of various thicknesses, ranging from 25 mm to 100 mm, and is sometimes protected on one face by wire netting. The mattresses are wrapped around the liners and held in position by steel strapping.

Moler liners are generally built to one of two designs (Fig 10.19); the first of these is the parallel type which is built from the base of the wind-shield or from a floor just below the flue inlet; the second is the tapered 'inverted flowerpot' design. In the latter design the moler liner is built off a series of floors 9 metres apart. The advantage of the second type is that it minimises expansion and contraction problems; but it has the disadvantage of increasing resistance to flue gases. Methods of weathering moler liners in concrete wind-shields are shown in Fig 10.20.

GRP liners are ideal for carrying acid fumes, but, as mentioned earlier, they have a temperature limitation. They are suitable for temperatures of up to 200°C and in some cases are claimed to be operating in temperatures above this; however, there are instances in which such liners have caught fire and been destroyed.

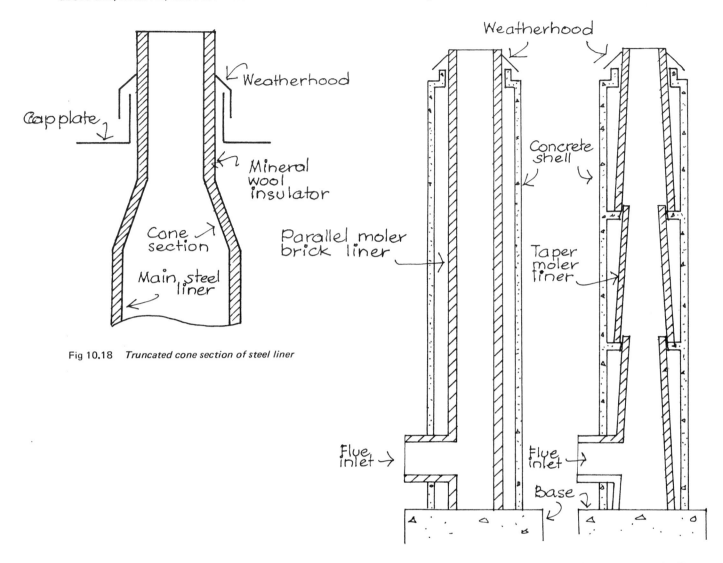

Fig 10.18   *Truncated cone section of steel liner*

Fig 10.19   *Two different methods of constructing moler liners*

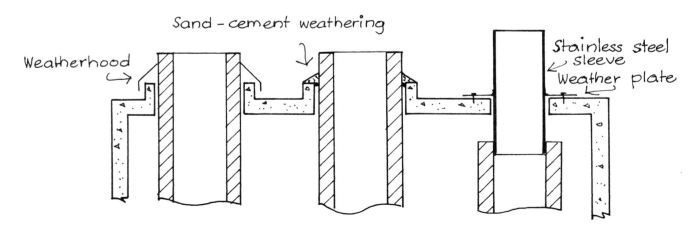

Fig 10.20   *Three ways of weathering moler liners passing through a concrete cap*

10.2.3 Demolition of tall chimneys

The method of demolishing a chimney will depend to a great extent on the material involved and its proximity to other buildings or obstacles. Steel chimneys should be dismantled in sections in the reverse order to that of erection; this method would also be used for GRP chimneys. Brick and concrete chimneys are best demolished by explosives, if space will permit. Where space or other factors prohibit this method of demolition, the chimney has to be demolished by expensive hand labour, the latter involving costly working platforms. Concrete chimneys which cannot be demolished by explosives may be cut down in sections by thermic lance; where this method is employed great care must be taken to confine the molten concrete. Generally, concrete chimneys in restricted areas are demolished by pneumatic breakers, oxy-acetylene being used to cut the reinforcement.

10.2.4 Cooling towers

Modern cooling towers (Fig 10.21) consist of a concrete shell supported on a series of concrete struts, and some form of cooling system housed in the base of the tower. Foundations for the tower are shown in Fig 10.22: they consist of a circular 'tee' beam formed by a wide concrete strip and inclined pond wall. This beam is necessary to resist the lateral thrusts. In addition to the 'tee' beam, piled foundations are normally used, the piles minimising any differential settlement which would otherwise lead to cracking in the tower. In a conventional cooling tower the water falls through the cooling stack and collects in a pond at the base of the tower, where the water is retained by an independent base slab and the pond wall.

Purpose and principles of cooling towers

The purpose of a conventional cooling tower (known as a 'wet system') is to reduce the temperature of the water used to condense steam in the condensers; the condensers convert exhaust steam from the turbines into water for re-use in the steam cycle. The circulating water passes through the condenser tubes, taking the heat out of the steam, and this is then sprayed over the cooling stack in the tower, falling as cooled water into the pond at the base of the tower for re-circulation to the condensers (Fig 10.23(a)).

The principle involved is as follows: the hot water is distributed by sprays over a large area of cooling stack, which increases the area of hot water being cooled either by providing a larger surface area over which the water runs, as with the film pack (Fig 10.24), or by breaking the falling water up into fine droplets, as with the splash pack. The main cooling effect is achieved by the water being evaporated by the rising air-stream. This evaporated water rises as a vapour out through the top of the towers, the cooled water falling into the pond. Since the hot air inside the tower is of a lower density than that outside, a suction flow is produced through the tower. The shape of the tower follows the flow pattern of the rising air-stream but does not restrict it, otherwise additional resistance to air flow would be involved. The shape used is the strongest and most economical that can be obtained without interference to the air flow.

This system of cooling loses a small amount of water by evaporation, usually about 1%, and also requires purging to clear away salts which are formed by continuous evaporation and re-circulation. The total loss due to evaporation and purging is made up from an outside source such as a river.

A dry cooling system incorporates a closed circulation system in which condensate is re-circulated through heat exchangers in the cooling tower and returned to the condenser as cooled condensate. The cooled condensate is sprayed into the steam within the condenser (known as a 'jet condenser'), reducing the steam to warm condensate and thereby completing the circuit. A small amount of condensate (2%) is continuously fed back to the boiler, the remaining 98% being re-circulated to the dry tower (Fig 10.23(b)).

Natural-draught cooling tower

The shell design is based on the hyperboloid, which has double curvature and can be analysed by modern methods for wind pressure; they can be constructed without ribs and buttresses (see Fig 10.24 for a diagrammatic sketch of a typical cooling tower). The tower, which may be 115 metres high, consists mainly of an empty shell, only the bottom 10 metres being used to house the cooling stack. The cooling stack, sometimes called the 'pack' structure', is fed with untreated hot water through sprays; the water falls through the stack into the pond area. Heat exchange takes place between the rising air and the falling water, the open structure at the base of the tower allowing a natural movement of air.

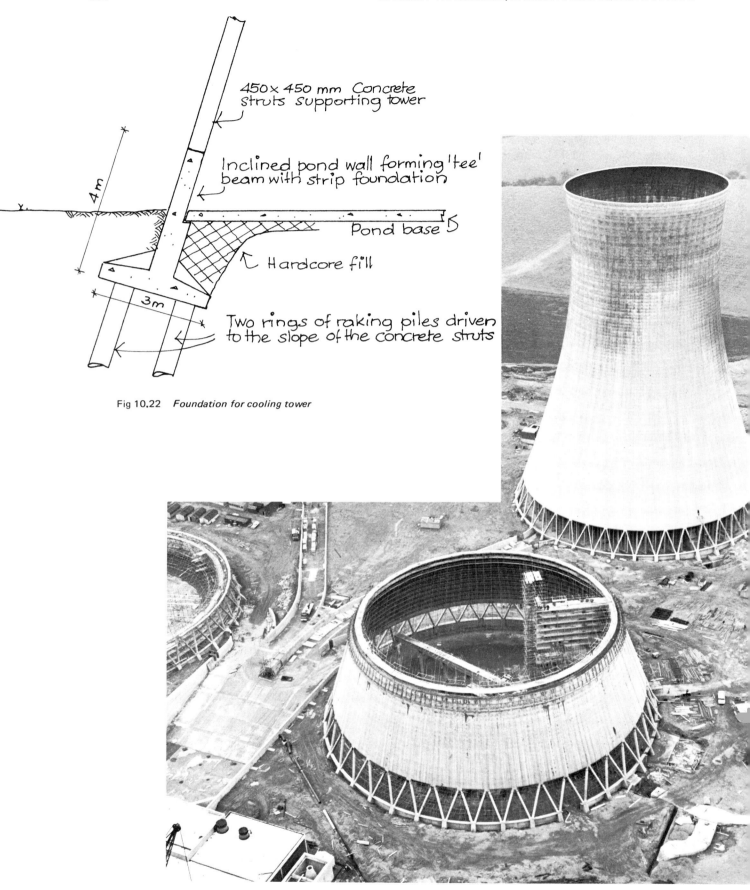

450 × 450 mm Concrete
Struts supporting tower

Inclined pond wall forming 'tee'
beam with strip foundation

4 m

3 m

Pond base

Hardcore fill

Two rings of raking piles driven
to the slope of the concrete struts

Fig 10.22   *Foundation for cooling tower*

Fig 10.21   *Progress view of construction of cooling towers at Eggborough Power Station* (Central Electricity Generating Board)

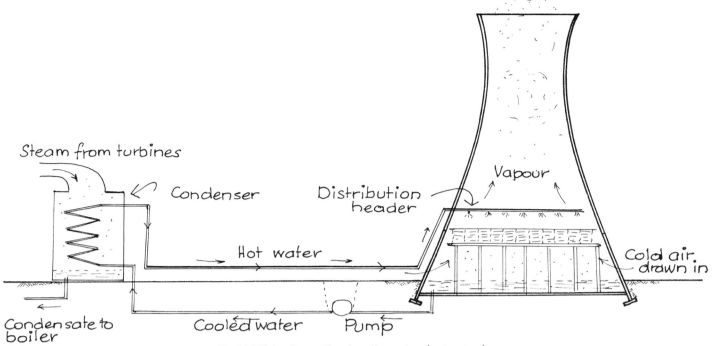

Fig 10.23(a) *Conventional cooling system (wet system)*

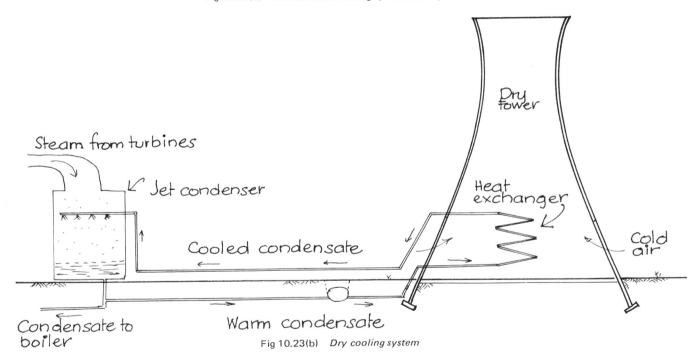

Fig 10.23(b) *Dry cooling system*

Stack construction

The cooling stack consists of packing which is used to increase the area between the hot water and the air flow. This is achieved in two ways; firstly by providing impregnated timber laths on to which the water can splash and break up into fine droplets, or secondly by passing the water between corrugated asbestos-cement sheets laid vertically on edge. The former is called a 'splash pack', the latter a 'film pack' (Fig 10.24). The stack is supported on reinforced concrete columns which are founded independently of the tower shell, so as to obviate damage which may be caused by a slight movement of the tower. The stack columns support perforated precast concrete beams into which the triangular-section timber laths are placed (Fig 10.24). Above the stack a layer of eliminators is constructed, these being either flat timber laths or corrugated asbestos-cement louvres (Fig 10.24). Eliminators intercept the droplets of water which would otherwise be carried up in the air-stream and deposited as fine rain.

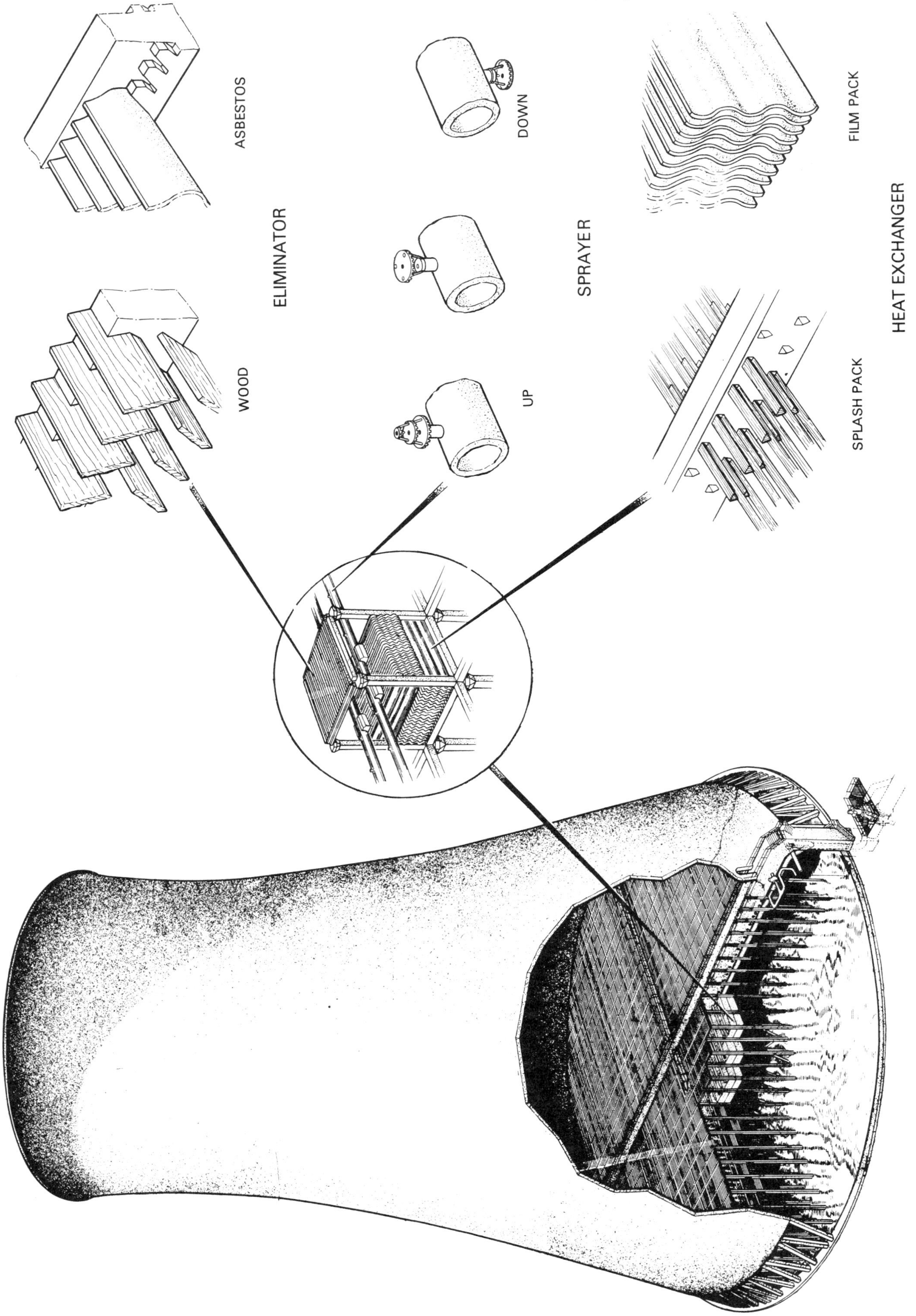

ASBESTOS

ELIMINATOR

WOOD

DOWN

SPRAYER

UP

FILM PACK

SPLASH PACK

HEAT EXCHANGER

Fig 10,24   *Typical natural draught cooling tower* (Central Electricity Generating Board)

Mechanical-draught towers

In this type of cooling tower the draught is provided by fans. They are used quite extensively in the UK, mainly in the oil and chemical industries where it is necessary to maintain or not to exceed a fixed temperature level in all ambient conditions. A close approach, i.e. difference between the ambient wet-bulb temperature and the cold-water temperature, or a situation in which the load factor is low, favours the use of mechanical draught towers. The cost of fan-power is high in this country, so the CEGB's practice is to use natural draught in preference to mechanical draught. This is because of the high load factor, wide approach and amenity considerations (the low-level plume from forced draught being abhorrent to planners).

Dry towers

The tower shell is similar in construction but considerably larger than a wet tower of the same rating; the heat exchange system is entirely different. The water is cooled by passing through aluminium tubes situated either within the tower shell or within the air opening. The principles of this system are shown in Fig 10.23(b).

Wet towers require make-up water from a suitable source; a 2000 MW station requires a gross make-up of 6.75 million litres/hr, net about 2.25 million litres/hr. In this country fuel supplies and water are usually found in reasonable proximity and for the present there is no call for a dry cooling system. In countries which lack adequate water supplies a dry tower will allow greater flexibility in the siting relative to fuel supplies.

INDEX

Access — site 44
Accommodation 33
Aggregates — general 299
          — bulk filling 50
Air Compressors 90
Airfield Construction — foundations 296
          — pavement design 296
          — pavement construction 296
Anchors — clay 196, 197
      — injection 196, 197
      — rock 196
Auger boring 205

Backfilling — rock 105
Basements 102
Benching 104
Bentonite — material 178
Bituminous mixing and laying plant 92 - 95
Blasting — see Explosives
Bolting 328
Borings — general 9
      — percussion 11
      — rig 10
      — rotary 11
Bricks 48
Bridges — arch bridge 281, 288
      — bascule 282
      — bearings 289
      — bridge decks 286
      — choice of system 282
      — erection 325 - 327
      — expansion joints 289, 290
      — falsework 286
      — formwork 287
      — foundations 284
      — surfacing of decks 291
      — suspension bridge 281, 288, 326 - 327
      — swing bridge 282
      — types 280
      — vertical lift 282
      — waterproofing 291
Bulb pressure 6, 8, 17

Cableways 75
Caissons — compressed air 233
      — design 232
      — introduction 232
      — open caissons 233
      — positioning and sinking 235
      — sealing and filling caissons 238
      — types and forms 232
Canals 255
Capping beams 166
Cathodic protection 145
Cements 47, 48
Chemical content — see Soil samples
Chimneys — demolition 33, 365
      — design factors 358
      — foundations 362
      — general 358
      — insulation 362 - 364
      — liners 362
      — materials and construction 358 - 361
Coastal defence 243
Cofferdams — cellular cofferdams 86, 230
      — economic factors 231
      — ground stabilisation 230
      — introduction 223
      — types 224
Compounds — storage 35
Compressed air — general 37
      — plant 90
      — tools 91
      — tunnels 213
      — working 46, 132

Contractors Plant — see Plant
Concrete — compliance testing 302
      — cutting and demolition 320
      — distribution and placing 71 - 77, 303, 304
      — formwork 239, 287, 305 - 308
      — general 48
      — gunite 317
      — jointing 310 - 311
      — materials 299, 300
      — mixing 70, 300
      — plant — see Plant
      — prestressed 312
      — ready-mixed 301
      — reinforcement 309
      — special concreting systems 317
      — steelcrete 319
      — water-cement ratio 302
Concreting — underwater 239
Contiguous piling 113, 183
Conveyors 65
Cooling towers — dry towers 369
      — foundations 366
      — general 365
      — mechanical-draught 369
      — natural-draught 365
      — stack construction 367
Core drilling 12
Costs — cost index 23
      — site investigation 26
Cranes — derrick 85, 86
      — mobile 83
      — tower 87 - 89
Crib walling 196, 198
Cut and fill 57, 102
Cut-off walling 112
Cuttings — setting out 59

Dangerous atmospheres 46
Demolition — concrete structures 320
      — general 30 - 33
Dewatering — equipment 98
      — general 116 - 126
      — wellpoints 120
Diaphragm walling — cofferdams 227
      — contiguous piling 183
      — diaphragms on legs 182
      — economic factors 187
      — introduction 178
      — plant and equipment 186
      — precast 182 - 185
      — specification of, 189 - 192
      — strip pile 181
      — thick cast insitu 179
      — thin cast insitu 179
Displacement piles 149
Docks — dry 242
      — wet 242
Dolphins 245
Drainage — runways 297
      — sewage treatment 342
      — surface water 278
Dredging — barges 252
      — canals and river works 255
      — construction 254 - 255
      — digging dredgers 249
      — general 247
      — materials 254 - 255
      — planning the work 248
      — plant and equipment 249
      — suction dredgers 250
Drilling — core 12
      — mud 11, 12
      — shot 12

Earthmoving plant 57
Earthworks — compaction of soil 101
            — duration and weather problems 101
            — economics 101
            — existing services and structures 100
            — general considerations 99, 267
            — (see Embankments)
            — ground conditions 100
Efficiency factors 67, 69
Electrical resistivity 22
Electricity supply — see Temporary services
Electro-osmosis 127
Embankments — in water 114
            — slopes of, 115
            — sloping ground 115
            — soft ground 115
Excavations — backfilling 105
            — bulk 102
            — explosives 104
            — methods of, 106
            — rock 103
            — support of, 107 - 112
            — trench 106
            — underwater 104
Explosives — blasting accessories 52
            — handling and storage 54
            — types of, 51, 104

Falsework 307, 308
Fenders 245
Flexible pavements 270
Floating pontoons 25
Footpaths and verges 279
Formwork — bridges 287
            — general forms 305 - 308
            — underwater 239
Foundations — bridge 284
            — runways 296
            — underwater 239
Freezing — ground support 127 - 132

Gabions 258
Gas supply — temporary 37
Gelignite — see Explosives
Geophysical surveys 22
Ground water control — compressed air 132, 213
                        — costs 134
                        — electro-osmosis 127
                        — freezing methods 127, 132
                        — grouting methods 133
                        — process, suitability of, 117
                        — pumping systems 116
                        — sandwicks 126
                        — wellpoints 120
Ground water level 8
Grouting — bentonite 133
            — bituminous 134
            — cement 133
            — chemical 133
            — methods and costs 134
            — methods of injection 134
            — resin 134
Gunite 317

Hard shoulders 279
Hardwood mats 29
Headings 12
Heating — temporary 37
Hoists — concrete 72
            — men and materials 89
Hover platform 25

Insurance 31
Investigation — see Site

Jetties 245
Joints — reservoirs 262
            — roads 275, 276
            — runways 297
            — types of, 310

Kerbs 279

Laboratory testing — see Testing
Lighting — tunnels 214
Linings — expanding 212
            — insitu 212
            — prestressed 212
            — tanks 266
            — tunnels 211
Liquid retaining tanks 261

Magnetic surveys 22
Marine works — breakwaters 246
            — docks 242
            — dolphins 245
            — dredging 247
            — fenders 245
            — groynes 246
            — jetties 245
            — moles 246
            — sea walls 242
            — wharves 245
Mass-haul diagram 57
Materials — bulk filling 50
            — concrete 299
            — explosives 51
            — general 47 - 50
            — reinforcement 309
            — storage 35
Mattresses — fascines 256
            — galvanised wire 258
            — nylon 256
Mobile units 34
Mono rail 72, 73

Oedometer 21, 22
Oil — storage 35
Organisation chart 35
Over break 2, 205, 207

Pavements — composite 277
            — concrete slab 273
            — roads 270, 271
            — runways 296, 297
Performance — plant 66
Petrol storage 35
Pierced steel planking 29
Piling: Bearing piles
            — bored piles 164
            — caps and capping beams 166
            — concrete preformed 150 - 153
            — displacement piles 150
            — driven piles 150
            — economics and selection 169 - 175
            — jetting piles 153
            — methods of driving 78, 163
            — modular piles 154 - 155
            — obstructions 171
            — pile linings 160
            — plant 78
            — preformed piles 150 - 155
            — preliminary piles 148
            — preliminary work 148
            — replacement piles 160
            — screw piles 160
            — specification for, 175 - 176
            — steel piles 156 - 160
            — stripping and lengthening 153
            — testing 168
            — timber piles 155
            — types 149
            — under-reaming 163

Piling: Sheet piles
            — contiguous 183, 186, 226
            — corrosion and protection 145
            — driving equipment 144
            — extraction 82, 145
            — methods of driving 142
            — pile guides 142 - 143
            — restricted headroom 144
            — selection and use of, 147
            — types of, 136, 138
Pipelines — construction methods 335 - 338
            — jointing 334
            — materials 331 - 333
            — protection 339 - 341
            — testing 340
            — thermal insulation 341
            — weight costings 341
Pipe jacking 202
Pits — trial 9
Plant — Bituminous mixing and laying 92 - 95
       — Compressed air 90
       — Concreting
              distribution 71 - 77, 273
              mixing 70
              selection 70
       — Craneage — see Cranes
       — Diaphragm walling 186
       — Earthmoving 57
              compaction 65
              excavation 58
              performance and outputs 66 - 69
              setting out for, 58
              transporting 63
       — Management of, 55
       — Pile driving 78, 79
              extractors 82
              hammers 80, 81, 144, 164
              winches 82
       — Pumps 74, 95 - 97
       — Safety 45
       — Transporting 63
Pneumatic tools 91
Pressure bulbs 6, 8
Pre-stressed concrete — circular tanks 317
                   — loss of stress 314
                   — materials 314
                   — post-tensioning 314
                   — pre-tensioning 312
Pulverised Fuel Ash 50
Pumping — see Ground water control
Pumping test 23, 126
Pumps 74, 96

Reinforcement 309
Reno mattress 258
Reports 26
Reservoirs — construction 261
              — expansion 263
              — in-ground storage 264
              — joints 262
              — linings 266
              — waterproofing 264
Retaining walls — methods of construction 194
                  — types of, 194
                  — waterproofing 198
Rigs — see Boring
River work — bank protection 256
              — dredging 255
              — gabions 258
              — mattresses 256
              — stone training work 258
Riveting 328

Roadwork — base materials 270
            — camber 278
            — composite pavement 277
            — concrete slabs 273
            — contraction joints 276
            — earthworks 267
            — flexible pavements 270
            — footpaths and verges 279
            — hard shoulders and kerbs 279
            — joints 275 - 277
            — joint filling and sealing 275
            — reinforcement 275
            — rigid pavements 271
            — road camber 278
            — slab laying plant 273, 274
            — sub-base 273
            — subgrade strength 268
            — super elevation 279
            — surfacing 271
            — wearing coat 271
Rock — anchors 196
      — back filling with, 105
      — bulk filling 50
      — classification 1
      — drilling 208 - 209
      — excavation 103
      — tunnelling 207
      — types of, 2

Safety 42, 213
Samples — see soil
Sand islands 236
Sand wicks 126, 268
Sea walls 242, 254
Seismic surveys 22
Services — pipelines 331 - 341
            — sewage treatment 342
Setting out 37 - 41, 59
Sewage treatment — general considerations 342
                    — layout of plant 348, 349
                    — methods of, 343 - 344, 347
                    — stages of, 345 - 346
Shafts — safety 43
Sheet piling — see Piling
Shotcrete — see Gunite
Site clearance 30
Site investigation — compact sites 7
                  — defects of failure for, 5
                  — existing works 5
                  — extended sites 7
                  — general enquiries 5
                  — information and costs 26
                  — inter-tidal 28
                  — methods of exploration 9
                  — new works 3
                  — objects of, 1
                  — off-shore 25
                  — preliminary work 5
                  — procedure 7
                  — specification of, 27
                  — types of, 3, 5
Site offices 33
Site organisation 29
Site survey 42
Skips — concrete 75 - 76
Sleeper mats 29
Soil — chemical content 22
     — classification of, 1, 4
     — consolidation 22
     — density 19
     — fill 50
     — movement 9
     — samples 14
     — shear strength 20
     — stabilisation 269

Specification — diaphragm walling 189 - 192
                — piling 175 - 176 (see site investigation)
Stabilisation of soil 269
Steel — sheet piling 136
      — types of, 47
Steelcrete 319
Steelwork — connections 328
          — erection of bridges 325 - 327
          — erection of buildings 324
          — types of structure 322
Stones 49
Subways — drainage 295
        — finishes 295
        — lighting 295
        — types of, 292 - 294
        — waterproofing 295
Support — excavations 107 - 112
Surveys — geophysical 22

Temporary roads 29
Temporary services 29, 36, 37, 44
Temporary works — design 43
                — general 54
Testing — CBR test 18
        — consolidation test 22
        — cost involved 26
        — geophysical surveys 22
        — insitu tests 15
        — laboratory 18
        — plate bearing test 17
        — pumping test 23, 126
        — reports 26
        — shear box test 20
        — standard penetration test 15
        — triaxial compression test 20
        — unconfined compression test 16
        — vane test 16
Thermic lance 32, 320, 321
Timber 49
Tools — compressed air 91
Tremie pipe 75, 241
Trench — excavation 106
       — support 107, 109
Trench sheeting 140, 141
Trial pits 9
Tunnelling — auger boring 205
           — compressed air 213

— control of water 200
— hard rock 209
— linings 211
— method of construction 200
— mini tunnels 205
— pipe jacking 202
— purpose of, 199
— removal of debris 200
— rock 207
— safety 43, 213 - 214
— shield 211
— soft ground 210
— soft rock 209
— type of ground 199
— ventilation and lighting 43, 214

Underpinning — chemical injection 200
             — methods of, 216
             — pedatifid system 217
             — pretest 219
Underwater construction — concreting 239 - 240
                        — excavation 239
                        — formwork 239
                        — tolerances 240

Ventilation — tunnels 37, 214
Verges 280
Vibroflotation 177
Vibro-replacement 177

Walling — cut-off 112
        — crib 196, 198
Wall sawing 322
Water — (see also Ground water control)
      — ground 8
      — lowering 117
      — supply 36
Waterproofing — bridge decks 291
              — reservoirs 264 - 265
              — retaining walls 198
              — subways 295
Welding 329
Wellhole blasting 104
Wellpoints 120 - 126
Wharves 245
Winches 82
Wirand concrete 318